GEOMETRY

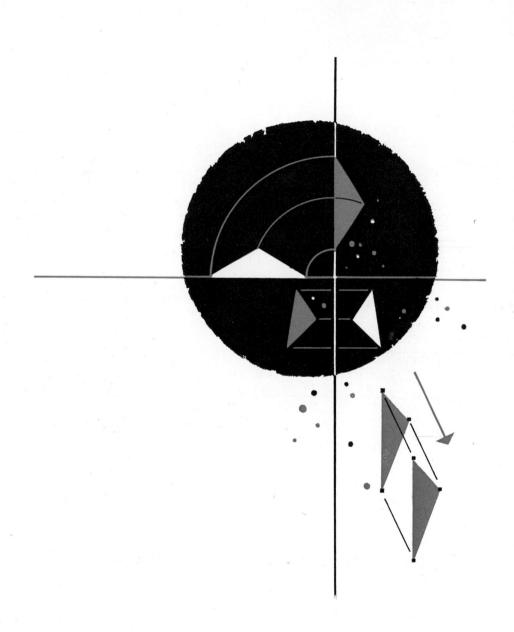

GEOMETRY

HOWARD F. FEHR

Professor of Mathematics, and Head, Department of Teaching of Mathematics, Teachers College, Columbia University

WALTER H. CARNAHAN

Formerly Assistant Professor of Education and Mathematics, Purdue University; Consultant in Secondary Mathematics Education for the State of Indiana

D. C. HEATH AND COMPANY BOSTON

Thematic representational drawings by

BILL H. ARMSTRONG

Library of Congress Catalog Card Number: 61-9693

PREFACE

Background of this book

At the present time there is a strong demand that all mathematics study make adjustments to modern concepts and applications of the subject. In this textbook, the authors have made all those adjustments which in their judgment are at present possible and desirable for a first course in deductive geometry. It is inevitable that some users of this book will think that the adjustments have gone too far while others will think that they have not gone far enough. Some of the adjustments made in this textbook are related to congruence as a transformation of a figure in a plane, systematic discussion of methods of proof, the introduction of coordinate geometry, and the inclusion of solid geometry.

The pedagogical features of the textbook have been accumulated out of teaching experience. The work on constructions, the discussion (not proof) of translation, reflection, and rotation as transformations of a figure, and the intuitive geometry of Chapter 1, are the result of classroom experimentation. Many of the exercises have been taken from accumulated practice materials that have been used for several years. The tests at the ends of chapters are types that have seen long use as measuring instruments.

The authors have studied various state syllabi as well as the reports, courses of study, and textual material of the Commission on Mathematics of the College Entrance Examination Board, the School Mathematics Study Group, and others. These reports and approaches to teaching geometry differ greatly in content and methods. No textbook could satisfy all of these programs in detail. This textbook presents material to permit a teacher to follow either the Commission Report or the School Mathematics Study Group's viewpoint as reflected in their publications. Adaptations to these various proposals are presented in the teachers manual.

New topics

In response to the demand that high school geometry should reflect modern developments in mathematical thinking, a chapter on coordinate geometry is included. The introduction of measures of line segments and angles by real numbers from the start has permitted shorter, simpler, and more easily understood proofs than those usually given in traditional treatments of synthetic geometry.

The modern development of transformations of a plane whereby one figure is mapped on another is reflected in the intuitive introduction to congruence, where figures are *not moved* but are mapped by using translations, rotations, and reflections of the plane. This approach builds correct mathematical concepts of congruence which are then applied in the usual manner to proofs of other theorems and original exercises.

Language of the book

A constant effort has been made to reduce so far as possible the language and vocabulary difficulties of students. We have used words as simple as are consistent with accuracy and clarity. However, mathematics shares with other subjects the requirement that the terms peculiar to that subject are among the facts that have to be mastered by the learner. These words have been discussed and defined in their proper places and added to the vocabulary of the subject for further use.

Conformity to recommended syllabi

The authors have read all published syllabi that deal with the subject matter of plane geometry. Since these syllabi do not agree in all respects, and many states are drastically revising their present syllabi to conform with modern viewpoints, decisions have had to be made as to what adjustments are required. Nevertheless, all essential materials recommended by leading syllabi will be found in this book.

Provisions for different abilities

This book has been prepared for all college-capable students. These students, however, show varying abilities in the learning of mathematics. In the treatment of both theorems and exercises the authors have had in mind the needs of students of various levels of ability and interest.

In some proofs we have given more of the detailed steps than is often done, and in the exercise lists we have provided many that are well within the ability of even the slowest students who are admitted to plane geometry. Many exercise lists are divided into three parts, each part suitable for students of one of three levels of ability. These divisions are conspicuously marked for the guidance of assignments.

Unit organization

This book is divided into twenty-one chapters. This organization makes for ease of learning and teaching. It also makes it possible to provide frequent summaries, reviews, and tests.

Summaries

At the end of each chapter is a brief summary of the subject matter of the chapter. These summaries help students to see the material as an organized whole and to concentrate on a small unit of material for review.

Reviews

At the end of each chapter that is part of the sequence there is a complete review of the chapter. Following Chapter 11 there are cumulative review tests covering the first eleven chapters. These serve as summary and evaluation of mastery of the materials presented in the first half of the course. Each review should be regarded as an essential part of the education experience of learners.

Tests

Each chapter that has a review also has one or two tests each of which covers the essential materials of the chapter. Many of these tests are of the objective type. Usually each test begins with very easy questions and progresses to more difficult ones. Of course, teachers will make their own class tests in the style they deem most suitable for evaluating student learning.

Discovery exercises

Wherever they can be naturally introduced, the authors have provided exercises which lead students step by step to discovery of some new fact or principle. These cultivate independence on the part of the learner. After each list of discovery exercises, the fact or principle is formally discussed.

Supplementary exercises

At the ends of all but a few chapters there are lists of Supplementary Exercises. These provide practice material and applications sufficient for the needs of any class. At the same time, they are set off to themselves so that they do not appear as part of the essential sequence of the course.

Discussion of logic

We have given discussions of methods of proof that are more complete than are generally to be found in high school textbooks. We have tried to make these discussions as brief as is consistent with conveyance of meaning, and we have included as much as it seems that high school students can profit from reading and discussing. The discussions have been written, studied, and rewritten in an effort to make them understandable and vital.

Howard F. Fehr
Walter H. Carnahan

CONTENTS

Chapter 0   **INTRODUCTION**   3

Chapter 1   **CONSTRUCTIONS**   23

Outline of Chapter 0 and Chapter 1, 33; Review of Chapter 0 and Chapter 1, 34; Yes-No Test on Chapter 0 and Chapter 1, 35; Completion Test on Chapter 0 and Chapter 1, 36; Supplementary Exercises on Chapter 0 and Chapter 1, 38

Chapter 2   **GEOMETRIC PROOF — ANGLE PAIRS**   43

Outline, 55; Review, 55; Yes-No Test, 56; Completion Test, 57; Supplementary Exercises, 58; Cumulative Review, 59

Chapter 3   **A NEW VIEW OF CONGRUENCE**   61

Outline, 87; Review, 88; Yes-No Test, 89; Completion Test, 90; Supplementary Exercises, 90

Chapter 4   **NATURE OF INDIRECT REASONING**   97

Outline, 106; Review, 106; Test, 107

Chapter 5   **PARALLEL LINES**   111

Discussion Exercises, 126; Outline, 129; Review, 129; Yes-No Test, 130; Completion Test, 131; Supplementary Exercises, 132

Chapter 6   **ANGLES OF POLYGONS**   135

Outline, 149; Review, 149; Yes-No Test, 150; Completion Test, 151; Supplementary Exercises, 152

Chapter 7   **PARALLELOGRAMS**   157
             Outline, 171; Review, 171; Completion Test, 173;
             Yes-No Test, 174; Supplementary Exercises, 174

Chapter 8   **DISTANCE**   181
             Outline, 201; Review, 202; Yes-No Test, 203; Com-
             pletion Test, 204; Supplementary Exercises, 205

Chapter 9   **INEQUALITIES**   211
             Outline, 220; Review, 220; Yes-No Test, 220; Com-
             pletion Test, 221; Supplementary Exercises, 223

Chapter 10   **CONCURRENT LINES**   227
             Geometry in Three-Space, 235; Outline, 244; Review,
             244; Yes-No Test, 245; Supplementary Exercises, 246

Chapter 11   **ANGLES AT THE CENTER
             OF A CIRCLE**   251
             Nongeometric Problems, 268; Outline, 270; Review,
             271; Yes-No Test, 271; Completion Test, 272; Sup-
             plementary Exercises, 274

             REVIEW TESTS — CHAPTERS 0 TO 11   278

Chapter 12   **LINES THAT INTERSECT A CIRCLE**   287
             Outline, 314; Review, 315; Yes-No Test, 316; Com-
             pletion Test, 317; Supplementary Exercises, 319

Chapter 13   **LOCUS**   327
             Outline, 344; Review, 344; Test, 345

Chapter 14   **RATIO, PROPORTION, AND
             PROPORTIONAL SEGMENTS**   347
             Outline, 364; Review, 365; Yes-No Test, 366; Com-
             pletion Test, 368; Supplementary Exercises, 369

Chapter 15   **SIMILARITY**   373
             Outline, 404; Review, 404; Yes-No Test, 406; Com-
             pletion Test, 407; Supplementary Exercises, 409

Chapter 16   **COORDINATE GEOMETRY**   415
             Outline, 437; Review, 438; Test, 439; Miscellaneous
             Exercises, 440

Chapter 17   **AREA**   443
Outline, 462; Review, 462; Yes-No Test, 463; Completion Test, 464; Supplementary Exercises, 466

Chapter 18   **REGULAR POLYGONS AND CIRCLES**   469
Outline, 488; Review, 489; Yes-No Test, 490; Completion Test, 491; Supplementary Exercises, 493

REVIEW TESTS — CHAPTERS 12 TO 18   495

Chapter 19   **POLYHEDRONS AND THE SPHERE**   503
Summary of Area and Volume Formulas, 523; Outline, 535; Review, 536; Test, 537

Chapter 20   **THE NATURE OF MATHEMATICAL REASONING**   539

SQUARES AND SQUARE ROOTS OF NUMBERS   556

INDEX   557

A Few Words to the Student

You have already studied geometry in the previous years of your schooling. The geometry you studied was a *physical* geometry because the lines, circles, and other figures were those you could see in the world about you. It was also intuitive, because you measured and drew pictures of these geometry figures to find their perimeters, areas, and size of angles. This was the geometry that the Egyptians studied more than three thousand years ago, because they were interested in practical applications.

The Greeks took this geometry and created out of it an organized sequential *logical* geometry. That is, they depended only on *reasoning* and not on measuring and seeing. For example, to the Egyptians, a point was a tiny dot on the earth or on papyrus (a sort of paper). The Greeks abstracted from this *physical point*, an *ideal point*, which could not be seen since it had no dimensions, but could only be a position on a line or in a plane. They made similar abstractions for a *line* (which had only one dimension), for a circle, and other geometric ideas.

While the Greeks drew illustrations of their geometric figures, they knew that these pictures were not the ideal things about which they talked. This book starts with the study begun by the Greeks. We shall study points, lines, circles, triangles, and many other geometric figures as ideal abstractions, but we use drawings or pictures to show what we mean. However we shall do this from a more modern viewpoint than that of the Greeks because we shall also use numbers to represent points.

GEOMETRY

CHAPTER 0

INTRODUCTION

BLAISE PASCAL was a famous French mathematician, scientist, and philosopher, who lived about three hundred years ago. When he was about twelve years old, he was once standing by his father's chair, looking on while the father worked at his desk. Blaise asked what his father was doing. The father replied that he was working at geometry. Blaise asked, "What is geometry?" His father replied, "Geometry is the construction of figures with exactness and studying what relations the parts have one with another." Now, this is not a very good definition of geometry, and the elder Pascal knew it, but it was as much as the boy could understand — and perhaps more.

Some time later the father noticed that Blaise was quiet and very busy. He looked and saw that the boy was drawing geometric figures with great exactness and studying them. This occupation held the boy's interest for days and weeks, and he kept coming back to it. Out of this activity of drawing figures and studying them, and with no systematic instruction, he worked out many original and interesting geometric facts, which he presented in an essay when he was sixteen years old.

In your study of geometry you will find it necessary to make many careful constructions as the basis of your work. In the first chapter you will review some constructions that you may have learned to do earlier, and you will learn some others. Later in the course you will learn how to *prove* that these constructions are correctly made. In this chapter you will learn many of the terms that you will use throughout your study of geometry.

0–1   Geometry   In geometry we study the properties of figures made up of points, lines, or surfaces. Plane geometry deals only with figures that can be represented on a plane (flat) surface. Solid geometry deals with such figures as cubes, spheres, and cylinders. In this book we shall study mainly plane geometry, but we shall discuss from time to time some of the properties of the solid geometry figures.

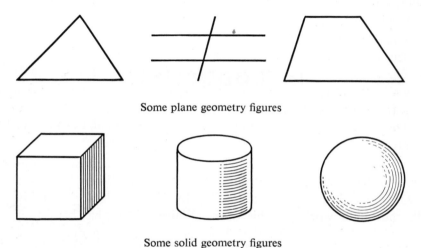

Some plane geometry figures

Some solid geometry figures

In the study of geometric figures we must reason; that is, we must try to draw justifiable new conclusions from previous conclusions that we have reached about these figures. The process of systematic reasoning is called logic. A simple example of logical reasoning in a nongeometric situation is the following:

If a pupil makes a grade of 70% or higher on a test, he passes. (This is a statement of fact.)
Harry made a grade of 83%. (This is another fact.)
83% is higher than 70%. (This is a third fact.)
Therefore, Harry passed the test. (This is a conclusion based upon the three facts.)

In our study of geometry we will learn some of the principles of reasoning so that we can draw logical conclusions. Once you have learned to apply the principles of reasoning in geometry, you will find that they can be applied also to other subjects, such as algebra, physics, and civil law.

0–2 Definitions In any kind of discussion it is important to be sure that one knows the meanings of the words and phrases that are being used. A <u>definition</u> is a statement of the meaning to be given to a term in a certain discussion. The definition of a particular word may not be the same in all discussions. For example, in the expressions *square table* and *square meal* the word *square* has quite different meanings.

Some characteristics of a good definition are the following:
1. It is brief, usually given in one sentence.
2. The other words used have accepted meanings.
3. The subject of the sentence is the name of the thing defined.
4. The predicate tells: (*a*) the smallest more general known class to which the thing belongs, and (*b*) the characteristics which distinguish it from other members of the class.
5. The meaning of the sentence must be the same if the subject and predicate are interchanged.

Suppose that we are to define the word *street*. We must consider what is the smallest more general known class to which it belongs. Now, a street can be classified as a *roadway*. Having decided on this classification, we must show how *street* differs from other members of this class. Then we can write a definition. Here is a possible one:

A street is a roadway in a city or a village.

The subject and predicate can be interchanged without changing the meaning:

A roadway in a city or a village is a street.

If we were stating a definition of *horse*, it would not be a proper definition to say that *a horse is a four-legged animal*. When this statement is reversed it becomes: *A four-legged animal is a horse.* What other four-legged animals can you think of?

Sometimes definitions are given that do not fit the description given above. Definitions in mathematics may be given in several ways. However, our discussion applies to nearly all definitions that you will have to consider in this book.

Designate the smallest more general known class to which each of the following belongs; give the characteristics which distinguish it from other members of the class, and thus define the word. Test each definition by interchanging the subject and predicate.

1. moon	2. clock	3. watch	4. knife
5. island	6. automobile	7. laborer	8. cereal
9. science	10. ice	11. gold	12. apple

0–3 Undefined Terms and Some Defined Terms. Line Segment. Broken Line. Curved Line The second characteristic of a good definition as stated on page 5 is that it is to be stated in words with accepted meanings. This does not mean that all words that are used must have been previously defined. If it were required that each definition must use only those words that have been previously defined, there would be no place to begin. We must have some words to start with. Each field of study has its own list of basic terms on which all definitions of special terms applying to that field are based. These basic terms are called <u>undefined terms</u>. Our first list of undefined terms for plane geometry is:

<u>point</u>   <u>line</u>   <u>straight line</u>   <u>plane</u>

Besides the defined and undefined terms of any field of study there are the words that are used in everyday conversation and in general writing, as well as in all fields of study, without definition. Some examples are *the, in, up, move, of, you, has;* there are many others. In our study of geometry we shall use these words without definition.

We represent a point by making a dot with a pencil on paper or with chalk on a board. We name a point by placing a capital letter such as *A* near it. We refer to the point as point *A* or simply as *A*.

A line is a set of points. (This statement is not intended as a definition, since we have accepted the word *line* as an undefined term, but as a description or statement of a characteristic. The word *set* is undefined.) We represent a line by making a continuous mark.

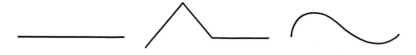

We represent a straight line by drawing a mark along the edge of a ruler or some other straight edge. When we use a ruler in this way in geometry, we disregard the marks on it and call the instrument a straight-edge. A straight line extends indefinitely in two directions. We name a straight line by designating any two points on it, or by using a single small letter, such as *l*.

$$\underset{\bullet}{\overset{A}{\vphantom{.}}} \hspace{3cm} \underset{\bullet}{\overset{B}{\vphantom{.}}} \hspace{0.3cm} l$$

Straight line *AB*, or straight line *l*

A designated point on a line separates the points of the line into three sets: (*a*) the designated point itself is a set of one point; (*b*) the set of points of the line that lie on one side of the designated point which we may call set *R*; (*c*) the set of points of the line that lie on the other side of the designated point which we may call set *L*.

$$\overset{L}{\hspace{2cm}} \underset{\bullet}{\overset{A}{\vphantom{.}}} \hspace{1.5cm} \overset{R}{\hspace{1cm}}$$

A plane is also a set of points, and a straight line separates the points of a plane into three sets: (*a*) the set of points that lie on the line; (*b*) the set of points that lie on one side of the line and which we may call set *R*; (*c*) the set of points that lie on the other side of the line and which we may call set *L*. A line connecting any point in set *R* with any point in set *L* will intersect the given line. Here, *intersect* means "have at least one point in common with."

The points of set *R* constitute a half-plane. The points of set *L* constitute a half-plane. The word *half* has an accepted meaning here different from that used in arithmetic; it does not mean one of two equal parts.

A geometric point does not move, and so the geometric points of a line do not move. However, in geometry we constantly find it necessary to draw lines by using pencil points, and in this process the point of the pencil moves. Furthermore, just as we move the point of the pencil to trace a line that goes through a number of points, so we can also move the straightedge to other positions in the plane; in doing this, we do not move the points that lie on any line that we have traced by using the straightedge. When we discuss angle (Sec. 0–10) we shall relate the motion of the straightedge to the angle but we shall not move the geometric lines nor the points on them. The student should keep in mind this distinction between the movement of the tools with which we work in tracing figures and the geometric elements of the figures themselves.

Of course, the marks that we make to represent points and lines have breadth, no matter how sharp a pencil we use. We must understand that they are only representations of abstractions that exist in our minds. A geometric point has no size, and a geometric line has no breadth. Likewise, a plane has no thickness. A piece of paper laid flat on a table can represent a portion of a plane but the thickness of the paper must be disregarded.

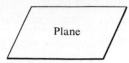

A line segment, or simply segment, consists of two designated points on a straight line and the part of the line that lies between them. The designated points are called the end points of the segment.

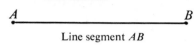

Line segment *AB*

In our definition of line segment we have made use of the following terms that are not in our list of undefined terms: *consists of, two, on, a, and, the, part of, that, lies between,* and *them.* These are terms that are familiar to us from conversation and everyday reading. Some of these terms have special importance in geometry and should be added to our list of undefined terms. The terms are:

point on a line   part of   lies between

A broken line is illustrated below.

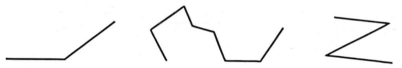

A curved line is a line that is neither straight nor broken.

Exercise. Name all segments on this line, including those that overlap.

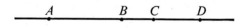

EXERCISES

Use your ruler as a straightedge in the following exercises.

1. Place a point on your paper. With straightedge and pencil draw a line through it. Draw another line. Another. How many lines can be drawn through the point?
2. Place two points on your paper. Draw a straight line that passes through both of them. Can you draw another straight line through them?

3. Place three points at random on your paper. Can you draw a straight line that passes through all three points?
4. Define line segment.
5. Draw a line segment on your paper and label it *RS.*
6. Draw a broken line *ABCDEFG.*
7. Place three points at random on your paper. How many line segments can you draw connecting them two by two?
8. Place four points at random on your paper. How many line segments can you draw connecting them two by two?

0–4   Relations between Points and Straight Lines   The following expressions are illustrated by the adjoining diagrams.

Point *P lies on* line *AB.*   (Or simply *P* lies on *AB.*)

Straight line *AB passes through* point *P.*

Point *P lies between* points *A* and *B* on straight line *AB.*

Points *A* and *B* lie *on opposite sides of* point *P.*

Straight lines *MN* and *RS intersect* in point *O.*   They have the point *O in common.*

Point *O* is the *point of intersection* of straight lines *MN* and *RS.*

Segment *EF intersects* segment *JK* in point *F.*

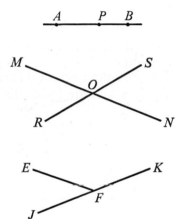

The intersection of two sets of points is the set of all the points they have in common.   In the case where the two sets are lines, their intersection will consist of a single point.   (Note that when reference is made only to *lines,* we shall mean *straight lines.*)

0–5   Some Instruments of Geometry.   Distance   In our study of geometry and in applying our knowledge we find it convenient to make use of various instruments for drawing and measuring figures.   However, for many hundreds of years it has been customary to limit the proofs of geometry to figures that can be made by use of only two instruments, the straightedge and a pair of compasses, and for the present we shall make use of these two instruments only.   We have discussed the straightedge in Sec. 0–3. The pair of compasses is an instrument that can be used for drawing circles or parts of circles. Hence, in geometry we shall usually be studying figures that are composed of straight lines and circles. A figure that is made by use of these two instruments only is called a geometric construction.

We assume that the compasses can be adjusted so that the points are as near to each other as we wish or as far apart as we wish. Also, we assume that any adjustment that we make will remain fixed until we change it. When we have adjusted the compasses for any particular opening, we call the length of the line segment determined by its two points the distance between them.

0–6 Plane Figure. Closed Figure. Closed Straight-line Figure. Closed Curve A plane figure is made up of points, lines, and line segments that lie in the same plane.

The illustrations below show examples of geometric figures which are called closed figures. Notice that each plane closed figure bounds a limited part of a plane. A plane closed figure separates the points of a plane into three sets: (*a*) the set of points that are on the figure; (*b*) the set of points that are inside the figure; (*c*) the set of points that are outside the figure. If any point *X* inside the figure is connected with any point *Y* outside the figure by a line, the line intersects the figure.

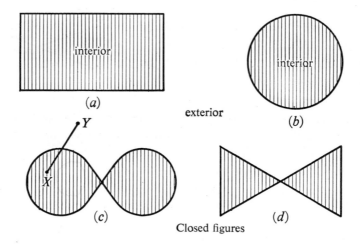

Closed figures

A plane closed straight-line figure is a plane figure that is made up of straight-line segments each of which has only the end points in common with one and only one other segment, such as figures (*a*) and (*d*).

In this book all plane closed figures with which we deal will be *simple* closed figures. Figures (*a*) and (*b*) are simple; (*c*) and (*d*) are not.

0–7 Circle. Concentric Circles A circle is a plane closed curved line all points of which are the same distance from a point inside called the center. The symbol for circle is ⊙.
If the center of a circle is M, we can call it circle M, or we can write ⊙ M.

The radius of a circle is a line segment drawn from the center to any point of the circle, as segment MP. We also use the word *radius* to indicate the distance from the center to a point of the circle. The plural of *radius* is *radii*. You are reminded that distance is a measure and is usually given as a number.

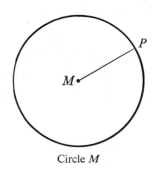

Circle M

To draw a circle, set the points of the compasses at the distance desired as the radius, place the metal point of the compasses on the point that is to be the center, hold the compasses by the knob at the top, and turn the pencil point around. It is best to use only thumb and forefinger.

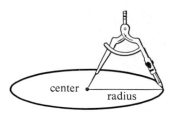

A diameter of a circle is a line segment that connects two points of the circle and passes through the center. We also use the word *diameter* to indicate the distance across a circle through the center.

An arc is a part of a circle.

Concentric circles are circles that have the same center. A circle is concentric to itself. Each can be named by designating its radius.

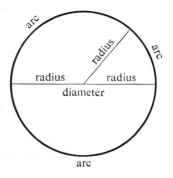

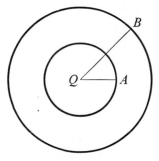

Concentric circles QA and QB

0–8 Relations between Straight Lines and Circles The following expressions are illustrated by the adjoining diagrams.

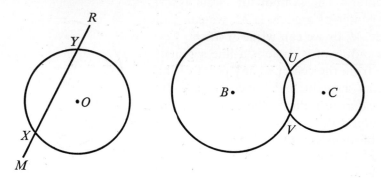

Circle *O intersects* the straight line *MR* in points *X* and *Y*. The straight line *MR intersects* circle *O* in points *X* and *Y*. The circle *O* and the straight line *MR* have points *X* and *Y in common*.

Circle *B* and circle *C intersect* in points *U* and *V*. They have points *U* and *V* in common.

EXERCISES

1. In what two ways did we use the word *point* in section 0–7?
2. Draw two straight lines *ST* and *VW* intersecting at *Z*.
3. Can you draw two straight lines that intersect in two points?
4. Can you draw two straight lines that do not intersect?
5. Draw a circle and name it *Q*.
6. Draw two concentric circles, *OA* and *OB*. Do they intersect?
7. Draw a circle *A*. Draw a line *EF* intersecting circle *A* at *H* and *K*.
8. Can you draw a straight line that intersects circle *A* in more than two points?
9. Can you draw a straight line that does not intersect circle *A*?
10. Let two circles intersect. How many points of intersection are there?
11. Draw a segment and label it *KL*. Draw a straight line and mark a point *M* on it. From point *M* mark off segments *MN* and *MP* (points *N* and *P* on opposite sides of point *M*) each equal to segment *KL*. Use your compasses for this.
12. Draw a straight line. Mark a segment *RS* on it. With your compasses mark off segments *ST*, *TU*, *UV*, and *VW*, in succession, each equal to *RS*.

EXERCISES

1. Copy the following figure by following the directions below it.

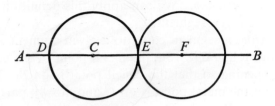

(a) Draw a straight line *AB*.
(b) Mark a point *C* on straight line *AB*.
(c) With *C* as center, draw a circle intersecting *AB* in points *D* and *E*.
(d) From point *E* mark off a segment *EF* equal to *CE*. *F* is on the opposite side of *E* from *C*.
(e) With *F* as center and *EF* as radius draw a circle.

2. Copy the following figures.

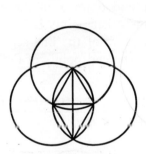

3. Make some other designs using straightedge and compasses.

4. Follow these directions and construct the figure described. (a) Draw a circle with center *O* and radius 1 inch. Let *A* be a point on it. (b) Keeping your compasses opened to 1 inch, step off *AB, BC, CD, DE, EF* on the circle. (c) Draw straight-line segments connecting the points. Can you name the figure?

5. On your copies of the figures in Ex. 2 above, label necessary points and tell the steps followed in making the figures.

6. Select one of the designs you made in Ex. 3, label the points, and tell how the figure was drawn.

0–9   Equal Line Segments.   Measurement of a Segment   We define equal line segments as segments that have the same measure, as described below. They may be radii of circles that are drawn with the same distance between the points of the compasses.   We can apply this definition to construct a segment equal to a given segment.

Thus, to construct a segment equal to a given segment *AB* we proceed as follows.   Draw a line *CD*.   Set the metal point of the compasses on *A* and adjust the opening so that the pencil point is on *B*.   Next move the compasses so that the metal point is on *C* and draw a part of a circle (an arc) that intersects *CD* at *E*.   Then *CE* = *AB*.

To measure a given line segment *ST* we first select an arbitrary line segment as a unit of length.   Using this segment as a radius and the initial point *S* of the segment as center, we construct an arc that intersects the segment at a point *U*.   Using the same radius and *U* as center, we construct an arc that intersects the line segment at *V*.   We continue this process until the last intersection reaches the end point *T* of the given segment.   Numbering the initial point 0 and the other points 1, 2, 3, and so on, the number of the end point is the measure of the line segment. We also say the number is the distance between the end points of the segment.

If it should happen that the segment *ST* does not contain an integral number of the selected unit, then we can do one of two things: either tell the number of units it contains approximately, or select some other unit and repeat the process. Whatever unit is selected, it usually happens that the segment being measured does not contain it an integral number of times, and so nearly every measurement is only an approximation. Later you will see that measurement of angles or of areas also results in approximations.

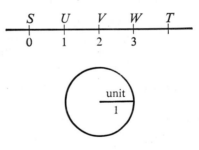

In reading or making scale drawings, in making machines or furniture, and in other mechanical operations we use rulers or scales that have units of linear measurement marked on them, such units as inch, centimeter, yard, and so on.

0–10 Half-line. Ray. Angle On page 7 we have seen that a designated point of a line separates the points of the line into three sets: (*a*) a set of one point, the designated point; (*b*) a set of points on one side of the designated point which we may call the set *R*; (*c*) a set of points on the other side of the designated point which we may call the set *L*. If any point in set *R* is connected with any point in set *L* by a line segment, the segment passes through the designated point.

A half-line is that part of a line which is on one side of the designated point. The designated point is called the vertex of the half-line. A half-line with its vertex is called a ray. The word *half-line* does not mean that a half-line is half as long as a line.

$$M \qquad\qquad N \longrightarrow$$

Ray *MN*, *M* is the vertex

Let *BA* and *BC* be two rays each of which has *B* as initial point. The figure *ABC* is called an *angle*. *B* is the *vertex* of the angle, and *BA* and *BC* are the *sides* of the angle. The symbol for angle is ∠.

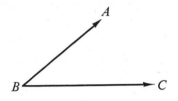

We summarize the definitions as follows.

An angle is a figure formed by two rays that have the same initial point. The sides of an angle are the rays that form it. The vertex of an angle is the initial point of the rays that form the angle.

The angle divides the entire plane into two regions, an interior and an exterior region. For the present we shall call that region the interior in which if any two points are joined to form a segment, the segment does not intersect the angle. In the figure, segment *AB* is in the interior of the angle. Show that points *P* and *Q* do not satisfy the definition of interior of an angle.

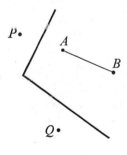

An angle is designated by naming a point other than the vertex on one side, then naming the vertex, then naming another point on the second side, as ∠*ABC* above. The letter that designates the vertex is always the second of the three letters that designate the angle. Sometimes, when there can be no confusion as to which angle is meant, we designate it by the vertex letter alone, as ∠*B*.

Usually the sides of an angle are not in the same straight line. However, they may be. If the sides of an angle are in the same straight line but on opposite sides of the vertex, we call the angle a <u>straight angle</u>. Either half-plane is the interior.

vertex

$A \longleftarrow$ one side $\quad O \quad$ other side $\longrightarrow B$

Straight angle AOB

Read each angle in these figures.

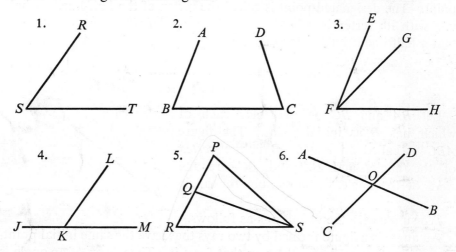

1. R, S, T
2. A, D, B, C
3. E, G, F, H
4. L, J, K, M
5. P, Q, R, S
6. A, D, O, B, C

In algebra you learned to use letters in various ways. For example, you met such expressions as "x has \$2," "Let x represent the number of inches," and "$y = 3x$." In the first example, x is the name of a person; in the second example, x represents an unknown number which has only one or possibly several values; in the third example, x is a variable that may take on an unlimited number of values. In geometry also a letter may have different meanings which are usually clear from context. For example, m may be used in some cases to name a line segment, and in other cases to represent its length.

0–11 The Use of Rotation On paper make a drawing of an angle having sides each 5 or 6 inches long. Now close the compasses and lay the instrument on the drawing of the angle in such a manner that the pivot pin is on the vertex and one arm of the compasses is on one side of the angle. Think of the two arms of the compasses as rays whose vertex in each case is the pivot pin. Keeping the one arm fixed, rotate the other arm about the pivot pin until this arm is on the second side of the angle. The moving arm of the compasses started in the position BA, at different times was in the positions BC_1, BC_2, BC_3, and so on. Two positions of the arm are of special interest. One of these is the position before it was moved, called the *initial position*. The other is the position at the end of the rotation, called the *terminal position*. Similarly, we call one side of the angle the initial side and the other the terminal side.

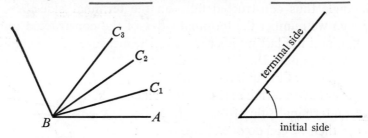

You can imagine a ray as rotating through an angle either in the direction in which the hands of a clock move, that is, clockwise, or in the opposite direction, that is, counterclockwise. The diagram above indicates counterclockwise rotation. An arrow is often used to indicate the direction of rotation.

0–12   Equal Angles.   Measurement of an Angle   Suppose that we are given an angle RST and a straight line AB. Then at a point P on AB there is one angle and only one, on one side of AB, that is equal to $\angle RST$. This angle can be constructed as follows.

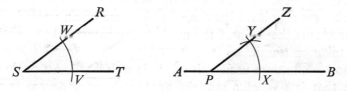

Draw any arc with center at S intersecting ST at V and SR at W. With P as center and the same radius draw an arc that intersects AB at X. Arc XY is part of this arc. Now adjust the compasses so that the opening is the distance VW. (This is the length of the straight-line segment from V to W.) With this radius and with X as center draw an arc that intersects the arc XY at Z. Use the straightedge to draw segment PZ. This makes $\angle XPZ = \angle RST$.

You can test the accuracy of your construction of the angle equal to the given angle by tracing $\angle XPZ$ on a piece of thin paper and laying this on $\angle RST$. In Chapter 3 we shall prove this construction is correct.

0–13   Measure of an Angle   In Sec. 0–9 there was described the measure of a line segment.   Similarly to measure an angle *HJK* we select an angle as a unit ($\angle DEF$).   Then beginning with the initial side of the angle *HJK* we construct an angle in the interior equal to the unit angle *DEF*.   Using the terminal side *JL* as a new initial side we again construct an angle equal to the unit angle *DEF*.   We continue this until the terminal side of the unit angle thus constructed falls on the terminal side *JK*.   In the figure shown we number the terminal sides of the constructed unit angle 0, 1, 2, 3, 4, and the last number gives us the measure; that is, angle *HJK* is 4 units, where angle *DEF* is the unit.

It can happen that the unit angles thus constructed never have a terminal side to coincide with *JK* (the terminal side of the angle to be measured); then we can do one of two things: either tell the number of unit angles it contains approximately, or select some smaller unit angle for the measurement.   Even if some smaller unit angle is selected, it usually happens that the angle being measured does not contain it exactly.   So, nearly every angle measurement is an approximation.   (Compare measurement of a segment, Sec. 0–9).

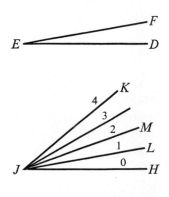

As you know, in measuring length we use a standard unit of length, such as a mile, an inch, or a centimeter.   When we say that the diameter of a ball is .01 inch, we mean that the diameter is .01 as long as a fixed length taken as a unit.   Likewise, the measure of an angle is a number which represents the ratio of the angle being measured to another angle which is taken as a unit.

The most commonly used unit angle is a <u>degree</u>.   An angle degree is an angle that is $\frac{1}{180}$ of a straight angle. $\frac{1}{60}$ of a degree is a <u>minute</u>. $\frac{1}{60}$ of a minute is a <u>second</u>.   25 degrees, 11 minutes, and 39 seconds is written 25° 11′ 39″.

When we say angles are equal we mean they have the same measure.

EXERCISES

1. Use your straightedge and draw any angle *AKM*.   Construct another angle equal to $\angle AKM$.
2. Draw any angle *PTY*.   Draw another angle *HKL* which is much smaller than $\angle PTY$.   Using $\angle HKL$ as a unit angle, measure $\angle PTY$.

0–14 How to Use a Protractor In mechanical drawing, building, or surveying, we use instruments that have unit angles marked. The unit is usually the degree. One such instrument is a protractor. A protractor is an instrument for measuring and drawing angles. At the middle of the straight side of the protractor is a mark or notch. Place this at the vertex of the angle to be measured and adjust the instrument so that the straight side lies along one side of the angle. The other side of the angle (extended, if necessary) intersects the curved part of the protractor. The number of degrees in the angle can be read at this intersection. $\angle ABC = 50°$.

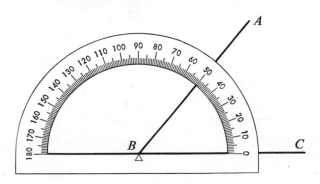

To draw an angle of a given size with a protractor, draw a line and on it indicate a point that is to be the vertex of the angle. Place the center of the protractor at this point with the straight side of the protractor on the line. Make a dot on the paper at the number of degrees desired, remove the protractor, and draw a line through the dot and the vertex. This gives the angle required.

WRITTEN EXERCISES

1. Draw a number of angles. Measure them with a protractor
2. Draw angles of 10°; 20°; 90°; 100°; 45°; 30°; 61°; 127°; 174°; 11°; 73°.
3. Draw six angles of various sizes and estimate the number of degrees in each; then measure with a protractor and write down the number of degrees difference between your estimate and the measurement.
4. With pencil and straightedge draw angles which you estimate to contain the number of degrees indicated: (a) 12°, (b) 30°, (c) 45°, (d) 60°, (e) 72°, (f) 90°, (g) 120°, (h) 150°. Test your estimates with a protractor and write down the difference between your angle and the given number of degrees.

0–15 Adjacent Angles Two angles have a <u>common side</u> if the same ray is a side of each angle.

<u>Adjacent angles</u> are angles that have the same vertex, a common side, and nonintersecting interiors.

In the figure on the left below, $\angle CBA$ and $\angle DBC$ have a common vertex B, a common side BC, and interiors that do not intersect. Therefore, they are adjacent angles. $\angle CBA$ and $\angle DBA$ have a common vertex B and a common side BA, but their interiors overlap. Therefore, they are not adjacent angles. They are called <u>overlapping angles</u>.

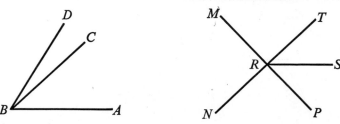

Exercise. Name the adjacent angles in the figure at the right above.

0–16 Right Angles. Perpendicular Lines A <u>right angle</u> is one of the angles formed by two straight lines that intersect in such a way that the adjacent angles are equal. A right angle has 90°. All right angles are equal.

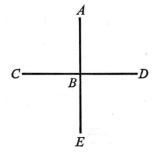

<u>Perpendicular lines</u> are lines that form right angles. In the figure we say that AE is perpendicular to CD and we write in symbols $AE \perp CD$.

$\angle ABC = \angle CBE = \angle EBD = \angle DBA$.
These are all right angles.

Two rays as well as two lines can form a right angle. Illustrate this.

0–17 Straight Angles. Oblique Angles A <u>straight angle</u> is an angle whose sides lie in a straight line on opposite sides of the vertex. The measure of a straight angle is 180°. All straight angles are equal. Compare page 16.

M————————N
MN is a straight line.
$\angle MON$ is a straight angle.

An oblique angle is an angle that is neither a right angle nor a straight angle. Are all oblique angles equal?

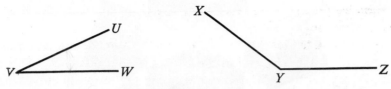

∠UVW and ∠XYZ are oblique angles

0–18 Acute Angle. Obtuse Angle An acute angle is an angle that is smaller than a right angle, such as ∠UVW.

An obtuse angle is an angle that is larger than a right angle but smaller than a straight angle, such as ∠XYZ.

ORAL EXERCISES

1. Which of these angles is largest? Smallest?

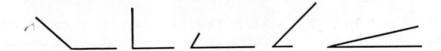

2. Read this angle with three letters; with one letter.

3. In this figure point out
   ∠YHK; ∠MHZ; ∠AHK.

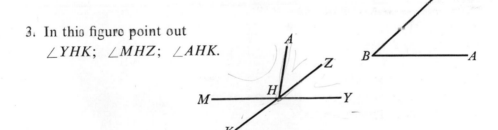

4. Read all the acute angles in the figure of exercise 3. Read the obtuse angles.
5. Name two angles adjacent to ∠AHZ.
6. What is the vertex of ∠PQR? What are the sides? Draw the angle and letter it.
7. Point out a number of right angles in the room.
8. Point out a number of straight angles in the room.

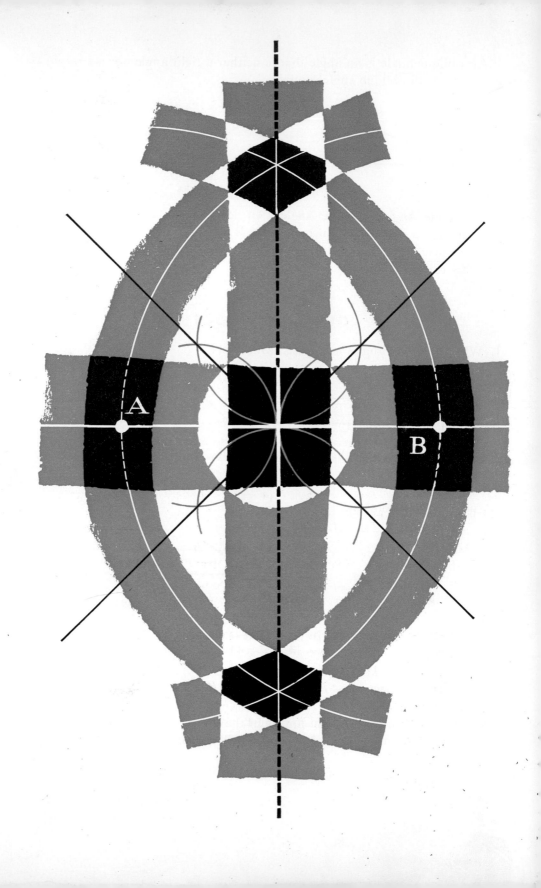

CONSTRUCTIONS

1-1 Bisect To bisect means to divide into two equal parts. The point that divides a line segment into two equal parts is called its mid-point.

The perpendicular bisector of a line segment is a line perpendicular to the segment at its mid-point.

1-2 Problem To construct the perpendicular bisector of a line segment.

Let *AB* be the segment that is to be bisected.

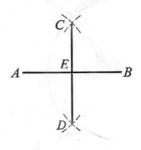

(*a*) With *A* as center and any radius that is longer than half of *AB*, draw an arc on each side of *AB*.
(*b*) With the same radius and with *B* as center, draw arcs that intersect the arcs with center at *A*. Let *C* and *D* be the points where these arcs intersect.
(*c*) Draw *CD* intersecting *AB* at *E*. The arcs are dashed because they are not part of what is given.

With the protractor measure $\angle AEC$ and $\angle BEC$.

Questions. (1) How do $\angle AEC$ and $\angle BEC$ appear to compare? (2) Are they adjacent angles? (3) Is $CE \perp AB$?

Open the compasses to the length of *AE*, and test to see whether $BE = AE$. (4) Does $BE = AE$? As a check, measure *AE* and *BE* with a ruler. (5) Does *CD* satisfy the definition of perpendicular bisector of *AB*?

1-3 Triangle A triangle is a figure formed by three distinct line segments joining three noncollinear points.

The sides of the triangle are the line segments that form it.

The vertices of the triangle are the points of intersection of the line segments.

The angles of the triangle are the angles that are formed by the rays which have the same vertices as those of the triangle and which contain the sides of the triangle.

The perimeter of a triangle is the sum of the lengths of the sides.

Kinds of Triangles

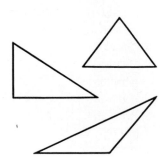

An acute triangle is a triangle all of whose angles are acute.

A right triangle is a triangle that has a right angle.

The side of a right triangle opposite the right angle is called the hypotenuse. The other sides are called arms.

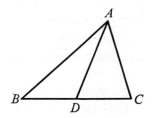

An obtuse triangle is a triangle that has an obtuse angle.

The symbol for triangle is △; for triangles, △s.

1-4 Median A median of a triangle is a line segment that joins a vertex to the mid-point of the opposite side.

AD is a median of $\triangle ABC$.

Is AD the only median of $\triangle ABC$?

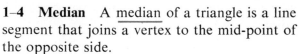

WRITTEN EXERCISES

1. Draw a segment AB more than two inches long on your paper, and divide it into four equal parts. This figure will suggest the method.

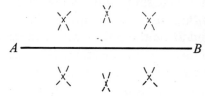

2. Draw a vertical segment and construct its perpendicular bisector. Use protractor and compasses as in Sec. 1-2 to see whether the constructed line is perpendicular to the segment at its mid-point.

3. Draw a circle O and draw a diameter AB. Construct the diameter which is the perpendicular bisector of AB.

4. Draw a segment *MN*. Construct its perpendicular bisector using two points on the same side of *MN*. To do this you will have to locate the two points by using radii of two different lengths.

5. Draw an obtuse triangle no side of which is less than two inches long. Construct the perpendicular bisectors of its sides.

6. Construct a right triangle. (See Sec. 0–16 and Sec. 1–3 for suggestions.) Construct the perpendicular bisectors of the sides of this triangle.

7. Draw an acute triangle. Construct the perpendicular bisectors of its sides.

8. What fact about the perpendicular bisectors of the sides of a triangle do you observe in your drawings in Ex. 5, 6, and 7?

9. In the drawings for Ex. 5, 6, and 7, draw the medians of the triangles.

10. What fact about the medians of a triangle do you observe in your drawings?

11. Draw a large triangle *ABC*, no two sides being equal. Construct medians *AX, BY, CZ* meeting at *O*. Measure and compute $AO \div AX$, $BO \div BY$, $CO \div CZ$.

1–5 Problem **To construct a line perpendicular to a given line at a given point on the line.**

First method. Let *AB* be the given line and *C* the given point on it. (*a*) With *C* as center and any convenient radius, draw arcs intersecting *AB* at *D* and *E*. (*b*) With *D* and *E* as centers and any radius longer than one half *DE*, draw arcs that intersect at *F*. (*c*) Draw *CF*. Then $CF \perp AB$ at *C*. Test your construction with a protractor.

Second method. Let *RS* be the line and *T* the given point on it. (*a*) Set the point of the compasses so it is not on *RS*. Call this point *V*. Open the compasses so that the pencil is on *T* and draw a circle that intersects *RS* at *T* and *W*. (*b*) Draw the diameter through *W* intersecting the circle at *W* and *X*. (*c*) Draw *XT*. Then $XT \perp RS$ at *T*. Test your construction with a protractor.

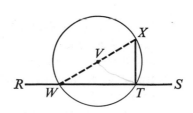

Question. Is $XT \perp RS$? See Sec. 0–16.

1. Draw a line *MN* and construct a perpendicular to it at *N*. In doing this, you may extend *MN* as far as you wish.
2. Draw a segment *XY* and construct a perpendicular to it at *Y* without extending the segment.
3. Draw a segment *AB* and construct a perpendicular to it at *A* and one at *B*. Extend these perpendiculars in both directions as far as the paper permits. Do they meet?

1-6 Distance to a Line The <u>distance from a point to a line</u> is the length of a perpendicular line segment from the point to the line. See Sec. 0–16.

1-7 Problem To construct a line perpendicular to a given line from a point not on the line.

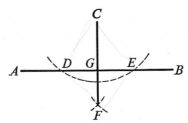

Let *AB* be the given line and *C* the given point. (*a*) With *C* as center and any convenient radius, draw an arc intersecting *AB* at *D* and *E*. (*b*) With *D* and *E* as centers and any radius more than half of *DE*, draw arcs that intersect at *F*. (*c*) Draw *CF* intersecting *AB* at *G*.

Question. Is *CG* ⊥ *AB*? Test your construction with a protractor.

1-8 Altitude of a Triangle An <u>altitude</u> of a triangle is the line segment from a vertex perpendicular to and terminating in the opposite side, or in the opposite side extended. How many altitudes has a triangle?

WRITTEN EXERCISES

C.

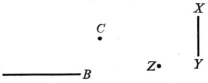

1. Reproduce each of these drawings on your paper. Construct a perpendicular from *C* to *AB*, and from *Z* to *XY*.
2. Repeat the construction described in Sec. 1–7, but have *F* on the same side of *AB* as is *C*. What advantages do you see in one plan over the other?

B.

3. Draw an acute triangle and construct its three altitudes.
4. Draw an obtuse triangle and construct its three altitudes.
5. Construct a right triangle and construct its three altitudes.
6. What fact about the altitudes of a triangle do you observe in Ex. 3, 4, and 5?

1–9 Problem   At a given point on a line to construct an angle equal to a given angle.

Let $\angle ABC$ be the given angle, MN the given line, and M the given point. (*a*) With B as center and any convenient radius, draw an arc intersecting AB at D and BC at E. (*b*) With M as center and the same radius, draw an arc intersecting MN at O. (*c*) With O as center and distance DE as radius, draw an arc intersecting the arc of M at P. (*d*) Draw MP.

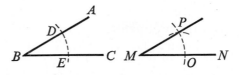

Use a protractor to test your construction.   Does $\angle PMO = \angle ABC$?

WRITTEN EXERCISES

1. On your paper draw a figure about like this but larger. Construct angles equal to each angle of the figure.

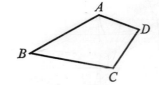

2. Draw an acute angle and construct another equal to it.
3. Draw an obtuse angle and construct another equal to it.
4. At two points on a line construct angles equal to each other and on opposite sides of the given line.

DISCOVERY EXERCISES

1. Study again Sec. 0–15 and Sec. 1–9. Can you use the principles learned there to construct the sum of two angles $\angle R$ and $\angle S$?
2. Draw $\angle R$ and $\angle S$, $\angle R$ being larger. Can you construct $\angle T$ such that $\angle T = \angle R - \angle S$?
3. Is Ex. 1 possible if $\angle R = \angle S$?
   Is Ex. 2 possible if $\angle R = \angle S$?
   Is Ex. 2 possible if $\angle S$ is larger than $\angle R$?
   NOTE: The symbol $>$ means *is greater than;* $<$ means *is less than.*

1–10   Problem   To construct an angle equal to the sum of two angles.
    Let ∠*ABC* and ∠*DEF* represent the angles the sum of which is to be

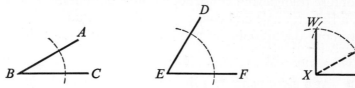

found.   (*a*) Draw a line *XY*.   (*b*) At *X* construct ∠*VXY* = ∠*ABC*.
(*c*) Construct ∠*WXV* = ∠*DEF* and adjacent to ∠*VXY*. (See Sec. 0–15.)
With the protractor measure ∠*ABC*, ∠*DEF*, and ∠*WXY*.
    Question.   Does ∠*ABC* + ∠*DEF* = ∠*WXY*?

1–11   Problem   To construct an angle equal to the difference of two angles.
    Let ∠*ABC* and ∠*DEF* represent the angles the difference of which is
to be found.   (*a*) Draw a line *XY*.   (*b*) At *X* construct ∠*VXY* = ∠*ABC*.
(*c*) Construct ∠*WXV* = ∠*DEF* and lying in ∠*VXY*. With the protractor
measure ∠*ABC*, ∠*DEF*, and ∠*WXY*.
    Question.   Does ∠*ABC* − ∠*DEF* = ∠*WXY*?

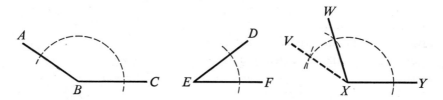

WRITTEN EXERCISES

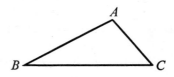

1. Draw an obtuse triangle about
   the shape of this one but larger.
   Construct an angle equal to ∠*A*
   and from it subtract ∠*B* and
   ∠*C*.
2. Construct an angle equal to ∠*A* + ∠*B* + ∠*C* in the above figure.
3. Draw an acute triangle and construct an angle equal to the sum of
   the angles of the triangle.
4. Construct a right triangle and construct an angle equal to the sum of
   the angles of the triangle.
5. With the protractor check your constructions in Ex. 2, 3, and 4.

1–12   Problem   To bisect an angle.

Let $\angle ABC$ be the angle to be bisected.
(*a*) With *B* as center and any convenient
radius draw an arc intersecting *AB* at *D*
and *BC* at *E*.   (*b*) With *D* and *E* as centers
and any radius greater than half of *DE*
draw arcs intersecting at *F*.   (*c*) Draw *BF*.
The ray *BF* is called the angle bisector.

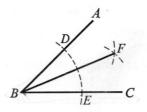

Test to see whether $\angle ABF = \angle CBF$.

Questions.   (1) What method for testing the equality of two angles
do you know?   (2) Is $\angle ABC$ bisected?

WRITTEN EXERCISES

1. Draw an acute angle and bisect it.
2. Draw an obtuse angle and bisect it.
3. Construct a right angle and bisect it.
4. Draw a straight angle and bisect it.   Compare Sec. 0–16.
5. Test the equality of your constructed angles in Ex. 1, 2, 3, and 4
   with a protractor.
6. Divide an angle into 4 equal parts.   Compare Ex. 1, Sec. 1–4.
7. Draw an acute triangle and bisect each of its angles.
8. Draw an obtuse triangle and bisect each of its angles.
9. Construct a right triangle and bisect each of its angles.
10. What fact about the angle bisectors of a triangle do you observe in
    Ex. 7, 8, and 9?

1–13   Congruent Triangles.   Corresponding Parts   In the first and second
figures, $AB = DE$, $AC = DF$, $BC = EF$, $\angle A = \angle D$, $\angle B = \angle E$, $\angle C$
$= \angle F$.   In these statements of relation we can translate this equals sign
into *has the same measure as.* $\triangle ABC$ and $\triangle DEF$ agree in their measurable parts and the equal parts are arranged in the same order.   That is, if
the measurable parts of $\triangle ABC$ are taken in counterclockwise order about
the figure, then the measurable parts of $\triangle DEF$ agree, part for part,
with those of $\triangle ABC$ if taken in counterclockwise order.

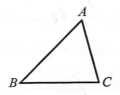 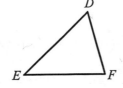 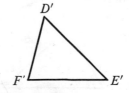

$\triangle ABC$ and $\triangle D'E'F'$ * also agree in their measurable parts but the equal parts are arranged in opposite order. That is, if the measurable parts of $\triangle ABC$ are taken in counterclockwise order about the figure, the measurable parts of $\triangle D'E'F'$, taken in clockwise order, agree, part for part.

For example, if we list the measurable parts of $\triangle ABC$ in counterclockwise order beginning with AB, they are as shown in the first row. If we list the measurable parts of $\triangle DEF$ in counterclockwise order beginning

$\triangle ABC$:	AB,	$\angle B$,	BC,	$\angle C$,	CA,	$\angle A$
$\triangle DEF$:	DE,	$\angle E$,	EF,	$\angle F$,	FD,	$\angle D$
$\triangle D'E'F'$:	$D'E'$,	$\angle E'$,	$E'F'$,	$\angle F'$,	$F'D'$,	$\angle D'$

with DE, they are as shown in the second row. If we list the measurable parts of $\triangle D'E'F'$ in clockwise order beginning with $D'E'$, they are as shown in the third row. Notice that the parts in each column are equal.

In either case, the triangles are said to be congruent.

A part in one of two congruent triangles and the part that agrees with it in the other have the same position in the two figures relative to the other parts that agree. In order to designate parts of congruent figures that agree, we use the word *corresponding*.

Corresponding parts of congruent triangles are parts that have the same size and the same relative position with respect to the other parts.

Corresponding parts of congruent triangles are equal. We abbreviate this to *c p c t e.*

Congruent triangles are triangles for which the corresponding sides and the corresponding angles are equal. $\cong$ means *congruent to*.

1–14 Problem To construct a triangle congruent to a given triangle using the three sides.

Let $\triangle ABC$ be the given triangle. (*a*) Draw line MN and on it mark off $MP = BC$. (*b*) With AB as radius and M as center draw an arc. (*c*) With AC as radius and P as center, draw an arc intersecting the first arc at R. (*d*) Draw MR and PR.

Measure the parts of $\triangle MPR$ and those of $\triangle ABC$ and compare corresponding measures.

Question. Is $\triangle MPR \cong \triangle ABC$?

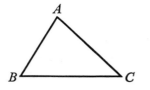
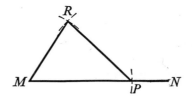

* D' is read "*D*-prime." $D'E'F'$ is read "*D*-prime *E*-prime *F*-prime."

WRITTEN EXERCISES

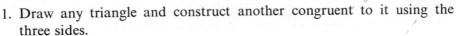

1. Draw any triangle and construct another congruent to it using the three sides.
2. Draw three segments with lengths 2 in., $2\frac{1}{2}$ in., and 3 in. Construct a triangle having sides equal to these lengths.
3. Can you construct a triangle the sides of which are 2 in., 3 in., and 5 in.? Try.
4. Can you construct a triangle the sides of which are 1 in., 2 in., and $3\frac{1}{2}$ in.? Try.
5. Can you state a fact indicated by Ex. 2, 3, and 4?
6. Construct a triangle having each of its sides 1 inch long.
7. Construct a triangle having one side 1 inch and two sides 2 inches each.

1–15   Included Parts in a Triangle   An angle that is formed by two rays is said to be *included by* them. A side of a triangle that connects the vertices of two angles is said to be *included by* them. It is a side of each of the two angles.

$\angle B$ is included by AB and BC, and BC is included by points B and C.

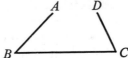

1–16   Problem   **To construct a triangle congruent to a given triangle using two sides and the included angle.**

Let $\triangle ABC$ be the given triangle. (*a*) Draw a line MN and on it mark off $MP = BC$. (*b*) At M construct $\angle PMQ = \angle B$. (*c*) On MQ mark off $MR = AB$. (*d*) Draw RP.

Measure the parts of $\triangle RMP$ and compare with the corresponding parts of $\triangle ABC$.

Question.   Is $\triangle RMP \cong \triangle ABC$?

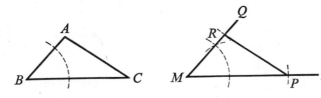

You can test for congruency two triangles on your paper by cutting out one and placing it on the other. Apply this test in Ex. 1, 2, 3 on page 32.

1. Draw an obtuse triangle. Using the obtuse angle and the two sides that include it construct another triangle congruent to it.
2. Draw any angle X. Draw any two segments VW and YZ. Construct a triangle having VW and YZ for two of its sides, and $\angle X$ for their included angle.
3. Using your ruler and protractor draw two lines each 3 inches and an angle of 40°. Using these parts as two sides and the included angle, construct the triangle.

1–17 Problem To construct a triangle congruent to a given triangle using two angles and the included side.

Study the figures and make the construction.

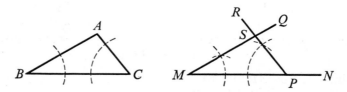

MISCELLANEOUS WRITTEN EXERCISES

B.

1. Draw any triangle PQR. Construct the median to the side PQ. Construct perpendiculars to this median from P and Q terminating in the median extended if necessary. Are these ⊥ line segments equal?
2. Construct a triangle having its base 1.5 inches, its altitude 1 inch, and the other sides equal.
3. Construct a right triangle having the sides that include the right angle 3 inches and 4 inches. How long is the third side? Measure it.
4. Construct a right triangle and bisect the side opposite the right angle. From this mid-point construct perpendiculars to the other sides.
5. Draw a circle and a diameter in it. From any point on the circle not an end of the diameter, construct a perpendicular to the diameter.
6. Draw an angle and bisect it. From any point on the bisector construct perpendiculars to the sides of the angle. Measure the perpendiculars and compare their lengths.
7. Construct a triangle that has three equal sides at least 3 inches long. From any point in the triangle construct perpendiculars to the sides.

8. Draw a circle and draw any triangle having its three vertices on the circle. From any point on the circle construct perpendiculars to the sides of the triangle. Connect the feet of the perpendiculars with straight lines. Do these lines coincide? (The Simson Line)

OUTLINE OF CHAPTERS 0 AND 1

These chapters introduce the following terms:

geometry	diameter	degree
compasses	arc	minute
straightedge	concentric circles	second
protractor	intersection	triangle
point	angle	right triangle
line	vertex	acute triangle
plane figure	side of angle	obtuse triangle
closed figure	initial and terminal sides	perimeter
line segment	angle bisector	median
straight line	adjacent angles	coincide
broken line	right angle	distance
half-line	perpendicular lines	length
ray	straight angle	altitude
half plane	oblique angle	congruent
circle	acute angle	corresponding parts
center	obtuse angle	definition
radius	bisect	undefined term

Chapter 1 has treated these constructions:

1. Perpendicular bisector of a line segment. Page 23
2. Perpendicular to a line at a point on the line. Page 25
3. Perpendicular to a line from a point not on the line. Page 26
4. Angle equal to a given angle. Page 27
5. Angle equal to the sum or difference of two angles. Page 28
6. Bisector of an angle. Page 29
7. A triangle congruent to a given triangle using:
   (a) The three sides. Page 30
   (b) Two sides and the included angle. Page 31
   (c) Two angles and the included side. Page 32

REVIEW

1. What is studied in geometry?
2. What are some of the characteristics of a good definition? Illustrate by defining some word with which you are familiar.
3. Why must there be some undefined terms in geometry?
4. What tools are recognized in making the constructions of geometry? What other tools are used in measuring and drawing geometric figures?
5. Illustrate a straight line; a broken line; a ray.
6. How is a line named?
7. Illustrate a circle; a radius; a diameter; an arc.
8. What are concentric circles? Illustrate.
9. How is a circle named?
10. What are intersecting lines? Illustrate.
11. Can curved lines intersect? Illustrate.
12. Draw a straight line RS that intersects $\odot O$ at P and Q.
13. What is an angle? What are its sides? What is its vertex? Illustrate each.
14. Draw an angle and letter it $\angle HTM$. Then draw another angle $\angle VCK$ such that $\angle VCK > \angle HTM$. Explain why $\angle VCK > \angle HTM$.
15. What is meant by the initial side of an angle? The terminal side? Illustrate.
16. Define adjacent angles. Illustrate.
17. Define perpendicular lines. Illustrate.
18. What is a right angle? An acute angle? An obtuse angle? A straight angle? Illustrate each.
19. Define *bisect*. What is a perpendicular bisector? Illustrate.
20. Construct a perpendicular bisector of a line segment and describe the process.
21. Construct the bisector of an angle and describe the process.
22. Construct a right triangle.
23. Draw an obtuse triangle.
24. What is a median of a triangle? Draw $\triangle ABC$ and construct one of its medians. Describe the process.
25. Construct a perpendicular to a given line at a given point on the line. Describe the process.

26. Construct a perpendicular to a given line from a given point not on the line. Describe the process.

27. Construct an angle equal to a given angle and describe the process.

28. Draw an oblique triangle and construct one congruent to it using the three sides.

29. Draw an acute triangle and construct one congruent to it using two sides and the included angle.

30. Draw an obtuse triangle and construct one congruent to it using two angles and the included side.

YES–NO TEST

Approximately 20 minutes

Copy on your paper the numbers of the following questions. If the answer to a question is *yes* under all conditions, place a plus sign (+) after its number. If the answer is *not yes* under all conditions, place a zero (0) after its number.

1. Is this figure a line?
2. Is a line segment the same as a line?
3. Is a radius of a circle equal to two diameters?
4. Are concentric circles the same size?
5. Is an arc a part of the compasses?
6. Does the size of an angle depend upon the lengths of the sides?
7. Does the vertex of an angle lie on both sides of the angle?
8. Does an angle have three sides?
9. Are two lines perpendicular if they form an angle of 90°?
10. Does *bisect* mean to divide a figure into two equal parts?
11. Is an oblique angle an obtuse angle?
12. Is a degree one sixtieth of a right angle?
13. Is a right angle an acute angle?
14. Does a perpendicular to a line bisect the line?
15. Is the distance from a point to a line measured on the perpendicular from the point to the line?
16. Is the distance between two points on a circle measured on an arc?

17. Do congruent triangles have the same shape?
18. Do congruent triangles have the same size?
19. Are all circles congruent?
20. Does a circle have length?
21. Is an obtuse angle larger than an acute angle?
22. Is a line segment a median if it contains the mid-point of a side of a triangle?
23. If a line passes through the mid-point of a line segment, is it the perpendicular bisector of the segment?

COMPLETION TEST

Approximately 25 minutes

Copy on your paper the numbers of the following statements. After each number write a word or expression which, if written in the blank, would complete the statement and make it true. If more than one blank occurs, give expressions to fill both. Do not write in your book.

1. A closed curve all points of which are equally distant from a fixed point is a _____.
2. Two rays with the same initial point form an _____.
3. If a geometric figure is divided into two equal parts, it is said to be _____.
4. A part of a circle is an _____.
5. The distance from a point on a circle to the center is a _____.
6. The angle included by rays drawn from a point is the angle that they _____.
7. The rays that form an angle are the _____ of the angle.
8. The point where two rays meet is called the _____ of the angle formed by them.
9. If two lines meet so as to form equal adjacent angles, the lines are _____.
10. If two angles have the same vertex, a common side, and nonintersecting interiors, the angles are _____.
11. If two lines meet so as to form equal adjacent angles, each angle is a _____ angle.

12. An angle greater than a right angle and less than a straight angle is ――――.

13. An angle less than a right angle is ――――.

14. The unit used in measuring angles is a ――――.

15. The tools used in making geometric constructions are (*a*) ――――
and (*b*) ――――.

Statement. On the basis of the sizes of their angles, triangles are right, acute, or obtuse.

16. △*ABC* is ―――― **17.** △*DEF* is ―――― **18.** △*JKL* is ――――

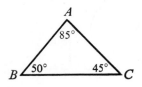
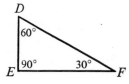
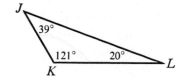

To construct the perpendicular bisector of line segment *AB*.

19. With *A* and *B* as centers draw arcs that intersect at *C* and *D* using a radius greater than ――――.

20. Draw ――――.

21. Then *AB* is bisected at ――――.

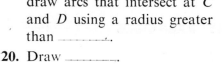

To construct a triangle congruent to a given triangle using the three sides of the given triangle *ABC*.

22. Draw any line ――――.

23. On *EG* mark off *EF*
= ――――.

24. With center *E* draw an arc with radius equal to ――――.

25. With radius equal to *AC* draw an arc with center at ――――.

26. The arcs intersect at ――――.

27. Draw ―――― and ――――.

28. The required triangle is ――――.

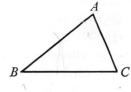
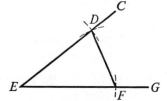

To bisect a given angle *ABC*.

29. Draw an arc intersecting *AB* at *D* and *BC* at *E*, the center of the arc being at _____.

30. With *D* and *E* as centers and any radius greater than $\frac{1}{2}DE$, draw arcs that intersect at _____.

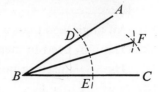

31. Draw _____.

32. _____ = _____

To construct a perpendicular to a line *AB* at a point *C* on the line.

33. With any radius draw arcs that intersect *AB* at *D* and *E*, the center being at _____.

34. Draw two arcs that intersect at *F*, the centers being at _____ and _____.

35. Draw _____.

36. *CF* ⊥ _____

SUPPLEMENTARY EXERCISES

Lines and Points

1. How many lines can be drawn through one given point? Illustrate your answer.

2. How many points can be on one given line? Illustrate your answer.

3. How many lines can be drawn through two given points? Illustrate.

4. How many points can be common to two straight lines that intersect? Illustrate.

5. How many lines at most are determined by three points placed at random? Illustrate.

6. Three lines drawn at random will intersect at most in how many points? Illustrate.

7. How is a point represented? Illustrate.

8. How is a line represented? Illustrate.

9. Can one segment be perpendicular to another without bisecting it? Illustrate your answer.

10. Can one segment bisect another without being perpendicular to it? Illustrate your answer.

11. Draw acute angles of two sizes.

12. Draw obtuse angles of two sizes.

13. Draw oblique angles of two sizes.

14. Draw two unlike angles that are neither acute nor obtuse. What kind of angle is each?

15. Draw two lines that do not form an angle.

16. In a drawing the sides of an acute angle are represented by 2 inch long segments, and the sides of an obtuse angle by 1 inch long segments. Which angle is larger?

17. Draw two adjacent acute angles.

18. Draw two adjacent obtuse angles.

19. Draw an acute and an obtuse angle that are adjacent.

20. How many sides has an angle?

21. Does every angle have a vertex?

22. How many vertices has an angle?

23. Draw an angle and letter it $\angle ABC$.

24. Draw an angle and letter it $\angle BAC$.

25. Draw an angle and letter it $\angle ACB$.

26. Construct a right angle.

27. Draw acute angle XYZ and bisect it. Test your construction by folding.

28. Draw straight angle PQR and bisect; then bisect each part again.

29. With the protractor make angles of 34°, 67°, 111°, 162°, 187°.

30. Fold down a corner of your paper and measure with the protractor the angle which the crease makes with the edge of the paper.

31. Draw two lines that intersect and measure each of the four angles formed by them.

32. Draw a triangle, letter it triangle ABC, measure the three angles and find their sum.

33. Draw a line segment, make an angle of 116° at one end and an angle of 20° at the other end. Measure the angle formed by the last lines drawn at the point where they meet.

34. Draw a triangle and construct the bisectors of its three angles.

35. Draw an obtuse angle and divide it into 4 equal angles, using the straightedge and compass.

36. Construct two perpendicular lines. What kind of angles are formed by them?

37. How many minutes are there in 14 degrees?

38. How many degrees are there in an angle of 420 minutes?

39. How many seconds are there in half a degree?

40. Change 12° 11′ 13″ to seconds.

41. Change 29° 42′ 5″ to seconds.

42. Draw an angle that contains 36,000 seconds.

43. Draw an acute angle and letter it $\angle ABC$. Construct $\angle XYZ = \angle ABC$.

44. Draw obtuse $\angle PQR$ and construct $\angle STV = \angle PQR$.

45. Draw an obtuse angle and an acute angle. Construct an angle equal to their sum. Construct an angle equal to their difference.

Circles

46. Does a circle have more than one center?

47. Can more than one diameter be drawn in a circle? Illustrate.

48. Can more than one radius be drawn in a circle? Illustrate.

49. Can two circles of different sizes have the same center? Illustrate.

50. Can concentric circles intersect each other?

51. Can circles of equal radii intersect each other? Illustrate.

52. Can circles having unequal radii intersect? Illustrate.

53. Can a straight line and a circle intersect? Illustrate.

54. Can you draw two diameters of a circle that do not intersect? Illustrate your answer.

55. Do two radii of a circle determine an angle? Illustrate your answer.

56. What is meant by the angle formed by two radii?

57. Can two circles be drawn so that they intersect in more than two points?

58. Draw an arc and letter it arc AB.

Triangles

59. How many sides has a triangle?

60. How many angles has a triangle?

61. How many vertices has a triangle?

62. Construct a right triangle.

63. Draw an acute triangle.

64. Draw an obtuse triangle.

65. Draw a triangle and construct its medians.

66. Draw a triangle and construct its altitudes.

67. Construct a triangle having sides 2 inches, $1\frac{1}{2}$ inches, and 1 inch.

68. Construct a triangle one side of which is 1 inch and each of the other sides is 2 inches.

69. Construct a triangle each side of which is 2 inches. Measure each angle with the protractor. How many degrees has each?

70. Draw any acute triangle and construct one congruent to it using the three sides. Test by measurement.

71. Draw any obtuse triangle and construct one congruent to it using two sides and the included angle. Test by measurement.

72. Draw any obtuse triangle and construct one congruent to it using two angles and the included side. Test by measurement.

CONSTRUCTIONS

To construct the perpendicular from a point P to a line ST.

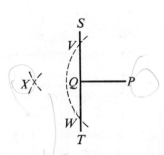

73. What is the center of arc VW?

74. What is the radius of arc VW?

75. What points are used as centers in drawing the arcs that intersect at X?

76. What radii are used in drawing the arcs that intersect at X?

77. What points determine the position of the perpendicular?

78. Do this construction on your paper and test by measuring $\angle SQP$.

Wayne State University, Detroit, Michigan

CHAPTER 2

GEOMETRIC PROOF — ANGLE PAIRS

In dealing with angles, we do not often consider one angle alone. Usually we compare one with another, or we combine two or more by addition or subtraction. We say: two angles are equal, or one is larger than the other; one is a definite number of times the size of the other; the sum or the difference of two or more angles is a definite quantity.

Often when we are conscious of dealing with only one angle, as when we measure it, we are really comparing it with another. For example, when you measure an angle with a protractor, or when the surveyor measures an angle with a transit, the process determines the number of times the given angle contains a unit angle called a *degree*.

In what follows, you are to learn about certain angle pairs which frequently occur throughout your study of geometry. In many familiar objects about you, such as floors, windows, gates, streets, bridges, machines, you will see illustrations of pairs of angles such as those whose relationships are to be studied in this chapter.

In order to study the relationships of angles, and to study other relationships, we need to know something about how conclusions are reached logically. We shall learn some of the principles of reasoning in connection with our study of angle pairs. These principles will then be applied throughout the study of geometry.

43

2–1 Conditional Statement. Hypothesis and Conclusion In geometry we find it necessary to do careful reasoning. Hence it is necessary to become acquainted with some of the terms and processes that are used.

You may have heard people make statements such as these:

If I miss the bus, then I shall be late for work.
If you keep a house well painted, then it will not decay.

Statements of this type assert that if certain conditions exist, then specific conclusions follow. Another way of expressing this is to say that if certain conditions are fulfilled, then certain results follow. *If . . ., then . . .* statements such as these we shall call conditional statements. The clause that is introduced by *if* expresses a condition. The clause introduced by *then* expresses a conclusion that follows.

We shall deal with many conditional statements in our study of geometry. Not every conditional statement contains the words *if* and *then*, but it does contain a condition and a conclusion. Some of the facts that we learned in Chapter 1 can be written as conditional statements. For example, the statement: *Corresponding parts of congruent figures are equal* can also be written in the form: *If two figures are congruent, then their corresponding parts are equal.* The condition of congruence implies the conclusion that the corresponding parts are equal.

Two points determine only one straight line is another conditional statement. It can be written in the form: *If two points are given, then only one straight line can be drawn through them.*

The clause introduced by the word *if* is called the hypothesis. It states at least one given condition. The clause introduced by the word *then* is called the conclusion. It states a consequence of the hypothesis.

EXERCISES

The following are conditional statements. Rewrite them in *if . . ., then . . .* form.

1. A right angle has 90°. *Hint.* If an angle is a right angle, then . . .
2. A right angle is an angle that is one half of a straight angle.
3. An acute angle is an angle that is smaller than a right angle.
4. A median of a triangle is a segment that is drawn from the vertex of an angle to the mid-point of the opposite side.
5. A person who is twenty-one years old or over has the right to vote. *Hint.* If a person is . . .
6. A triangle is a geometric figure that has three sides.

2–2   What Assumption Means   A city election was to be held in Bolton. Mr. Ridley said to Mr. Patton, "I assume that you will go to the polls next Tuesday.   Vote for Lewman for city treasurer.   He is a successful businessman."

Now, Mr. Ridley had said three things.

(1) He had stated the assumption that Mr. Patton would go to the polls.

(2) He had recommended Mr. Lewman as city treasurer.

(3) He had given a reason for his recommendation.

An assumption is a statement held as true without proof and used as the basis for further reasoning.

It is clear that Mr. Ridley had made an assumption other than the one that he had stated:

(4) He assumed that the candidate who is successful in his private business will make the best city treasurer.

Since this assumption (4) was not stated nor mentioned in the conversation quoted above, it is called a tacit assumption.

Often when an assumption is made, it would be possible to choose another assumption.   In considering the characteristics of a good definition, we pointed out the impossibility of giving a definition of every term because you need some words to start.   In the very same way it is not possible to prove every assertion that is made in a discussion.   The only reasonable way out is to accept some unproved statements or assumptions as a start.

2–3   Postulate   In geometry we state our assumptions explicitly and make systematic use of them.   In mathematics an assumption is usually called a postulate or an axiom,   In this book we shall use only the word *postulate* to designate an assumption.

A postulate is a statement assumed to be true.   For example, we have a postulate which states: If equal quantities are added to equal quantities of the same kind, the sums are equal.

We shall introduce the postulates as they are needed.   A list of these may not agree with a list that you may find in another book.   You should remember also that in any particular case it may be possible to select some postulate other than the one that is stated.   However, we could not choose a postulate that contradicts one that we have previously accepted or that contradicts any statement proved as the result of using any of our postulates.   The whole structure of our subject would be destroyed by such a contradiction.

2–4 Theorem. Deductive Reasoning Using our definitions and postulates, we can, by a process of reasoning, arrive at new if-then or conditional statements that are true. These new conditional statements are called *theorems*.

A theorem is a statement that can be derived from the postulates, definitions, undefined terms, and previously proved statements by reasoning. An example of a theorem, which will be proved later in this book, is the following:

If in a triangle two sides are unequal, then the two angles in the triangle opposite these sides are unequal.

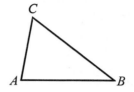

The figure is an illustration of this theorem. In the triangle *ABC*, side *BC* is not equal to side *AC*. The conclusion is that angle *BAC*, opposite side *BC*, is not equal to angle *CBA*, which is opposite side *AC*.

You can now leaf through this book and read many more theorems which you will study and prove.

The type of reasoning we do in showing that the theorem is a true statement is called deductive reasoning. Below are two simple examples of such reasoning. In each case the first two statements are given as accepted facts. The third statement is then a conclusion logically implied by the first two.

Example 1:

   (1) If a closed plane figure is a triangle, it has three sides.
   (2) A given figure is a triangle.

Therefore

   (3) The given figure has three sides.

Example 2:

   (1) If an angle is less than a right angle, it is an acute angle.
   (2) Half of a right angle is less than a right angle.
   (3) Half of a right angle is an acute angle.

By continuing a number of arguments in this fashion, starting with certain hypotheses, we can arrive at a *valid* conclusion. The hypotheses and conclusions thus form a theorem.

Exercise. Follow the pattern of Example 2 above and show that if $\angle V$ is $1\frac{1}{2}$ rt. $\angle$s it is obtuse. You must show two things. See Sec. 0–18.

2–5 Demonstration After each of the constructions done in Chapter 1, we applied tests and made observations on the basis of which we drew conclusions. Such conclusions are not deductive in a mathematical sense and cannot be accepted with entire confidence for a number of reasons. (*a*) There is always the possibility that our instruments do not give wholly accurate figures. (*b*) The human eye cannot detect very small differences in lengths and sizes of figures. (*c*) The figures are illustrations and may not be truly representative of all possible figures for which we wish to make a general statement of fact.

When we make a statement of fact, we want to know with reasonable assurance that it is true for every instance, and we want to be able to give a proof so that no one can have any doubt as to its truth. Such proof of a statement in geometry is called a *demonstration*.

A demonstration is a chain of reasoning by which we prove that a stated conclusion logically follows from stated hypotheses. A demonstration makes use of

(*a*) certain undefined terms
(*b*) certain defined terms
(*c*) certain accepted statements called postulates
(*d*) certain previously proved statements
(*e*) laws of logic.

2–6 Parts of a Demonstration For convenience, a geometric demonstration is usually divided into five parts. (*a*) The *statement* of the theorem that is to be proved. (*b*) A *figure* which illustrates the theorem. (*c*) Statement of the *hypothesis* in terms of the figure. (*d*) Statement of the *conclusion* in terms of the figure. (*e*) The *proof*, which consists of a series of statements with a reason for each.

When helping lines are to be used in the figure, it is well to insert a step between (*d*) and (*e*) describing the construction of these lines. Often a geometric demonstration may require two or more figures while at other times it may be impossible to draw a suitable figure.

In making a geometric demonstration, one of the important steps is to analyze the theorem and decide correctly what is the hypothesis and what is the conclusion.

Often the hypothesis has two or more parts. When this is the case, each of the parts should be carefully set down. For example, look at Ex. 21 on page 52. The hypothesis has two parts. Sometimes the conclusion has two or more parts. For example, look at Ex. 5 on page 115. The conclusion has two parts.

EXERCISES

Below are given a number of theorems. Copy each, draw a figure to illustrate it, and tell what is given and what is to be proved, or what is required to be done. No proof is to be attempted here. The first exercise is worked out completely. The others should be done in the same manner.

1. Theorem. Any two right angles are equal.
    Hypothesis. *ABC* and *DEF* are rt. ∠s.
    Conclusion. ∠*ABC* = ∠*DEF*

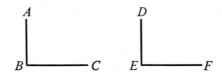

2. Theorem. If two sides of a triangle are equal, the angles opposite these sides are equal.
3. Theorem. If the three sides of a triangle are equal, the three angles are equal.
4. Theorem. If the three angles of a triangle are equal, the three sides are equal.
5. Theorem. If the three angles of a triangle are added, the sum is a straight angle.
6. Theorem. A diagonal of a square divides it into two congruent triangles.
7. Theorem. If the radius of a circle is *r*, its area is πr^2.

Quantity We use the word *quantity* to mean anything that can be measured, such as angles, line segments, surfaces, and so on. Measures are expressed by numbers. When we refer to addition and subtraction of quantities of the same kind, we refer to the addition and subtraction of the measures of quantities of the same kind. Line segments and angles are not quantities of the same kind so it would not make sense to combine their measures. An area of a triangle and an area of a circle are quantities of the same kind; they are measures of surfaces which may be combined or compared.

Two quantities are either equal, or one is greater than the other. $a = b$ is read "*a* equals *b*"; $r > s$ is read "*r* is greater than *s*"; $v < w$ is read "*v* is less than *w*." A cancel line means *not*. Thus, $c \neq d$ is read "*c* does not equal *d*"; $e \nless f$ is read "*e* is not less than *f*." How do you read $g \ngtr h$?

2–7 POSTULATE 1 The whole of any quantity is equal to the sum of its distinct parts.

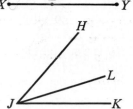

By <u>distinct parts</u> we mean that no part includes or overlaps any other part.

Example 1: $XY = XZ + ZY$
Example 2: $\angle HJK = \angle HJL + \angle LJK$

2–8 POSTULATE 2 In any equation or inequality a quantity may be substituted for one that is equal to it.

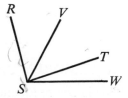

Example: Suppose that $\angle RSV = \angle VST$ and that $\angle VST + \angle TSW = 60°$. We may substitute $\angle RSV$ for $\angle VST$ in the equation $\angle VST + \angle TSW = 60°$. Then $\angle RSV + \angle TSW = 60°$.

2–9 POSTULATE 3 If equal quantities are divided by the same number, not zero, the quotients are equal.

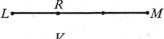

Example: If $LM = ST$,
   then $\frac{1}{3}LM = \frac{1}{3}ST$.

2–10 POSTULATE 4 If equal quantities are multiplied by the same number, the products are equal.

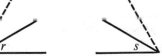

Example: If $\angle r = \angle s$,
   then $2\angle r = 2\angle s$.

2–11 POSTULATE 5 If equal quantities are added to equal quantities of the same kind, the sums are equal.

Example: If $\angle x = \angle y$ and $\angle z = \angle w$,
   then $\angle x + \angle z = \angle y + \angle w$.

2–12 POSTULATE 6 If equal quantities are subtracted from equal quantities of the same kind, the remainders are equal.

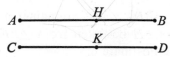

Example: If $AB = CD$ and $AH = CK$,
   then $AB - AH = CD - CK$,
   or $HB = KD$.

2–13 THEOREM **A right angle is one half of a straight angle.**

Proof Let AB be $\perp CD$. Then $\angle ABC$ and $\angle ABD$ are right angles. (See Sec. 0–16.) Now $\angle ABC + \angle ABD = \angle CBD$ by Postulate 1, and $\angle CBD$ is a straight angle. By Postulate 2 we can substitute $\angle ABC$ for $\angle ABD$ and thus $2\angle ABC = \angle CBD$. Hence, $\angle ABC = \frac{1}{2}\angle CBD$ by Postulate 3.

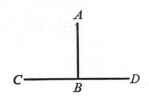

2–14 POSTULATE 7 **Any two straight angles are equal.**

Example: $\angle HJK = \angle LJM$

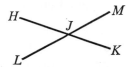

2–15 THEOREM **Any two right angles are equal.**

This is a consequence of Sec. 2–13, and Postulate 7.

2–16 POSTULATE 8 **At a point on a given line there can be at least one line that is perpendicular to the given line.**

2–17 THEOREM **At a point on a given line there can be only one line perpendicular to the given line.**

If there were more than one perpendicular, we should have unequal right angles, which contradicts Sec. 2–15, that all right angles are equal.

2–18 Complementary Angles Complementary angles are two angles whose sum is a right angle. Each angle is called the *complement* of the other.

2–19 THEOREM **Complements of the same angle or of equal angles are equal.**

Proof Let $\angle CBD = \angle GFH$, $\angle ABC$ be the complement of $\angle CBD$, and $\angle EFG$ be the complement of $\angle GFH$. $\angle ABD = \angle EFH$ since both are right angles. If $\angle CBD$ be taken from $\angle ABD$, $\angle ABC$ remains, and if $\angle GFH$ be taken from $\angle EFH$, $\angle EFG$ remains. Then $\angle ABC = \angle EFG$ by Postulate 6.

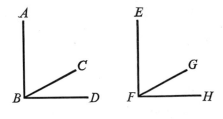

2–20 Supplementary Angles Supplementary angles are two angles whose sum is a straight angle. Each angle is called the *supplement* of the other.

2–21 THEOREM Supplements of the same angle or of equal angles are equal.

Exercise. Prove the theorem just stated. Follow a plan like that used in Sec. 2–19.

EXERCISES

Oral

1. ABC is a straight line. Therefore $\angle ABC$ is a _____ angle.

2. AC is bisected at B. Therefore _____ = _____.

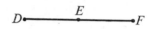

3. $\angle DEF$ is a straight $\angle$. Therefore DEF is a _____ line.

4. $DE = EF$. Therefore DF is _____ at E.

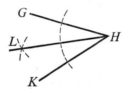

5. $\angle GHK$ is bisected. Therefore _____ = _____.

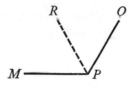

6. $\angle MPR = \angle RPQ$. Therefore $\angle MPQ$ is _____.

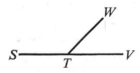

7. $\angle STW$ and $\angle WTV$ are supplementary. Therefore $\angle STW + \angle WTV =$ _____°.

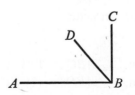

8. $\angle ABD + \angle DBC =$ a rt. $\angle$. Therefore $\angle ABD$ and $\angle DBC$ are _____ angles.

9. $\angle EFH + \angle HFG$ = a st. $\angle$. Therefore $\angle EFH$ and $\angle HFG$ are _____ angles.

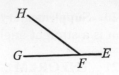

10. $\angle JKM$ and $\angle MKL$ are complementary. Then $\angle JKM + \angle MKL$ = a _____ $\angle$.

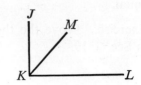

11. $\angle OPQ$ is a st. $\angle$. SP bisects $\angle OPR$ and TP bisects $\angle RPQ$. How many degrees are there in $\angle SPT$?

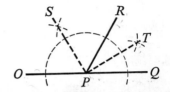

12. $WV \perp UV$. YV bisects $\angle UVX$, and ZV bisects $\angle XVW$. How many degrees are there in $\angle YVZ$?

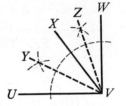

13. Which is the larger, an acute angle or its supplement?
14. How many degrees are there in the difference between the complement and the supplement of an angle?
15. How many degrees are there in a straight angle? A right angle?
16. Find the complement of an angle of 11°. Find its supplement.

Written

C.

17. What is the complement of 47° 12'? Of 86° 29'?
18. How many degrees are there in the supplement of 161° 26'?
19. Draw $\angle ABC$. Construct its supplement.
20. Draw an acute $\angle XYZ$ and its complement.

B.

21. Hyp. $\angle ABC$ = 1 rt. $\angle$, $\angle DBE$ = 1 rt. $\angle$
    Con. $\angle ABD = \angle CBE$

22. An angle is twice its complement. How many degrees does it contain? *Suggestion.* Let x = number of degrees in the complement; $2x$ = _____. $x + 2x = $?

23. An angle contains 4° more than its supplement. Find the number of degrees in the angle and in its supplement.

24. Find the number of degrees in an angle the sum of whose complement and supplement is 200°.

25. Draw acute $\angle RST$. Construct its supplement $\angle X$. Construct its complement $\angle Y$. Construct $\angle X - \angle Y$. With the protractor measure $\angle X - \angle Y$. How many degrees are there in $\angle X - \angle Y$?

The following theorem and steps show one way of presenting a proof. The reason supporting a statement is given to the right of the statement. Note that the last statement is the conclusion of the theorem and that the hypotheses were used in earlier statements. Thus granting the hypotheses we have established the conclusion. The theorem is proved.

2–22 Vertical Angles If two angles have the same vertex, and the sides of one are extensions of the sides of the other through the vertex, the angles are called vertical angles. The extension of a ray is the other half-line.

2–23 THEOREM Vertical angles are equal.

Hypothesis Lines AB and CD intersecting at E forming pairs of vertical angles 1 and 2, 3 and 4

Conclusion $\angle 1 = \angle 2$; $\angle 3 = \angle 4$

The plan is to show that vertical angles are supplements of the same angle.

Proof

1. $\angle 1$ and $\angle 3$ are adjacent angles.   1. Sec. 0–15
2. $\angle 1$ and $\angle 3$ are supplementary.   2. Sec. 2–20
3. $\angle 2$ and $\angle 3$ are adjacent angles.   3. Same as 1 above
4. $\angle 2$ and $\angle 3$ are supplementary.   4. Same as 2 above
5. $\angle 1$ and $\angle 2$ have the same supplement, $\angle 3$.   5. Statements 2 and 4
6. $\angle 1 = \angle 2$ 6. Sec. 2–21
7. $\angle 3 = \angle 4$ 7. Steps 1 to 6 using $\angle 1$ as the common supplement

MISCELLANEOUS WRITTEN EXERCISES

C.

1. Write out all the steps to prove statement 7 in the theorem above.
2. $\angle A$ and $\angle B$ are complementary. $\angle A = 2x$ degrees; $\angle B = 3x$ degrees. Find the number of degrees in each angle.
3. $\angle C$ and $\angle D$ are supplementary. $\angle C = 7x$ degrees; $\angle D = 3x$ degrees. Find the number of degrees in each angle.

B.

4. What is the sum of all the angles about a point that fill the plane but do not overlap?
   Suggestions. Draw a line through the point. What is the sum of all the angles on one side of the line?
5. Six angles fill the plane about a point. Measured in degrees, the angles are x, $\dfrac{x}{2}$, $2x$, $\dfrac{3x}{4}$, $2\tfrac{1}{4}x$, and $\dfrac{3x}{2}$. Find the number of degrees in each angle.
6. What is the size of each of the four angles that fill the plane about a point if each angle after the first is twice as large as the one preceding it?

7. What is the sum of the three angles inside $\triangle ABC$?

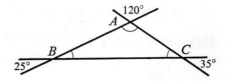

8. What is the sum of the three angles inside $\triangle DEF$?

9. What is the sum of the four angles inside the figure $GHKL$?

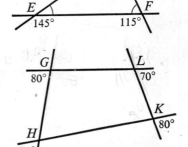

OUTLINE OF CHAPTER 2

This chapter introduces the following terms:

conditional statement	postulate	demonstration
hypothesis	axiom	complementary angles
conclusion	theorem	supplementary angles
assumption	distinct parts	vertical angles
tacit assumption	deductive reasoning	

This chapter presents information concerning:

1. Conditional statement. Page 44
2. The nature of a postulate. Page 45
3. The parts of a demonstration. Page 47
4. The essential parts of a theorem. Page 46
5. How a geometric proof is made. Page 47
6. How to organize a geometric proof. Page 53
7. Eight postulates. Pages 49, 50
8. Relation between right angles and straight angles. Page 50
9. Relation between any two right angles. Page 50
10. Relation between complements or supplements of equal angles. Pages 50, 51
11. Relation between vertical angles. Page 53

REVIEW

1. What is a conditional statement? Illustrate.
2. What is meant by hypothesis? By conclusion? Illustrate.
3. Put into *if* . . ., *then* . . . form the statement "A triangle has three sides." What is the hypothesis? What is the conclusion?
4. What is an assumption? Illustrate.
5. What is meant by tacit assumption? Illustrate.
6. What is a postulate? Give three examples.
7. Would you expect that the list of postulates given in one geometry textbook would agree in all details with the list given in another? Why?
8. What is a theorem? Illustrate by stating a geometric theorem.

9. What is meant by deductive reasoning?

10. What is meant by demonstration? What are the principal parts of a geometric demonstration?

11. Theorem. If the three angles of a triangle are equal, the three sides are equal. In this theorem what is the hypothesis? What is the conclusion?

12. Theorem. Complements of the same angle are equal. Give a deductive proof of this theorem.

13. An angle is three times its supplement. How many degrees are there in the angle?

14. What are vertical angles? Illustrate.

15. Give a demonstration that vertical angles are equal.

YES—NO TEST

Time: about 5 minutes

Copy on your paper the numbers of the following questions. If the answer to a question is *yes* under all conditions, place a plus sign (+) after its number. If the answer is *not yes* under all conditions, place a zero (0) after its number.

1. Is a straight line a straight angle?
2. Is a straight angle half a right angle?
3. Are all right angles equal?
4. Is the sum of complementary angles 180°?
5. Is the complement of an angle equal to its supplement?
6. Are complementary angles adjacent?
7. Are angles of 80° 10′ and 100° 50′ supplementary?
8. Are angles of 26° 30′ and 63° 30′ complementary?
9. Are vertical angles complementary?
10. Is a 60° angle half its supplement?
11. Is a postulate a theorem?
12. Is a hypothesis a part of a theorem?
13. Is deductive reasoning used in geometry?
14. Is a postulate an assumption?

COMPLETION TEST

Time: about 5 minutes

Copy on your paper the numbers of the following statements. After each number write the word, or letters, or number, or expression which if written in the blank would complete the statement and make it true.

1. $\angle ABC$ can be denoted with one letter, $\angle$_____.

2. $\angle C$ can be denoted with three letters, $\angle$_____.

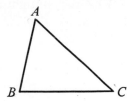

3. Two angles are supplementary if their sum is _____.

4. Two angles are complementary if their sum is _____.

5. Vertical angles are $\angle a$ and $\angle$_____.

6. Adjacent angles are $\angle c$ and $\angle$_____.

7. $\angle x =$ _____°

8. $\angle y =$ _____°

9. $\angle z =$ _____°

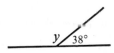

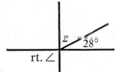

10. $\angle ABC$ contains _____ degrees.

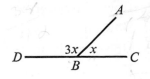

11. $\angle EFG =$ a rt. $\angle$; $\angle HJK$ = a rt. $\angle$; $\angle r = \angle s$ because _____ of equal angles are equal.

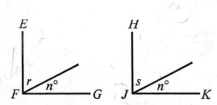

12. $\angle x = \angle y$ because _____ of equal angles are equal.

13. AB is _____ to BC.

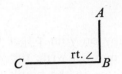

14. $\angle XYZ$ is a straight angle. WY bisects $\angle XYZ$. $\angle WYZ$ is a _____ angle.

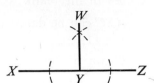

SUPPLEMENTARY EXERCISES

C.

1. What is the complement of each of the following angles? (*a*) 21°; (*b*) 1°; (*c*) 89°; (*d*) 51°; (*e*) 63°; (*f*) $82\frac{1}{2}°$; (*g*) 31° 14′; (*h*) 46° 46′; (*i*) 13° 21′ 46″

2. What is the supplement of each of the following angles? (*a*) 90°; (*b*) 30°; (*c*) 146°; (*d*) 1°; (*e*) 179°; (*f*) $62\frac{1}{3}°$; (*g*) 26° 19′; (*h*) 129° 52′; (*i*) 112° 14′ 28″

3. What is the complement of each of the following angles? (*a*) $x°$; (*b*) $d°$; (*c*) $90° - 12°$; (*d*) $90° - a°$; (*e*) $60° - b°$; (*f*) $40n°$; (*g*) $5t°$

4. What is the supplement of each of the following angles? (*a*) $r°$; (*b*) $m°$; (*c*) $90° - 32°$; (*d*) $90° - c°$; (*e*) $180° - d°$; (*f*) $90° - e°$; (*g*) $(h + k)°$

B.

5. How many degrees are there in an angle that is $\frac{2}{3}$ its complement?

6. How large is an angle that is 5 times its complement?

7. How large is an angle that is $1\frac{1}{2}$ times its supplement?

8. How many degrees are there in an angle that is 5 times its supplement?

9. What angle is 12° 40′ more than its complement?

10. What angle is 35° 41′ less than its complement?

11. What angle is 88° 28′ less than its supplement?

12. What angle is 11° 20′ more than its supplement?

13. Is there an angle the supplement of which is twice its complement?

14. The supplement of an angle is 10° more than three times its complement. Find the angle.

15. The sum of the supplement and complement of an angle is 170°. Find the complement of the angle.

16. $\angle x$ and $\angle y$ are complementary vertical angles. Find each angle.

17. $\angle A$ and $\angle B$ are vertical angles. $\angle A$ contains $x°$, and $\angle B$ contains $90° - 2x°$. Find each angle.

CUMULATIVE REVIEW

1. An angle is 125% of its complement. What angle is it?

2. An angle is 60% of its supplement. What angle is it?

3. An angle is 25% larger than its complement. How many degrees does it contain?

4. One half of a certain angle added to one third of it equals its complement. How many degrees does it contain?

5. An angle minus its complement is 50°. How large is each?

6. Angle A is three times as large as angle B. How large is angle A if angle B is 15° 20'? If angle B is 21° 37'? 17° 56'? 12° 15' 11"?

7. The difference of two supplementary angles is 42°. Find the angles.

8. Two supplementary angles are $(5x - 7y + 27)$ degrees and $(3x + 4y - 35)$ degrees. Write in simplest form an equation that expresses this fact.

9. Two complementary angles are $(7a + 8b - 62)$ degrees and $(2b - 9a + 15)$ degrees. Write in simplest form an equation that expresses this fact.

10. An angle contains $(2x + 11)$ degrees and its vertical angle contains $(5x - 22)$ degrees. Find the number of degrees in each angle.

11. Can the complement of an angle equal its supplement? Explain.

12. Can vertical angles be supplementary? Explain.

13. Write in symbols sixty degrees nine minutes seventeen seconds.

14. What is the complement of an angle that contains $\frac{1}{4}$ of a right angle?

15. What is a diameter?

16. Draw an oblique angle and bisect it.

17. Draw a scalene triangle and construct one congruent to it using two angles and the included side.

18. Construct the perpendicular bisector of a vertical line segment.

19. What is a theorem?

CHAPTER | 3

A NEW VIEW OF CONGRUENCE

THE geometric figures that we have studied consist of points, lines, line segments, planes, rays, angles, triangles, circles, and other figures made by combining these figures in various ways. A line segment consists of two end points and all the points that are between these points and on the line that passes through them. Therefore, we say that a line segment is a figure made up of a set of points. By the word *set* we here mean a collection of all points which have the property of belonging to the line segment. Rays, lines, angles, circles, and triangles also are made up of sets of points. Thus any plane geometric figure that we study can be considered as a set of points in the plane so defined that each point of the set belongs to the figure. None of the other points of the plane belong to the figure.

3–1 One-to-One Correspondence One-to-one correspondence is one of the most fundamental ideas of comparing one set of objects with another set of objects. You have used this idea many times. For example, when you count the chairs in a room, you make a one-to-one correspondence between the counting numbers and the chairs. In doing this, you assign a chair to number one, another chair to number two, and so on until each chair has been assigned a number.

In drawing a graph of a straight line in algebra, you made a one-to-one correspondence between points in a line and ordered pairs of numbers. A point is usually represented by a dot and the ordered pair of numbers is in the form (x,y). The ordered pair of numbers designates the coordinates of the point. Thus, in this figure (0,2) corresponds to point A, and (3,4) corresponds to point B. To each point in the line there corresponds only one ordered pair of numbers, and to each of the ordered pairs of numbers that satisfy a given equation there is only one point in the line.

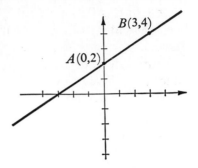

We can sometimes make a one-to-one correspondence between two sets of points. In the figure at the right the points in line segment AB and those in line segment CD are put in one-to-one correspondence by extending CA and DB to meet at P. Then a line from P to any point Q in CD intersects AB at a point R which corresponds to Q. It is easy to see that in this manner any point in CD is matched with only one point in AB. This is a way of matching sets of points in certain line segments, whether the segments are equal or unequal.

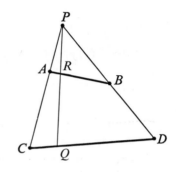

3–2 Geometric Transformation of a Point When a point A is related to another point A' in a plane by a definite process, we say A has been transformed into A'. There are three fundamental processes by which such a transformation can be made. We shall discuss each of these.

Translation Translation is a process by which a point is transformed into another at a given distance and in a given direction. In this figure we are given point A, a ray l, and a distance d. We are to transform A into A' which is a distance d from A and in the direction indicated by l. First, we construct through A a ray m parallel to l. Second, on m we measure $AA' = d$. Thus A is transformed into A' according to the stated conditions.

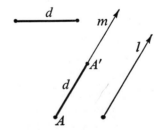

To transform a line segment by translation we (theoretically) translate each point of the line segment. In this figure we are given line segment CD, a ray r, and a distance s; we are to transform CD through a distance s in the direction indicated by r. Through points of CD (the figure shows three representative points C, X, D) we construct rays parallel to r.

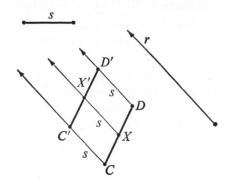

On each of these rays we measure the distance s. Thus CD is transformed into $C'D' = CD$. Such a transformation of a line segment always preserves form and distance between pairs of corresponding points. Thus, $C'X' = CX$, $X'D' = XD$, and so on. Proof of this statement depends upon a property of parallelograms which is dealt with later. Page 159

Note that translation establishes a one-to-one correspondence between points in the given line segment and points in the segment obtained by translation.

Rotation   Rotation is a process by which a point is transformed into another point through a given angle. In this figure we are given point H and angle HKL. Using K as center and KH as radius, we draw arc HH' intersecting KL at H'. Thus, H is transformed by rotation into H'.

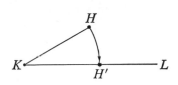

To transform a line segment by rotation we (theoretically) rotate each point of the segment through the given angle, thus establishing one-to-one correspondence between each point in the given segment and a point in the figure resulting from the transformation. In

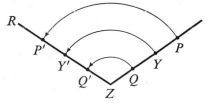

this figure we are given line segment PQ and angle RZP. Through each point in PQ (the figure shows three representative points P, Y, Q) we draw arcs with center Z, intersecting ZR. Thus PQ is transformed into $P'Q'$. Such a transformation always preserves form and distances. Thus, $PY = P'Y'$, $PQ = P'Q'$, and so on. Proof of this statement follows from subtraction of radii.

Reflection Reflection is a process by which a point is transformed into another through a distance which is bisected at right angles by a given line. In this figure we are given point A and line l. We are to transform A into A' so that l is the perpendicular bisector of the line segment AA'. First, we construct $AT \perp l$. Second, we extend AT through T to A', making $A'T = AT$. Thus A is transformed into A' by a reflection into the line l.

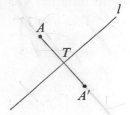

To transform a line segment by reflection we (theoretically) reflect each point in the given segment. In this figure we are given line segment RS and line j. We construct perpendiculars to j through each point in RS (the figure shows the details for representative points R, V, S). Such a transformation always preserves form and distances.

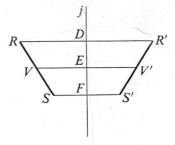

Proof of this statement depends upon a property of trapezoids which is dealt with later. Page 186

Not only points and line segments can be transformed by translation, rotation, and reflection but other geometric figures can be thus transformed, point by point. The figures below show a circle transformed by translation, a parallelogram transformed by rotation, and a triangle transformed by reflection.

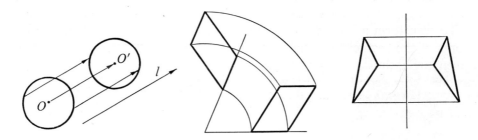

Carry out in detail the transformations suggested above and show the one-to-one correspondence of selected pairs of points. Now you see why we often say that these transformations *take one figure into another*. To take one figure into another simply means to transform a given figure by translation, rotation, or reflection.

3-3 Geometric Transformations and Congruent Figures In the work that follows, we shall use these transformations in reverse; that is, we shall be given two figures and asked if by the use of one or more of the three transformations we can take one figure into the other. If we can, we shall say the figures are congruent. We use congruent figures so often in our proofs that we have a special symbol, ≅, which is read *is congruent to* . . .

In the figures of section 3–2, $CD \cong C'D'$, $PQ \cong P'Q'$, and $RS \cong R'S'$. Here the order of the letters indicates that the initial and terminal points are to be taken in the order given. Thus, C is the initial point of CD, and Q is the terminal point of PQ.

The figure at the right shows that segment CD can be transformed into segment DC by rotating 180° about its mid-point M. C is transformed into D; P is transformed into P' where $CP = DP'$, and so on; M corresponds to itself. Since we can make a similar

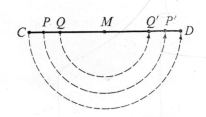

transformation of any line segment, we see that two equal line segments are congruent regardless of the order in which the initial and terminal points are taken.

POSTULATE 9 **Any two equal line segments are congruent.**

It is also true that two congruent segments are equal.

EXERCISES

1. Using a figure as shown, first reflect ABC about l. Then reflect the new figure about m. Show that the third figure could be obtained from the first by one translation.

2. Using a figure as shown, first rotate $ABCD$ about C through an angle equal to x where $CE ⫫ A'D'$. Then show how to obtain $A'B'C'D'$ by a translation.

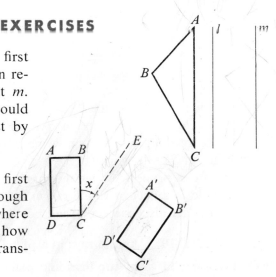

3. Place two congruent letters *A* like the one shown at different places on a sheet of paper. Discover several transformations (2 or 3 in each case) that transform one figure into the other.

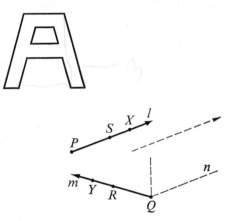

Suppose we are given two rays in a plane, *l* and *m*, with initial points *P* and *Q*. Are these rays congruent? On ray *l* we select any point *S* forming segment *PS*. Then on ray *m* we find point *R* so that *QR* = *PS*. In the same manner, to *any point X* on *l* there can be made to correspond one and only one point *Y* on *m* so that *PX* = *QY*. Then segment *SX* = segment *RY*.

By the use of properly placed mirrors, or by geometric transformations, it is possible to reflect or rotate ray *m* into *n* and then translate *n* into *l*. Without further discussion, we shall postulate:

POSTULATE 10   Any two rays in a plane are congruent.

POSTULATE 11   Any two lines in a plane are congruent.

3-4 The Triangle We shall now think of a triangle as a collection of points. Let $A, B,$ and C be three points not all in the same line or, in other words, noncollinear (Fig. I). These points may be the end points of three line segments $AB, BC,$ and CA (Fig. II). The figure consisting of three noncollinear points and all the points of the line segments connecting these three points is a triangle. To designate sets of points we write the symbols of the points in braces. Thus $\{A,B,C\}$ is a set of three points. If they are noncollinear, they determine a triangle.

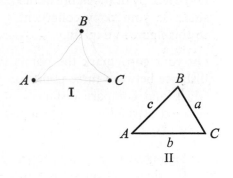

The three points are called the vertices of the triangle. The three line segments are called the sides. The sides are also named by using the small letter of the vertex of the triangle not in the segments. Thus side BC is also named a, since vertex A is not on segment BC. We also say side a is opposite vertex A. Sides AB and CA are named respectively c and b.

Point A is the vertex of ray l containing side AB. It is also the vertex of a ray m containing side AC (Fig. III). These rays, l and m, form an angle. We call this angle an angle of the triangle, naming it angle A or angle CAB. (In naming an angle we usually go counterclockwise in the plane as shown by the arrow in Fig. III. Thus side CA comes first, then side AB, and the angle is CAB. The same angle could be labeled BAC going in clockwise direction.) Similarly the angles formed at vertex B and vertex C are called angles of the triangle.

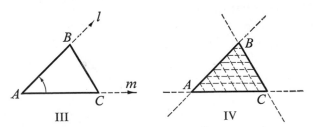

Fig. IV shows the part of the angle interiors that all three angles of the triangle have in common. This region is called the interior of the triangle. The part of the plane that is neither the triangle itself nor the interior of the triangle is called the exterior of the triangle.

EXERCISES

1. Use transparent paper and make a copy of the figure at the side. Is your copy congruent to this figure? Explain.

2. On your copy mark the points that correspond to *A* and *B*. Is the distance between these points on your copy equal to the distance *AB*? Mark and compare distances of several other corresponding points selected at random on the figure shown. What conclusions can you draw?

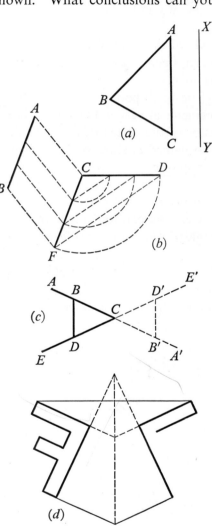

3. Make a copy of Fig. (*a*) shown on the right and on your copy construct a figure congruent to *ABC*, by dropping perpendicular lines to *XY* and extending them. Describe your construction.

4. In Fig. (*b*) *AB* and *CD* are equal line segments. Explain how the correspondence was constructed using the idea of rotation and translation.

5. Using a method similar to that in Sec. 3–3 show how to make *AB* in Fig. (*b*) correspond with *DC*. Note the order in which the points are given.

6. In Fig. (*c*) tell how ∠*E′CA′* was constructed to be congruent to ∠*ECA*. Tell which lines correspond and in what order.

7. Copy Fig. (*d*) shown at the right and complete the construction of the second letter. Describe exactly how you did the construction.

8. Using mirrors or construction, find a method to transform the first *L* into the second *L*.

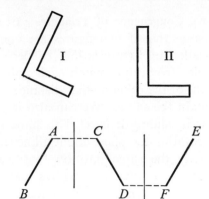

9. The figure shows how *AB* ≅ *CD* and *CD* ≅ *EF*. What conclusion can you draw about *AB* and *EF*?

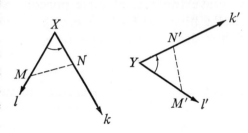

3–5 Congruence of Angles   An angle consists of two rays with the same initial point. If two angles are given in a plane, we have four rays. Let us make a transformation on the one angle so that the ray *l* is taken into ray *l'*. If the *same transformation* takes the ray *k* into the ray *k'*, we shall then say the angles are congruent. From our previous study of measurement of angles, it is evident that congruent angles are equal. It is also obvious that equal angles can be transformed into one another and are therefore congruent.

POSTULATE 12   Two equal angles are congruent.

EXERCISES

1. Is an angle congruent to itself? Explain your answer.
2. If ∠*X* is congruent to ∠*Y*, how can you show ∠*Y* is congruent to ∠*X*?
3. Given ∠*X* is congruent to ∠*Y*, and ∠*Y* is congruent to ∠*Z*. What is true of ∠*X* and ∠*Z*? Prove your statement.
4. In the figure for Sec. 3–5 we showed how ∠*MXN* was congruent to ∠*M'YN'*. Show how in this case ∠*MXN* is also congruent to ∠*N'YM'* where the order of the letters indicates the correspondence.
5. State the converse of Postulate 12. Is it true? Illustrate this converse. (*Hint.* Two congruent angles . . .)

3–6 Congruence of Triangles In the foregoing discussion we have indicated that if two figures are congruent we can, by properly drawing parallel lines (translating) or perpendicular lines (reflecting) or arcs of circles (rotating), match each point of one figure with a corresponding point of the other so that distances between pairs of corresponding points remain the same. We can also imagine this as moving the whole plane, that is, sliding it parallel to some given line, or rotating about a point, or rotating the plane about a line (reflecting) until the one figure occupies exactly the same position that was originally occupied by the other. Thus: Congruence of figures means a correspondence of the points by translation, reflection, or rotation so that distances between pairs of corresponding points of the figures are equal. We shall think of congruence in this manner in the rest of this book. We shall also say that the one figure has been made to *coincide* with the other.

When we say three noncollinear points *determine* a triangle, we mean that the three points select in the plane a particular triangle. Suppose we have two sets of three noncollinear points which we represent by $\{A,B,C\}$ and $\{D,E,F\}$. We wish to know what it means to say that the points determine two congruent triangles, and under what conditions they do so.

If we can transform one triangle so that the transformed triangle will occupy exactly the same position as the other triangle, the triangles are congruent. This is the same as saying that one triangle can be made to coincide with the other. *The corresponding sides are equal, and the corresponding angles are equal.* This is what is meant by saying triangles are congruent.

We use the symbol c p c t e for *corresponding parts of congruent triangles are equal.* Also see page 30.

First Case Suppose the selected points are such that $AB = DE$, $AC = DF$, and $\angle BAC = \angle EDF$. From the previous discussion, since the angles are equal they are also congruent and hence $\angle BAC$ can be made to coincide with $\angle EDF$. Since segment $AB = DE$, we know point B can be made to coincide with point E. Similarly since $AC = DF$, point C can be made to coincide with F. Then segment BC coincides with DF. (Two points determine only one segment.) Since now all points of $\triangle ABC$ are paired with points of $\triangle DEF$ and corresponding distances are equal, the triangles are congruent.

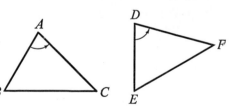

POSTULATE 13 **Two triangles are congruent if two sides and the in-cluded angle of one are equal respectively to two sides and the included angle of the other.** We abbreviate this to (sas).

3–7 Congruence of geometric figures uses the following three relations:

(a) A geometric figure is congruent to itself. This is the <u>identity relation</u>. Thus we say, for example, segment $AB \cong AB$ by identity.

(b) If one figure is congruent to a second, then the second figure is con-gruent to the first. This is the <u>symmetric relation</u>. Thus we say: If $\angle X \cong \angle Y$, then $\angle Y \cong \angle X$.

(c) If one figure is congruent to a second, and the second is congruent to the third, then the first figure is congruent to the third. This is the <u>transitive relation</u>. Thus we say, for example, if $\triangle ABC \cong \triangle DEF$, and $\triangle DEF \cong \triangle XYZ$, then $\triangle ABC \cong \triangle XYZ$.

Study these relations, replacing the word *figure* successively with *seg-ment, ray, line, angle,* and *triangle.*

3–8 Analyzing a Situation to Discover a Method of Proof In proving exercises and propositions, it often happens that one cannot see immedi-ately from the hypothesis through the various steps to the conclusion. It is often helpful to start at the conclusion and work back, step by step, until the hypothesis is reached. This process is called *analysis.* After the various steps are discovered, one can then write the proof in direct order.

Example: Hypothesis. $AD \perp BC, BD = DC$ Conclusion. $AB = AC$

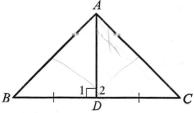

One may reason:

$AB = AC$ if $\triangle ABD \cong \triangle ACD$.

But $\triangle ABD \cong \triangle ACD$ if the conditions of Postulate 13 are met. Now, $BD = DC$, $\angle 1 = \angle 2$ (Why?), and $AD = AD$.

$\therefore \triangle ABD \cong \triangle ACD$ and hence $AB = AC$.

NOTE: The symbol $\therefore$ is read "therefore" or "hence."

Proof.
1. $BD = DC$
2. $\angle 1 =$ a rt. $\angle$
3. $\angle 2 =$ a rt. $\angle$
4. $\angle 1 = \angle 2$
5. $AD = AD$
6. $\triangle ABD \cong \triangle ACD$
7. $\therefore AB = AC$

1. Hyp.
2. Sec. 0–16
3. Why?
4. Post. 2
5. By identity
6. s a s
7. c p c t e

In the following exercises and throughout your work in geometry, carefully analyze a situation whenever necessary to find a method for proving difficult relations. Such analysis is a part of your work in preparing to write out a demonstration or to give a proof in the classroom and usually need not be given on your paper or in recitation.

EXERCISES

C. Oral

1. Which of the following triangles are congruent? Why?

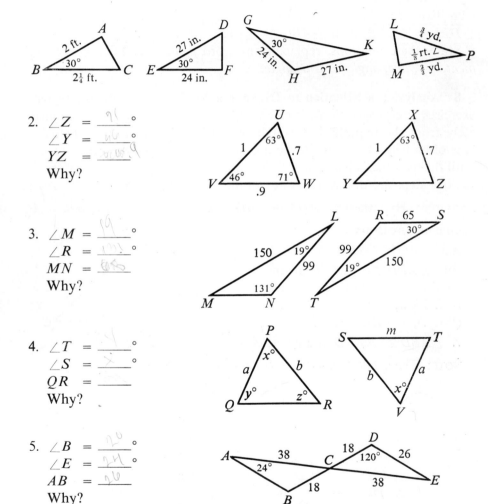

2. $\angle Z$ = \underline{91} °
   $\angle Y$ = \underline{46} °
   YZ = \underline{.9}
   Why?

3. $\angle M$ = \underline{19} °
   $\angle R$ = \underline{131} °
   MN = \underline{65}
   Why?

4. $\angle T$ = \underline{\quad} °
   $\angle S$ = \underline{\quad} °
   QR = \underline{\quad}
   Why?

5. $\angle B$ = \underline{120} °
   $\angle E$ = \underline{24} °
   AB = \underline{26}
   Why?

Study the following example:

Hyp. $\angle 1 = \angle 2$; $AD = CD$
Con. $\triangle ABD \cong \triangle CBD$

Proof.

1. $\angle 1 = \angle 2$ 1. Hyp.
2. $AD = CD$ 2. Hyp.
3. $BD = BD$ 3. By identity
4. $\triangle ABD \cong \triangle CBD$ 4. s a s

In Exercises 1–6 copy the hypothesis, the conclusion, and the figure and write out the proof as in the Example.

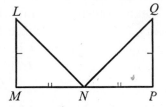

1. Hyp. $XY = XZ$; $\angle 1 = \angle 2$
    Con. $\angle Y = \angle Z$

2. Hyp. $LM \perp MP$; $QP \perp MP$;
           $MN = NP$; $LM = QP$
    Con. $\angle L = \angle Q$; $LN = QN$

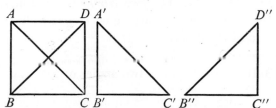

3. Hyp. $AB \perp BC$;
           $CD \perp BC$;
           $AB = CD$
    Con. $\triangle ABC \cong \triangle BCD$

Suggestion. In this and other proofs in which one triangle overlaps another, it will be found helpful to make a supplementary drawing in which the triangles do not overlap. That is, translate one of the triangles. Study the new figures in connection with the given one.

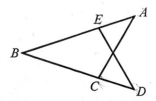

4. Hyp. $AB = BD$; $AE = CD$
    Con. $\triangle ABC \cong \triangle BDE$

5. Hyp. *RT* and *SV* bisect each
   other at *O*.
   Con. $\angle RST = \angle RVT$;
   $\angle VRS = \angle VTS$;
   $RS = TV$; $RV = ST$

6. Hyp. *ZW* is the perpendicular
   bisector of *XY*; *P* is any
   point on *ZW*.
   Con. $PX = PY$

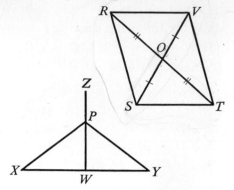

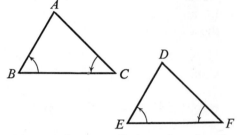

3–9 Second Case Suppose two triangles are determined in a plane by
the sets of points $\{A,B,C\}$ and
$\{D,E,F\}$ so that $BC = EF$, $\angle CBA$
$= \angle FED$, and $\angle ACB = \angle EFD$.
We can transform *BC* into *EF*.
Then since the angles are equal,
ray *BA* is transformed into *ED*,
and ray *CA* into *FD*. Since two
nonparallel rays can meet in only
one point, the point *A* is transformed into point *D* and thus the triangles
are congruent.

**POSTULATE 14 Two triangles are congruent if two angles and the in-
cluded side of one are equal respectively to two angles and the included
side of the other.** (asa)

3–10 How to prove two angles or two line segments equal.

To prove two angles equal, you now have these possible methods.
1. Show that they are vertical angles.
2. Show that they are complements or supplements of the same angle.
3. Show that they are both right angles or both straight angles.
4. Show that they are equal to the same or to equal angles.
5. Show that they are halves of the same or equal angles.
6. Show that they are corresponding parts of congruent triangles.

To prove two line segments equal, you have these possible methods.
1. Show that they are equal to the same or to equal line segments.
2. Show that they are halves of the same or equal line segments.
3. Show that they are corresponding parts of congruent triangles.

EXERCISES

C. Oral

1. Which of the following triangles are congruent?   Why?

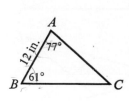 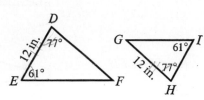 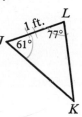

2. $\angle R$ = _____° SR = _____
   RT = _____   Why?

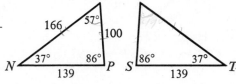

3. $\angle K$ = _____° XY = _____
   YZ = _____   Why?

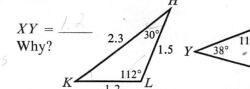

4. $\angle A$ = _____° AC = _____
   Why?

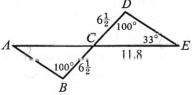

B. Written

5. Hyp. MO bisects $\angle LMN$ and $\angle LON$.
   Con. $LM = MN$

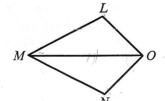

6. Hyp. $\angle 1 = \angle 2$; $\angle 3 = \angle 4$
   Con. $AD = BC$; $AB = CD$

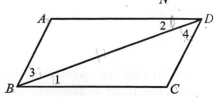

7. Hyp. $\angle 1 = \angle 2$; $AB \perp BC$;
   $CD \perp BC$
   Con. $AB = CD$

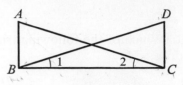

8. Hyp. $\angle E = \angle H$; $EF = FH$
   Con. $EG = HK$

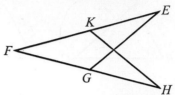

9. Hyp. $RT = SV$;
   $\angle RST = \angle STV$;
   $\angle 1 = \angle 2$
   Con. $RS = TV$

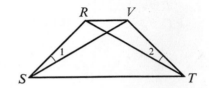

3–11   Third Case   It is easy to see that with three sticks, such that the sum of any two is greater than the third, you can arrange only one triangular shape. In Chapter 1, you found that you could construct only one triangle given three segments, with the sum of any two of these segments greater than the third.

In a plane, if three noncollinear points are given, the sum of two of the segments determined by these points is always greater than the third segment. (Why?) We now suppose we have given two sets of noncollinear points, $\{A,B,C\}$ and $\{D,E,F\}$, so that $AB = DE$, $BC = EF$, and $CA = FD$. Is it reasonable to assume that the triangles thus determined are congruent? The answer is yes.

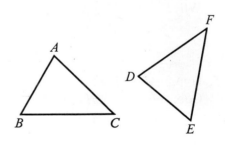

If we think of transforming AB so that it coincides with (corresponds to) DE, then point C must coincide (correspond) with F, for if it did not, either AC would not be equal to DF, or BC would not be equal to EF.

POSTULATE 15   **Two triangles are congruent if the three sides of one are equal respectively to the three sides of the other.** (sss)

EXERCISES

C. Oral

1. Which of the following △s are ≅? Why?

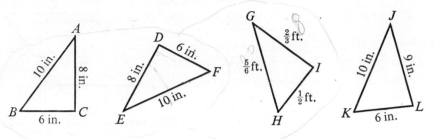

2. $\angle R = \underline{51}°$ $\angle Y = \underline{46}°$
   $\angle Z = \underline{83}°$ Why?

3. $\angle A = \underline{29}°$ $\angle M = \underline{31}°$
   $\angle N = \underline{120}°$ Why?

4. $\angle x = \underline{127}°$ $\angle y = \underline{18}°$
   $\angle z = \underline{35}°$ Why?

B. Written

Write out each proof completely.

5. Hyp. $AB = CD;$ $AD = BC$
      Con. $\angle A = \angle C$

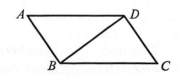

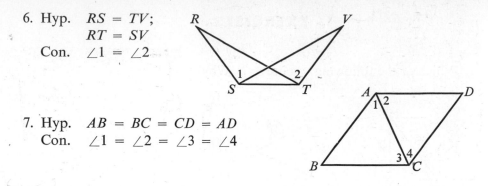

6. Hyp. $RS = TV$;
$RT = SV$
   Con. $\angle 1 = \angle 2$

7. Hyp. $AB = BC = CD = AD$
   Con. $\angle 1 = \angle 2 = \angle 3 = \angle 4$

3–12 POSTULATE 16 Through two points one and only one straight line can be drawn. (See Sec. 0–3)

3–13 POSTULATE 17 There can be one and only one straight line that bisects a given angle.

3–14 Problem. Proposition In our study of geometry we shall use the word *problem* to mean a construction to be done. Proof must always be given that the construction does what we started out to do.

The word *proposition* is used to refer to either a theorem or a problem. (Compare Sec. 2–4.) Just as we say that three selected noncollinear points determine a triangle, so we also say that when selected points enable us to construct a segment, or ray, or angle, or any geometric figure, that the figure is <u>determined</u>. *To determine means to select a particular figure in the plane.*

3–15 Problem To construct an angle equal to a given angle. Let the pupil give the proof. See Sec. 1–9 for the construction.

3–16 Problem To bisect an angle.

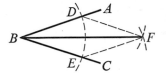

Given $\angle ABC$
Required To bisect $\angle ABC$

Construction. With B as center and any convenient radius draw an arc intersecting AB at D and BC at E. With D and E as centers and any radius greater than one half of the distance from D to E draw arcs that intersect at F, F not being the same as point B. Draw BF. Then $\angle ABF = \angle CBF$ and $\angle ABC$ has been bisected.

Proof Draw DF and EF and complete the proof.

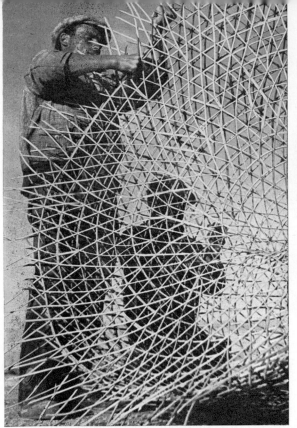

Top: A quilt design
Left: Fishermen mending a wicker net

3–17 Isosceles Triangle   An isosceles triangle is a triangle that has two equal sides.

The vertex angle of an isosceles triangle is the angle formed by the two equal sides.   The side opposite the vertex angle is called the base of the triangle.   The angles having the base as one side are called base angles.

3–18 THEOREM   **The angles opposite the equal sides of an isosceles triangle are equal.**

> **Hypothesis**   Isosceles $\triangle XYZ$ with $XY = XZ$
>
> **Conclusion** $\angle Y = \angle Z$

The plan is to determine the mid-point of YZ and connect it to the vertex with a line segment.   Then prove the resulting triangles congruent.

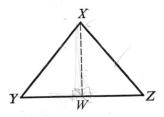

Proof   Let the student prove $\triangle XYW \cong \triangle XZW$ and complete the demonstration.

3-19 THEOREM If two angles of a triangle are equal, the triangle is isosceles.

Hypothesis XYZ is a triangle with $\angle Y = \angle Z$.

Conclusion $XY = XZ$

The plan is to construct a triangle congruent to the given triangle by reflection. At any point of YZ extended draw $l \perp$ to YZ. Then construct $\triangle X'Y'Z' \cong \triangle XYZ$ by reflection about the line l.

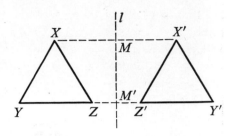

Proof

1. $\angle Y = \angle Y'$; $YZ = Y'Z'$;   1. cpcte
   $XY = X'Y'$
2. $\angle Y = \angle Z$ 2. Given
3. $\angle Z = \angle Y'$ 3. Why?
4. $\angle Z = \angle Z'$; $\angle Y = \angle Z'$ 4. Steps 1 to 3
5. $\triangle XYZ \cong \triangle X'Z'Y'$ 5. a s a = a s a (Note order of parts)
6. $XZ = X'Y'$ 6. cpcte
7. $XY = XZ$ 7. See steps 1 and 6.

NOTE: Another statement of this theorem is given in Chapter 5 under the discussion of converse and "If, and only if." Can you prove the above theorem using only the figure XYZ and proving $\triangle XYZ \cong \triangle XZY$ (note the order of correspondence)?

NOTE: A figure that has two pairs of adjacent equal sides and two pairs of adjacent unequal sides, such as $ABCD$ in Ex. 1 below, is called a *kite*.

EXERCISES

1. Prove:

   Hyp. Kite $ABCD$, $AB = AD$,
   $CB = CD$, $AB \neq CB$

   Con. $\triangle ABC \cong \triangle ADC$

2. Prove:

   Hyp. In this figure $RS = RT$,
   $SW = TW$.

   Con. $\angle WSR = \angle WTR$

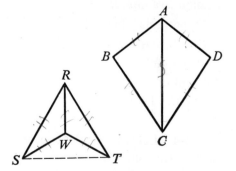

3–20 Equilateral Triangle. Equiangular Triangle An equilateral triangle is a triangle all sides of which are equal. An equiangular triangle is a triangle all angles of which are equal.

3–21 Corollary In any mathematical subject, once we have proved an important theorem, we can use it in the proof of many other theorems. When a theorem can be proved in one or two steps from a major theorem it is usually referred to as a corollary, which means a consequence that follows immediately.

To be isosceles a triangle must have two equal sides. Since any equilateral triangle certainly has any two sides equal it is isosceles. Is every isosceles triangle equilateral? From the previous theorems on the isosceles triangle and on triangles with two equal angles it is easy to prove the following corollaries.

3–22 Corollary The three angles of an equilateral triangle are equal.

3–23 Corollary The three sides of an equiangular triangle are equal.

3–24 Scalene Triangle A scalene triangle is a triangle that has no two sides equal.

EXERCISES

C. Oral

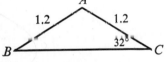

1. $\angle B =$ _____ °
   Why?

B. Written

Prove:

2. Hyp. $\triangle XYZ$ is isosceles;
   $\angle 1 = \angle 2$
   Con. $\triangle XMN$ is isosceles.

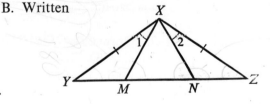

3. Hyp. $\triangle BDE$ is isosceles;
   $AE = CD$
   Con. $\triangle ABC$ is isosceles.

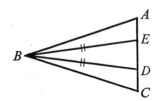

4. **Hyp.** △*MNO* is isosceles;
   △*MPO* is isosceles.

   Con. ∠*NMP* = ∠*NOP*

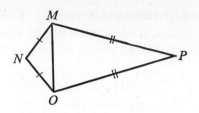

5. **Hyp.** △*ABC* is isosceles;
   △*ABD* is isosceles.

   Con. ∠1 = ∠2

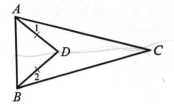

6. Prove: The median to the base of an isosceles triangle bisects the vertex angle.
7. Prove: The bisector of the vertex angle of an isosceles triangle is perpendicular to the base and bisects it.
8. Prove: Bisectors of any two angles of an equilateral triangle are equal. Are two angle bisectors of an isosceles triangle equal? Prove this.
9. Problem. To construct a perpendicular to a given line at a given point on the line.
   Give a complete demonstration of the first method used in Sec. 1–5.
10. Problem. To construct the perpendicular bisector of a given segment.
    See Sec. 1–2. Draw *AC, BC, AD,* and *BD.* Prove △*ACD* ≅ △*BCD.* ∴ ∠*ACD* = ∠*BCD.* Prove △*ACE* ≅ △*BCE.* ∴ ∠*AEC* = ∠*BEC.* Now use Sec. 0–16. Also, *AE* = *BE.* (Why?) Give a complete demonstration.
11. Problem. To construct the perpendicular to a line from a point not on the line.
    See Sec. 1–7. Draw *CD, CE, DF,* and *EF.* As in Ex. 10, prove *CF* is the perpendicular bisector of *DE.* Does this make *CG* ⊥ *AB*?
12. Theorem. If two points are each equally distant from the end points of a line segment, they determine the perpendicular bisector of the segment.
13. Draw ∠*HJK* and bisect it. Let *JT* be the bisector. At *T* construct a line perpendicular to *JT*, intersecting *HJ* at *R* and *JK* at *S*. Prove *RT* = *ST*.
14. Under what conditions are the bisector of an angle of a triangle and a median the same line?

3–25 THEOREM Two right triangles are congruent if the hypotenuse and an arm of one are equal respectively to the hypotenuse and an arm of the other. (h s)

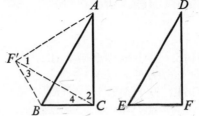

Hypothesis $\triangle ABC$ and $\triangle DEF$ with $\angle C$ and $\angle F$ right angles; $AB = DE$; $AC = DF$

Conclusion $\triangle ABC \cong \triangle DEF$

The plan is to construct a triangle on AB opposite vertex C which is congruent to $\triangle DEF$.

Proof

1. Construct $\angle F'AB = \angle FDE$ and make $AF' = DF$. Draw $F'B$ and $F'C$.	1. Give reasons
2. $\triangle F'AB \cong \triangle FDE$	2. s a s = s a s
3. $AF' = AC$	3. Why?
4. $\angle 1 = \angle 2$	4. Why?
5. $\angle AF'B$ is a rt. $\angle$.	5. c p c t e
6. $\angle AF'B = \angle ACB$	6. All right $\angle$s are $=$
7. $\angle 3 = \angle 4$	7. Why?
8. $F'B = BC$	8. Why?
9. $BC = EF$	9. $EF = BF'$, c p c t e
10. $\triangle ABC \cong \triangle DEF$	10. Why?

EXERCISES

C. Oral

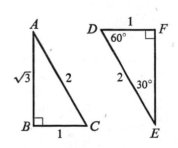

1. $EF = $ _____ $\angle A = $ _____ °
   $\angle C = $ _____ °   Why?

B. Written

Prove:

2. Hyp. $PR \perp QS$; $PQ = PS$
   Con. $QR = RS$

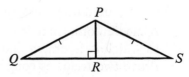

3. Hyp. $\angle A = \angle D = $ a rt. $\angle$;
$AB = CD$
   Con. $AC = BD$

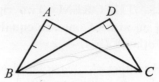

4. Hyp. $\angle 1 = \angle 2 = $ a rt. $\angle$;
$HK = LM$
   Con. $\angle HML = \angle HKL$

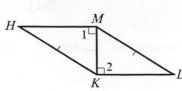

5. Hyp. $\angle A = \angle C = $ a rt. $\angle$;
$AB = CD$
   Con. $\angle ABC = \angle ADC$

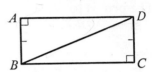

6. Prove: The altitude drawn from the vertex angle of an isosceles triangle bisects the base.

MISCELLANEOUS EXERCISES

C.

1. Construct a right triangle having the hypotenuse 3 inches and an arm 2 inches.

2. Construct a right triangle having the hypotenuse h and an arm a.
   NOTE: When you use small letters for lengths, we mean you are to use arbitrarily selected line segments. In order to have a triangle, what conditions are imposed on your selection?

3. With the protractor draw a 25° angle; then construct a right triangle having the hypotenuse 2 inches and an acute angle 25°.

B.

4. Construct a right triangle with hypotenuse x and an acute angle z.
   NOTE: When we use small letters for angles, we mean you are to use arbitrarily selected angles. In order to have a triangle what conditions are imposed on your selection?

5. A median of a triangle is extended by its own length through the side to which it is drawn and the end point is connected with a vertex. Prove two triangles congruent.

6. Prove: Two triangles are congruent if two sides and the median to one of them are equal respectively to two sides and the corresponding median of the other triangle.

7. Prove: If the median drawn from the vertex of a triangle to the base equals half the base, the vertex angle equals the sum of the base angles.

8. In order to determine the length of a lake, some boys measured off $AB = BC$ and $BD = BE$. They then measured the distance from C to E. Prove that CE equals the length of the lake.

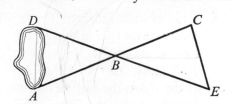

9. The distance across a stream may be found approximately in this way: Stand on the edge of the stream and look across at the other side. Pull down your hat until you can just see the other bank under it. Keep your head at the same angle

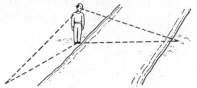

and turn about. Select a spot that can be seen on the ground directly under the hat brim. Measure the distance from the point of observation to this spot. Prove that the measured distance equals the width of the stream.

10. Before the modern spirit level was invented, the plumb level was used. It was made by constructing a wooden or metal isosceles triangle ABC and hanging a weight D by a cord from the vertex. Prove that when D is at the mid-point of BC, the base of the triangle is level. (*Level* means at right angles to a vertical line.)

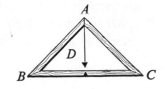

11. A triangle is called a rigid figure because with sides of a given length its shape remains always the same. Is this true of a figure of four or five sides riveted at the joints? Why are the geometric figures used in bridge construction usually triangles?

12. A carpenter can bisect an angle as follows: Mark off $AB = AC$. Place the steel square so that it passes through B and C and so that $BD = CD$. Prove that a line from A to D bisects $\angle BAC$.

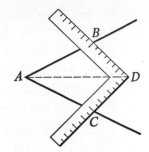

13. A ray of light reflected from a mirror leaves the surface at the same angle at which it strikes it. That is, $\angle LPA = \angle EPN$, where MN is the surface of the mirror. Does the image appear as far back of the mirror as the object is in front of it? That is, does $LA = L'A$? Prove it.

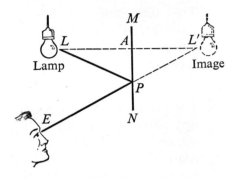

A.

14. A messenger is to go from H to the river ST where he is to receive a sealed message to be carried to an army division at B. Where should he arrange to meet a boat along the river so that he shall travel the shortest possible distance?

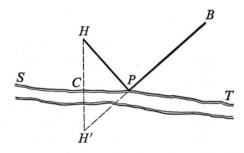

Suggestions. Draw $HCH' \perp ST$, making $CH' = CH$. Draw straight line BH' intersecting ST at P. Draw HP. Does $HP = H'P$? Is $H'PB$ shorter than any other line from H' to B?

15. The 8-ball on a pool table is directly between the cue ball and the 9-ball. A player wants to hit the 9-ball. Make a drawing and explain how he can do this. Does he have more than one choice? Assume that a banked ball behaves like reflected light.

16. Prove: Any two isosceles triangles are congruent if the base and a base angle of one are equal respectively to the base and a base angle of the other.

This chapter introduces the following terms:

interior, exterior angles
one-to-one correspondence
geometric transformation
translation
rotation
reflection
noncollinear
symmetric relation
transitive relation
analysis
identity
problem

proposition
determine
isosceles triangle
vertex angle
base angles
equilateral triangle
equiangular triangle
scalene triangle
hypotenuse
arm
corollary

This chapter presents information concerning:

1. One-to-one correspondence and its use in translation, rotation, and reflection.   Pages 61–64

2. Corresponding parts of congruent figures.   Page 70

3. The relation between two triangles having two sides and the included angle of one equal respectively to two sides and the included angle of the other.   Page 71

4. Analysis as a way of discovering a proof of a theorem or an exercise.   Page 71

5. The relation between two triangles having two angles and the included side of one equal respectively to two angles and the included side of the other.   Page 74

6. The relation between two triangles having the three sides of one equal respectively to the three sides of the other.   Page 76

7. Methods of bisecting and duplicating an angle and proof of the constructions.   Page 78

8. The relation between the base angles and the equal sides of an isosceles triangle.   Pages 79–80

9. The relation between the sides of a triangle that has two equal angles.   Page 80

10. The relation between two right triangles having the hypotenuse and an arm of one equal respectively to the hypotenuse and an arm of the other.   Page 83

REVIEW

1. Illustrate the translation of a line segment *AB*.

2. Draw a capital letter *I*. Rotate this figure through an angle of 45°. (Rotate about the mid-point of its vertical part.)

3. Fold a piece of paper. With a sharp instrument of any kind cut a design through the folded sheet. Open the paper. Explain how one figure could be obtained from the other by reflection.

4. What is translation of a figure? Make drawings to illustrate your definition.

5. If you know that two triangles are congruent, how many equations of corresponding parts can be written? Illustrate.

6. Give the postulate symbolized by the letters s a s.

7. Give the postulate symbolized by the letters a s a.

8. Give the postulate symbolized by the letters s s s.

9. What is meant by the statement that two figures are congruent?

10. Draw a scalene triangle *HJK* and construct triangle *H′J′K′* which is a copy of *HJK*, using the three sides. (See Sec. 1–14.) Is $\angle H = \angle H'$? Why? Is $\angle J = \angle J'$? Why? What other equality can be written and proved by the principle of congruence?

11. Draw an angle and bisect it. (See Sec. 1–12 and 3–16.) Prove that your construction bisects the given angle.

12. The angles opposite the equal sides of an isosceles triangle are equal. Give a complete proof of this theorem.

13. Draw isosceles triangle *RST*, with *RS* = *RT*. Construct *V*, the mid-point of *ST*. Draw *RV*. Prove that $\angle SRV = \angle TRV$.

14. Construct a perpendicular to a given line from a point that is not on the line. (See Sec. 1–7.) Prove that the construction gives a perpendicular.

15. Construct isosceles $\triangle ABC$, with *AB* = *AC*. Construct $AD \perp BC$. Prove that $\triangle ADB \cong \triangle ADC$.

16. What is the hypotenuse of $\triangle ADC$ in Ex. 15?

17. Prove: Two right triangles are congruent if the hypotenuse and an arm of one are equal to the corresponding parts of the other.

18. Prove: Two right triangles are congruent if an arm and its adjacent acute angle of one triangle are equal to the corresponding parts of the other.

YES–NO TEST

Approximately 10 minutes

Copy on your paper the numbers of the following questions. If the answer to a question is *yes* under all conditions, place a plus sign (+) after its number. If the answer is *not yes* under all conditions, place a zero (0) after its number.

1. Are corresponding parts of congruent triangles equal?
2. Are two triangles congruent if three angles of one are equal respectively to three angles of the other?
3. Are two triangles congruent if two sides and an angle of one are equal respectively to two sides and an angle of the other?
4. May any angle of an isosceles triangle be called its vertex angle?
5. If two sides of an equilateral triangle are each 3 feet, can the other side be 2 feet?
6. Can a scalene triangle be congruent to an isosceles triangle?
7. If the sides of a triangle are 3, 4, and 5, is it congruent to a triangle the sides of which are 5, 4, and 3?
8. Is a side adjacent to a right angle of a right triangle called the hypotenuse?
9. Can there be more than one perpendicular from a given point to a given line?
10. If the two arms of one right triangle are equal respectively to the two arms of another, are the triangles congruent?
11. Are all equilateral triangles congruent?
12. Can a right triangle be isosceles?
13. The sides of a right triangle are 6, 8, and 10 inches. Is the 10-inch side an arm?
14. An angle has 19°; it is bisected. Does each part have 38°?
15. The sides of one triangle are 2 feet, 3 feet, and 4 feet. The sides of another are 36 inches, 24 inches, and 48 inches. Are the triangles congruent?
16. In $\triangle ABC$, $\angle A = 25°$, $\angle B = 60°$, $AB = 3$ inches. In $\triangle XYZ$, $\angle X = 60°$, $\angle Y = 25°$, $XY = 3$ feet. Are the triangles congruent?
17. If $\triangle A$ is congruent to $\triangle B$, and $\triangle B$ is congruent to $\triangle C$, is $\triangle A$ congruent to $\triangle C$? Use Postulate 2.

COMPLETION TEST

Approximately 10 minutes

Copy on your paper the numbers of the following statements. After each number write a word, or a letter, or a number which, if it were written in the blank, would complete the statement and make it true.

1. If one triangle can be taken into another by translation, the triangles are ____.
2. A triangle has three sides and three _____.
3. The side opposite the right angle of a right triangle is called the _____.
4. Corresponding parts of _____ triangles are equal.
5. In $\triangle ABC$, $AB = 5$ in., $AC = 9$ in., $BC = 10$ in., $\angle A = 88°$, $\angle B = 71°$, $\angle C = 21°$. In $\triangle DEF$, $\angle D = 88°$, $\angle E = 21°$, $\angle F = 71°$. In $\triangle GHK$, $GH = 9$ in., $GK = 10$ in., $HK = 5$ in. $\triangle ABC \cong$ _____.
6. In $\triangle PQR$, $PQ = 22$ cm., $QR = 13$ cm., $\angle Q = 70°$. In $\triangle STV$, $SV = 13$ cm., $VT = 22$ cm., $\angle V = 70°$. In $\triangle XYZ$, $XY = 22$ cm., $YZ = 13$ cm., $\angle Z = 70°$. $\triangle PQR \cong$ _____.
7. In $\triangle ABC$, $AB = 7.3$ ft., $AC = 8.2$ ft., $BC = 5.9$ ft., $\angle B = 74°$, $\angle C = 61°$. In $\triangle DEF$, $EF = 5.9$ ft., $\angle E = 74°$, $\angle F = 61°$. $DE =$ _____.
8. In $\triangle SVT$, $\angle T$ is a right angle, $ST = 21$ cm., $SV = 26$ cm. In $\triangle PQR$, $\angle R$ is 90°, $PQ = 26$ cm., $RQ = 21$ cm., $\angle P = 57°$. $\angle$ _____ has 57°.

SUPPLEMENTARY EXERCISES

C.

1. Is $\triangle ABC \cong \triangle DEF$?

   Why?

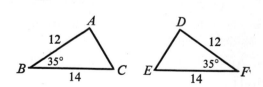

2. Is $\triangle GHI \cong \triangle JKL$?

   Give a reason for your answer.

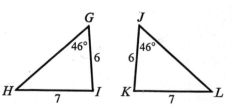

3. Is $\triangle PQR \cong \triangle STV$?

Why?

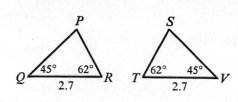

4. Is $\triangle ABC \cong \triangle DEF$?

Why?

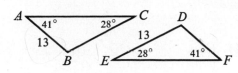

5. Is $\triangle OPQ \cong \triangle RST$?

Why?

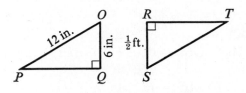

6. Is $\triangle ABC \cong \triangle DEF$?

Why?

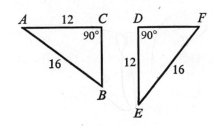

7. Is $\triangle GHI \cong \triangle JKL$?

Why?

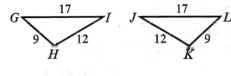

8. Hyp. $JH \perp GI$
Is $\triangle GHJ \cong \triangle IHJ$?

Why?

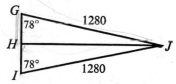

B.

9. Hyp. $BD = CD$; $AD \perp BC$
Is $\triangle ABC$ isosceles?

Prove.

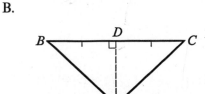

Prove:

10. Hyp. $EF = FG$; $EK = GL$;
$KH \perp EG$; $LJ \perp EG$
Con. $\triangle EHK \cong \triangle GJL$

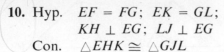

11. Hyp. $OS = OQ$; $\angle 1 = \angle 2$
Con. $\triangle OPQ \cong \triangle OSR$

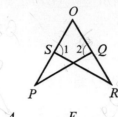

12. Hyp. $AB \perp BD$; $FC \perp BD$;
$ED \perp BD$; $BC = CD$;
$AC = EC$
Con. $\angle 1 = \angle 2$

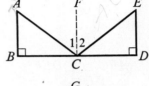

13. Hyp. $HG = GK$; GJ bisects
$\angle HGK$.
Con. $\angle HJG = \angle KJG$

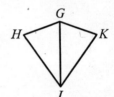

14. Hyp. $\angle 1 = \angle 2$; $OP = OR$
Con. $\angle Q = \angle S$

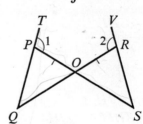

15. Hyp. $\angle 1 = \angle 2$; $\angle 3 = \angle 4$
Find the length of AB and the
length of BC.

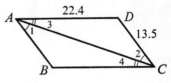

16. Hyp. $JK \perp EI$; $FE = FI$;
$JK \perp GH$
Con. $\triangle FGH$ is isosceles.

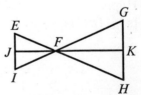

17. Hyp. $AB = BC$; $AE = DC$;
BF bisects $\angle EBD$.
Con. $AF = CF$

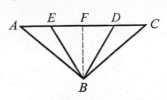

18. Hyp. $\angle 1 = \angle 2$; $\angle 3 = \angle 4$
Con. $\angle 5 = \angle 6$

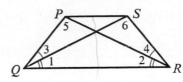

19. Hyp. $AB = BC$; $\angle 1 = \angle 2$
Con. $\angle 3 = \angle 4$

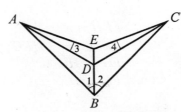

20. Hyp. $FH = HJ$; $GH = HK$
Con. $LH = HM$

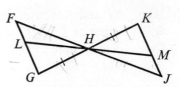

21. Hyp. $OP = QR$; $\angle 1 = \angle 2$;
$PX = RX$
Con. $SX = TX$

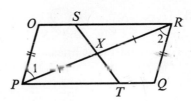

22. Hyp. $BC = DF$;
$\angle C = \angle D$;
$\angle ABD = \angle CFE$
Con. $AC = DE$

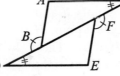

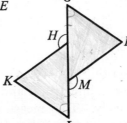

23. Hyp. $\angle G = \angle L$;
$\angle GHK = \angle LMP$;
$GH = LM$
Con. $\angle K = \angle P$

24. Hyp.   *VS* is bisected at *R*;
               QR = *RT*;
               ∠*QRV* = ∠*SRT*
    Con.   *QS* = *VT*

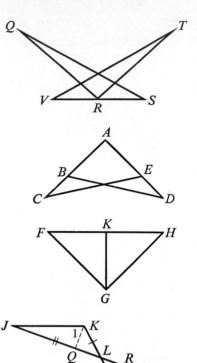

25. Hyp.   *AB* = *AE*; *AC* = *AD*
    Con.   *BD* = *CE*

26. Hyp.   *FKH* is a st. line;
               ∠*FKG* = ∠*HKG*;
               FG = *HG*
    Con.   *FK* = *HK*

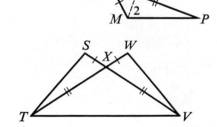

27. Hyp.   *JP* and *KM* bisect each
               other at *L*; ∠1 = ∠2
    Con.   *KQ* = *MR*

28. Hyp.   *SX* = *WX*; *TX* = *VX*;
               TXW and *SXV* are
               straight lines.
    Con.   ∠*S* = ∠*W*

29. To find the distance between two inaccessible points *F* and *G*, some boys locate a point *H* in line with *F* and *G*. They then lay off line *HK* at right angles to *FGH* and find its mid-point *J*; next they lay off *KM* at right angles to *KH* and on this set up stakes at *L* and *M* in line with *G* and *F* respectively. They measure the distance *LM*. Prove *LM* = *FG*.

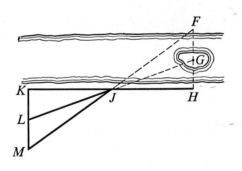

30. Prove: If the perpendicular bisector of one side of a triangle passes through the opposite vertex, the triangle is isosceles.

31. Prove: If the bisector of an angle of a triangle is perpendicular to the opposite side, the triangle is isosceles.

32. Prove: The perpendiculars drawn to the equal sides of an isosceles triangle from the mid-point of the base are equal.

33. Prove: The medians drawn to the equal sides of an isosceles triangle are equal.

34. Prove: The altitudes drawn to the equal sides of an isosceles triangle are equal.

A.

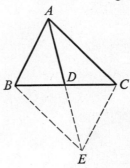

35. Prove: The length of a median of a triangle is less than one half the sum of the sides from the same vertex.

Hint. Extend the median its own length and connect the terminal point to the other two vertices of the triangle.

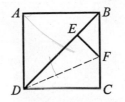

36. On the diagonal *DB* of a square *ABCD*, a segment *DE* is made equal to a side of the square, and *EF* is drawn ⊥ *DB* meeting *BC* at *F*. Prove that *EF* = *FC*.

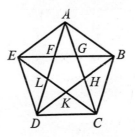

37. A regular pentagon has 5 equal sides and 5 equal angles. If all the diagonals are drawn a smaller pentagon is formed inside the first one. Prove the smaller pentagon is also regular.

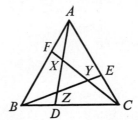

38. In an equilateral △*ABC*, the sides are trisected in order at *D*, *E*, and *F*. (*BD* = ⅓*BC*, etc.) The lines *AD*, *BE*, and *CF* form △*XYZ*. Prove △*XYZ* is equiangular.

NOTE: △*XYZ* is also ⅐ the size of △*ABC* but you cannot prove this as yet.

CHAPTER 4

NATURE OF INDIRECT REASONING

4-1 Direct Reasoning In the theorems you have proved thus far you reasoned from the given hypothesis until you reached the conclusion. This is called direct reasoning. To compare this type of reasoning with another type called indirect reasoning, we shall first review direct reasoning. Consider the following exercise.

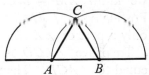

Hypothesis *A* is the center of circle with radius *AB*. *B* is the center of circle with radius *BA*. The circles meet above the line at *C*.

Conclusion △*ABC* is an equiangular triangle.

We start with our hypothesis: Since *A* is the center of a circle, $AB = AC$, because radii of the same circle are equal. Similarly, since *B* is the center of a circle, we have $BA = BC$. Then $AB = BC = CA$ (give the reason), and △*ABC* is equilateral (by definition). Finally we reach the conclusion $\angle A = \angle B = \angle C$ because an equilateral △ is also equiangular. (See Sec. 3–22.)

The following theorem is also proved by direct reasoning. First we introduce a new definition.

4–2 Exterior Angle In a triangle, if one side is produced beyond the vertex, this extended ray forms with the adjacent side of the triangle an angle that is outside the triangle. This angle is called an exterior angle of the triangle. Thus BCD is an exterior angle.

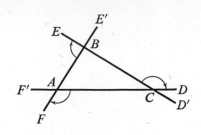

A triangle has six exterior angles, two at each vertex. However, the two exterior angles at the same vertex angle are equal. Why? (See Sec. 2–23.) Note that an exterior angle and interior angle at the same vertex are supplementary. Why? We now study how an exterior angle is related to the opposite interior angles. Note also that the vertical angle to the interior angle is not an exterior angle of the triangle; that is, $\angle EBE'$ is not an exterior angle of $\triangle ABC$.

4–3 THEOREM **An exterior angle of a triangle is greater than either nonadjacent interior angle of the triangle.**

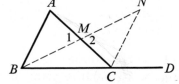

> **Hypothesis** $\angle ACD$ is an ext. $\angle$ of $\triangle ABC$
>
> **Conclusion** $\angle ACD > \angle A$; $\angle ACD > \angle B$

Proof Bisect AC at M (Sec. 1–2) and draw BM. Then extend BM to N so that $BM = MN$. Next draw NC. Now, in $\triangle ABM$ and $\triangle MNC$ we know $AM = MC$, $BM = MN$, and $\angle 1 = \angle 2$ (Sec. 2–23). By Postulate 13 $\triangle AMB \cong \triangle MNC$ and $\angle A = \angle MCN$. But $\angle MCN$ is only a part of $\angle ACD$. Hence $\angle ACD > \angle A$.

To prove $\angle ACD > \angle B$, use the other exterior angle at C which is equal to $\angle ACD$. Then draw a line from A to the mid-point of BC and continue as in the above proof. The student should carry out this proof.

4–4 Indirect Proof Can all theorems be proved directly? In Chapter 2 it was proved (Sec. 2–17) that on a plane at a point in a line, only one line could be drawn perpendicular to the line. Let us see if direct reasoning was used in proving this theorem.

> **Hypothesis** C is a point on AB. $CD \perp AB$
>
> **Conclusion** CD is the only line $\perp AB$ at C.

Let us start with our hypothesis $CD \perp AB$. What shall we do next? We can say $\angle ACD$ and $\angle DCB$ are right angles, and then they are equal, but this does not help us arrive at our conclusion.

So we start with something other than our hypothesis. We assume that there is also another line $CE \perp AB$. Note well that this is not a permissible or known construction, but merely an *assumed* (maybe true, maybe false) construction. Then we reason that $\angle ECB$ and $\angle DCB$ are equal since they are both right angles. This is one conclusion from our assumption. But *we know* they are unequal angles since one is a part of the other. We thus have arrived at two conclusions that contradict each other. Since *we know* one of these statements, namely that the angles are unequal, is true, we conclude that the other is false, that is, we know that ECB is not a right angle and hence CD is the only perpendicular. Notice that the procedure was systematic.

Since we started with something other than our hypothesis, we call this an indirect method of proof. In this chapter we shall study this method of proof more carefully, since it is a very useful way of reasoning in everyday problems as well as in mathematics. We first study different types of statements.

4–5 Contradictory Statements Consider the two statements:

(*a*) It is raining.   (*b*) It is not raining.

If either of these is true, the other is false. Two statements of this kind are said to be contradictory.

Similarly, the contradictory statement to

$\triangle ABC$ is an isosceles triangle

is

$\triangle ABC$ is not an isosceles triangle.

If a statement is given, we can write the contradictory of the statement by denying it is true. Thus the contradictory of

AB is not perpendicular to CD

is

AB is perpendicular to CD.

Notice that the word *not* in the examples above gives a clue to the contradictory relation. In the first example *not* is absent in the given statement; the contradiction is obtained by inserting this word in the second statement. Discuss the second example.

EXERCISES

Write the contradictory statement to exercises 1–10. You are not to consider whether the contradictory statement is true or false.

1. Triangle *ABC* = triangle *DEF*.
2. The base angles of an isosceles triangle are equal.
3. Angle *A* is supplementary to angle *B*.
4. Angle *A* is equal to angle *B*.
5. Angle *A* is greater than angle *B*. (Be careful!)
6. Thursday comes after Friday.
7. 6 is greater than 10. (Be careful!)
8. Truth is stranger than fiction.
9. Point *M* bisects segment *AB*.
10. Line *AB* bisects angle *A*.
11. What can you say about the truth of statements in Ex. 6 and 7?
12. What can you say about the truth of contradictory statements to Ex. 6 and 7?
13. If you know a statement is true, what do you know about its contradictory statement?
14. If a statement is false, what do you know about its contradictory statement?
15. Make three statements, either true or false, and write their contradictory statements. In each case what can you say about the truth or falsity of the statement and its contradictory statement?

4–6 Law of Contradiction The foregoing exercises illustrate a very important rule of reasoning. *For two contradictory statements, if one is true, the other must necessarily be false, and if one is false, the other must be true.*

This is sometimes called the law of contradiction.

In applying this rule we must be sure that the two statements considered are really contradictory. A statement may disagree with another statement and yet not be the contradictory statement. Consider:

A. Jane is a daughter of Mrs. Jones.
B. Jane is a niece of Mrs. Jones.

The second statement is different from (does not agree with) the first, yet if the second statement is false, the first is not necessarily true. To show this we could write:

C. Jane is the sister of Mrs. Jones.
D. Jane is a friend of Mrs. Jones, etc.

Statements B, C, and D are contrary to statement A but not contradictory. The contradictory to statement A is

A'. Jane is *not* a daughter of Mrs. Jones.

Thus if A is true, A' is false, and if A is false, then A' is true.

Similarly, if we make the statement concerning two numbers a and b that $a < b$, then $a = b$ and $a > b$ are both contraries. The contradictory to $a < b$ is $a \not< b$ which is read, "a is not less than b."

EXERCISES

For each of the following statements write at least two contrary statements and the one contradictory statement.

1. $\angle A$ is a right angle.
2. $\triangle ABC$ is scalene.
3. $\triangle ABC$ is a right triangle.
4. Mr. Jones is the father of James.
5. Segment AB = segment CD.
6. Circle O > circle Q.
7. $\angle A < \angle B$.
8. J comes before K in the alphabet.
9. Bill has a higher average than Jack.
10. The United States is the nation with the greatest production of goods.
11. An arm of a right triangle is greater than the hypotenuse.
12. The three angles of a scalene triangle are equal.
13. The statement that Mr. Jones is a politician contradicts the statement that he is honest.
14. Susan is writing a novel.
15. Lincoln said, "The world will little note nor long remember what we say here, but it can never forget what they did here."

4–7 Inconsistent Statements Two statements that cannot both be true at the same time are inconsistent. Thus two contradictory statements are always inconsistent. In geometry, it is important that we be able to tell which of two contradictory statements is the true one. To do this we usually start with the statement we believe to be false and reason directly from it to a fact that contradicts something we know to be true. This means that the statement we began with is a false statement and therefore its contradictory is true. Two statements are consistent when both can be true at the same time.

EXERCISES

In each of the following sets of statements prove that the contradictory of the first statement is false when the second and third statements are true. Arrive at a false statement. The first example is worked through as an illustration. S_1 means *first statement*, and so on.

NOTE: The symbol $\not\perp$ means *is not perpendicular to*.

1. S_1: $AB \neq AC$
   S_2: $BM = MC$
   S_3: $AM \not\perp BC$

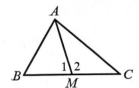

Assume $AB = AC$; we know that $BM = MC$, and $AM = AM$. Thus, $\triangle ABM \cong \triangle AMC$ and $\angle 1 = \angle 2$. This means that $\angle 1$ and $\angle 2$ are right angles (Sec. 0–16) and $AM \perp BC$. But it is known that $AM \not\perp BC$ (by S_3). We have reached a contradiction, so our assumption $AB = AC$ is false. We conclude that $AB \neq AC$.

2. S_1: Mr. A averages more than 40 mi. per hr.
   S_2: Mr. A travels 4 hrs.
   S_3: Mr. A goes 180 miles.

3. S_1: $AB \neq AC$
   S_2: ABC is a triangle.
   S_3: $\angle B \neq \angle C$

4. S_1: $AC \not\perp DE$
   S_2: $AB \perp DE$
   S_3: B and C are on line DE.

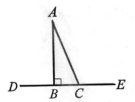

5. S_1: $AM \not\perp BC$
   S_2: $BM = MC$
   S_3: $AB \neq AC$

6. S_1: $X + Y \neq 10$
   S_2: X is 2.
   S_3: Y is less than 8.

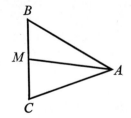

7. S_1: $a + b = 1$
   S_2: a and b are different positive numbers.
   S_3: $a^2 - b^2 = a - b$

Hint. $a - b \neq 0$; divide both sides of S_3 by $(a - b)$

4-8 Indirect Proof To prove a theorem indirectly we proceed as follows:

1. Assume the contradictory of the conclusion in the theorem.
2. Reason from this assumption (and any of the hypotheses of the theorem) to a statement known to be false.
3. Then the theorem consisting of the hypotheses and the conclusion is a true statement and the theorem is proved. This is a valid form of reasoning.

The following examples illustrate this method of proof.

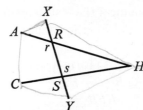

Example 1. If two intersecting lines AH and CH are cut by a third line XY, $\angle r$ is not equal to $\angle s$.

1. Assume $\angle r = \angle s$. (This is the contradictory of the conclusion.)
2. Figure RHS is a triangle, $\angle r$ is an exterior angle of this triangle, and $\angle s$ is a nonadjacent interior angle. This would lead to the conclusion that an exterior angle equals a nonadjacent interior angle. This is false and hence $\angle r = \angle s$ is false.
3. Hence $\angle r \neq \angle s$ because the contradictory of a false statement is true.

Example 2. An officer said in court that an autoist traveled 250 miles on a parkway in 4 hours and therefore exceeded the speed limit of 60 m.p.h.

1. Assume that the autoist did not exceed 60 m.p.h. (This is the contradictory of the officer's conclusion.)
2. Then in 4 hours the greatest distance the autoist traveled was 4×60 or 240 miles. This is false, since he traveled 250 miles. Hence, the statement that the autoist never exceeded 60 m.p.h. is false.
3. Then the statement that the autoist exceeded the speed limit at some time in his trip is true.

Example 3. If two angles of a triangle are unequal, the sides opposite these angles are unequal.

Hypothesis. $\angle B \neq \angle C$
Conclusion. $AB \neq AC$

1. Assume $AB = AC$. (The contradictory of the stated conclusion.)
2. If $AB = AC$, then $\angle B = \angle C$, but this is false since it contradicts the known true hypothesis. Thus the statement $AB = AC$ is false.
3. Then $AB \neq AC$. (The contradictory of a false statement is true.)

4–9 THEOREM In the same plane two lines that are perpendicular to the same line do not intersect.

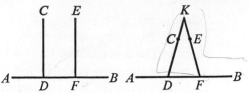

Hypothesis $CD \perp AB$;
$EF \perp AB$

Conclusion CD does not meet EF.

Proof

1. Assume the statement CD meets EF. (See figure at right.)
2. Then CD meets EF at some point K to form a triangle KDF.
3. $\angle KFB > \angle KDF$
4. But $\angle KFB = \angle KDF$
5. CD meets EF is false.

6. CD does not meet EF.

1. Assumption

2. Def. of $\triangle$

3. Ext. $\angle$ of $\triangle$
4. All right angles are equal.
5. Since step 3 contradicts step 4, which is true.
6. Contradictory of a false statement is true.

4–10 Corollary From a point not on a line only one line can be drawn perpendicular to the given line.

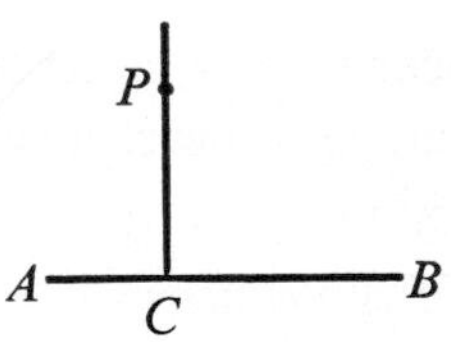

Hypothesis Point P is not on AB.
$PC \perp AB$

Conclusion PC is the only $\perp$.

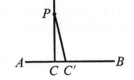

Proof

Assume PC' is another perpendicular from P to AB. Now show that this assumption leads to a contradiction of a statement that is known to be true and hence the assumption is false. Hence . . .

EXERCISES

Prove the following theorems by indirect reasoning.

1. A line from the vertex of a scalene triangle to the mid-point of the opposite side is not perpendicular to the base.

   Hint. Assume that this line is perpendicular to the base, etc.

2. The line from the vertex of a scalene triangle to the opposite side and bisecting the angle at the vertex is not perpendicular to that side.

3. If in $\triangle ABC$, $\angle B \neq \angle C$, then $AC \neq AB$.

4. If in $\triangle ABC$, $AC > AB$, then $\angle B \neq \angle C$.

   Hint. On AC lay off AD = AB and compare the angles marked.

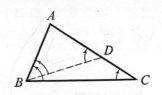

5. In the figure $CM \perp AB$, AM = MB, and P is not on CM. Prove $PA \neq PB$.

   Hint. Draw PM.

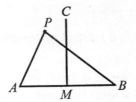

6. If zero is divided by a number n where $n \neq 0$, then the quotient is zero.

   Hint. Assume $\dfrac{\text{zero}}{n} = x$ where x is not zero.

7. If $x + y = 6$ and $x + y = 8$, then there is no common solution to the two equations.

   Hint. Assume there is a common value for y. Solve one equation for y and substitute in the other equation, etc.

8. If a man travels 100 miles in 2 hours, at some time he exceeds 45 miles per hour.

9. If two lines AB and CD are cut by a third line XY so that $\angle 1 = \angle 2$, then AB does not meet CD to the right of the line XY.

   Hint. Assume the second figure and get a contradiction. Recall that RSP is a $\triangle$ with ext. $\angle 1$.

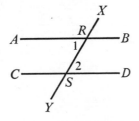
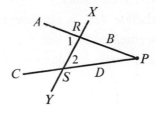

10. Use the same hypothesis as in Ex. 9 and prove AB and CD do not meet to the left of line XY.

11. What conclusion can you draw from Ex. 9 and 10?

12. Write an explanation of proof by using the indirect method.

OUTLINE OF CHAPTER 4

The following words and phrases were studied in this chapter:

contradictory statement   consistent statements

contrary statement   inconsistent statements

direct proof   true and false statements

indirect proof

In this chapter you learned or reviewed:

1. The meaning of direct proof. Page 97
2. The meaning of indirect proof. Pages 98–99
3. The distinction between contradictory and contrary statements. Pages 99–101
4. How to prove a statement to be false. Page 101
5. If an assumed statement is false, its contradictory statement is true. Page 103

REVIEW

1. What is direct reasoning?
2. State the law of contradiction.
3. What are contradictory statements? Give an example.
4. What are contrary statements? Give an example.
5. State and prove the relation between an exterior angle of a triangle and a nonadjacent interior angle.

In exercises 6–12 write *a* contrary statement and *the* contradictory statement.

6. Today is Wednesday.
7. The triangle ABC is equilateral.
8. Line segment $AB >$ line segment CD.
9. Line a is perpendicular to line c.
10. $XY \parallel AB$
11. $2 = 5$
12. The product of two negative numbers is a positive number.
13. If it is false that $a > b$, write the contradictory statement. Is this statement true?
14. If it is false that $a > b$, write two contrary statements. Are these statements both true?

15. How do you prove a statement to be false?

16. What is a consistent set of statements?

17. What is indirect reasoning?

18. Given *ABC* is a triangle and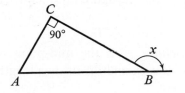
(1) $\angle C = 90°$, (2) $\angle x$ is an exterior angle at *B* equal to 80°. Are these two statements consistent? Explain.

19. Prove indirectly: If 12 oranges cost 96 cents and all cost the same amount, then they cost less than 10 cents each.

20. Prove indirectly: If each man can make 12 articles in a week, then 15 men each working a week cannot make 210 articles in a week.

TEST

Approximate time: 30 min.

1. Write the contradictory statement of:
   (a) The number of prime integers is endless.
   (b) $\sqrt{2}$ is a fraction.
   (c) There is only one line through a point parallel to a given line.

2. Hyp. $AB \neq AC$, *M* is the mid-point of *BC*, line *AM*.
   Con. ?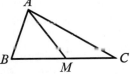
   (a) Write two contradictory statements concerning the perpendicularity of *AM* and *BC*.
   (b) Assume the statement in part (a) you believe to be false and reason to a statement that you know to be true.
   (c) Write the conclusion that is missing in order to make a valid geometric statement.

3. Prove: Two lines perpendicular to the same line do not meet. Use an indirect method in your proof.

4. In the figure, $\angle A = \angle ABC$. Prove $AC = BC$ as follows: Assume $BC \neq AC$. Lay off $AD = BC$ and draw *BD*. Then compare $\triangle ADB$ with $\triangle ABC$.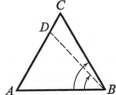

SUPPLEMENTARY EXERCISES

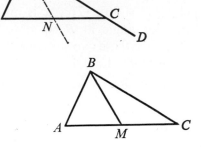

1. Given the figure in which ACD is an exterior angle of $\triangle ABC$. Prove $\angle ACD > \angle A$.

    Hint. N is the mid-point of AC; extend BN its own length, etc.

2. In $\triangle ABC$, AC is bisected at M. Also $AB = BM$. Prove $\angle A > \angle C$.

3. In Ex. 2 prove $AB \neq AC$.

4. Write the contradictory to each of the following statements.

    (*a*) George is ill.

    (*b*) There is a school session on Saturday.

    (*c*) Three lines are perpendicular to each other in pairs.

    (*d*) In a trapezoid two angles have different sizes.

    (*e*) Mr. A is the father of John.

    (*f*) Indirect proof is easy to learn.

    (*g*) All theorems can be proved by indirect reasoning.

    (*h*) A is not greater than B.

    (*i*) Life exists on Mars.

    (*j*) Five minus two equals seven.

    (*k*) Alpha always exceeds be a.

    (*l*) Larry has no hat.

    (*m*) M is the mid-point of AB.

    (*n*) A times B equals B times A.

    (*o*) The first and second statements imply the third.

5. Given a line AB through points A and B. Show that the statement "there is another straight line through A and B" is false by assuming this statement and getting a contradiction.

6. Prove that if two triangles have two sides of one equal to two sides of the other, but the included angles are unequal, then the triangles are not congruent. What can you then say about the third sides of these triangles?

7. Prove: If two sides of a triangle are equal to the two sides of another triangle, but the third sides are unequal, the angles included by the equal sides are not equal. Use the indirect method of proof.

8. If lines *AB* and *CD* are cut by a third line *EF* so that ∠1 > ∠2, prove indirectly that *AB* and *CD* will not meet to the left of line *EF*.

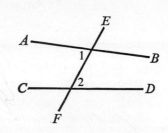

9. If a statement *A* is the contradictory of a statement *B*, and the statement *B* is the contradictory of a statement *C*, what relation is the statement *A* to the statement *C*? Give an example.

10. Hyp.   *AB* ⊥ *DB*; *AC* ⊥ *CD*;
    A is inside ∠*BDC*;
    AB ≠ *AC*

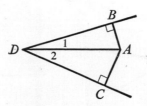

    Con.   ∠1 ≠ ∠2; that is, *AD* is not an angle bisector. Prove by using the indirect method of proof.

11. Hyp.   In △*ABC*, *AD* ⊥ *BC*;
    AB ≠ *AC*

    Con.   *D* is not the mid-point of *BC*. Prove by using the indirect method of proof.

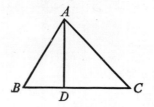

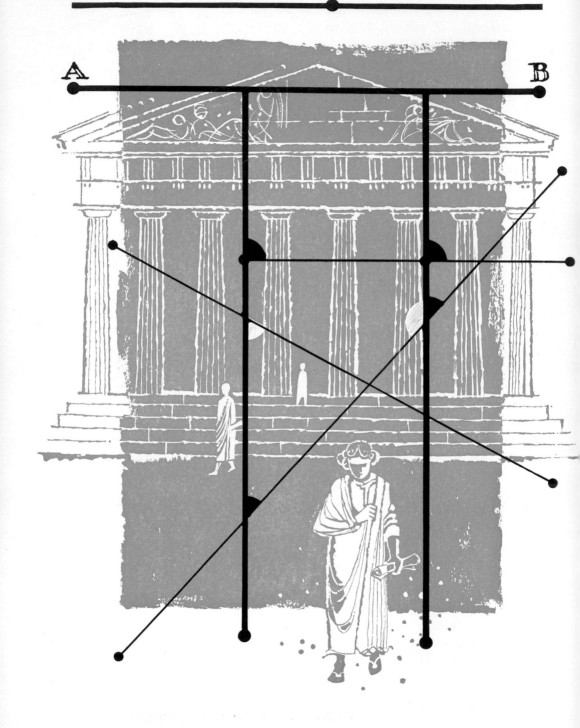

CHAPTER 5

PARALLEL LINES

WE make use of parallel lines in so many ways that it is hard to conceive of a world in which they do not exist. In a floor the edges of the boards are parallel. When a train runs on a straight track the rails are parallel. The farmer plows a field making parallel furrows. In a room parallel lines abound in the windows, walls, and ceilings. The folds in the window curtains hung without a tie are parallel straight lines. The strips in venetian blinds are parallel. The lines on writing paper are parallel. These are only a very few of the many common examples of parallel lines. It is the geometry connected with such lines that we are to study in this unit.

5–1 Parallel Lines Parallel lines are lines that lie in the same plane and satisfy one of the following conditions.

1. They have no points in common.
2. They have all points in common, that is, they are the same line.

Note that condition 2 says "a line is parallel to itself." We can write this $a \parallel a$. $\parallel$ is read *is parallel to*.

Note also that if $x \parallel y$, then $y \parallel x$; that is, if a first line *is parallel to* a second, then the second line *is parallel to* the first line.

$$x$$
$$y$$

We say that *is parallel to* is a *relation* that exists between two lines. Here are some other relations.

is perpendicular to
is congruent to
is equal to

Whenever one geometric element is related to another geometric element of the same kind by a property, or characteristic, we call this property a relation. We shall now study the *is parallel to* relation.

5–2 THEOREM If two lines are perpendicular to the same line, they are parallel.

This theorem is a restatement of Sec. 4–9 and has been proved. What is the difference between the present wording and that in Sec. 4–9?

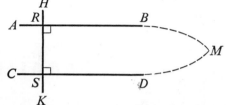

5–3 POSTULATE 18 Through a given point that is not on a given line, only one line can be drawn parallel to the given line. (The <u>Parallel Postulate</u>)

For example, given the line AB and point P not on AB, it is possible to draw one line through P parallel to AB. If CD is parallel to AB and passes through P, then there can be no other line through P parallel to AB.

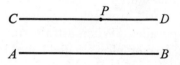

The Parallel Postulate Mathematicians have spent much time in studying this postulate and in trying to prove it. When, without using other equivalent postulates, all attempts to prove it failed, they considered whether some other postulate might be substituted for it. Other postulates have been suggested. Two of these are: (*A*) No line can be drawn through a point parallel to a given line. (*B*) Two lines can be drawn through a point parallel to a given line. If either of these postulates is substituted for our Postulate 18, the theorems based on this postulate must be re-examined. The conclusions of some theorems have to be changed. Since the geometry of this book is based upon the parallel postulate which was used by Euclid, it is called Euclidean geometry. The geometries based upon Postulate *A* and Postulate *B* are called non-Euclidean geometries. Sometime you may read about these geometries or study them.

5–4 THEOREM If a line is perpendicular to one of two parallel lines, it is perpendicular to the other.

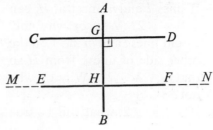

Hypothesis $AB \perp CD$; $CD \parallel EF$

Conclusion $AB \perp EF$

The plan is to consider the contradictory of the conclusion, or that $AB \not\perp EF$.

Construction. Suppose that AB is not $\perp EF$. Through H, the point of intersection of AB and EF, draw $MN \perp AB$.

Proof

1. $MN \parallel CD$
2. But $EF \parallel CD$
3. MN and EF both contain H.
4. Statements 1, 2, and 3 are inconsistent.
5. $EF \perp AB$, that is, $AB \perp EF$

1. Sec. 5–2
2. Hypothesis
3. Construction and given
4. Postulate 18
5. Sec. 4–8

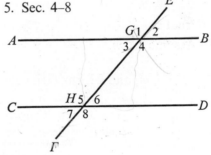

5–5 Transversal A transversal is a line that intersects two or more lines.

Interior angles are angles formed by the transversal and two lines that it intersects and lying between the lines intersected. $\angle 3$, $\angle 4$, $\angle 5$, and $\angle 6$ are interior angles.

Exterior angles lie outside the intersected lines. $\angle 1$, $\angle 2$, $\angle 7$, and $\angle 8$ are exterior angles.

Alternate angles are nonadjacent angles not on the same side of the transversal. $\angle 1$ and $\angle 8$, $\angle 2$ and $\angle 7$, $\angle 3$ and $\angle 6$, $\angle 4$ and $\angle 5$ are alternate angles.

Corresponding angles are angles on the same side of the transversal and on the same relative sides of the lines intersected. That is, if one angle is above one line, its corresponding angle is above the other line, etc. $\angle 1$ and $\angle 5$ are one pair of corresponding angles.

Alternate interior angles are angles that are both alternate and interior. For example, $\angle 3$ and $\angle 6$.

Alternate exterior angles are angles that are both alternate and exterior. For example, $\angle 1$ and $\angle 8$.

1. If lines *l* and *m* meet at *H*, can
   $\angle 1 = \angle 2$? Why or why not?
2. Could lines *l* and *m* meet on the
   other side of line *k* from *H* so
   that $\angle 1 = \angle 2$? Why or why
   not?
3. If $\angle 1 = \angle 2$, what will be true
   of the lines *l* and *m*? Can you
   prove your answer?

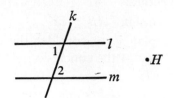

5–6   THEOREM   If two lines are cut by a transversal so that a pair of alternate interior angles are equal, the lines are parallel.

Hypothesis   *k* intersects *l* and *m*; $\angle 1 = \angle 2$
Conclusion   *l* ∥ *m*

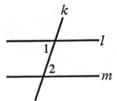

Proof

1. Assume *l* ∦ *m*.

2. Then *l*, *m*, and *k* form a triangle
   with $\angle 1$ and $\angle 2$, one an exterior and the other a nonadjacent interior angle of the
   triangle.
3. $\angle 1 > \angle 2$ or $\angle 2 > \angle 1$
4. $\angle 1 = \angle 2$
5. 3 and 4 are contradictory statements.
6. *l* ∥ *m*

1. Contradictory of conclusion;
   additional hypothesis
2. Def. of △

3. See Sec. 4–3.
4. Given
5. See Sec. 4–5.

6. See Sec. 4–6.

5–7   Corollary   If two lines are cut by a transversal so that a pair of corresponding angles are equal, the lines are parallel.

5–8   Corollary   If two lines are cut by a transversal so that a pair of alternate exterior angles are equal, the lines are parallel.

5–9   Corollary   If two lines are cut by a transversal so that two consecutive interior angles are supplementary, the lines are parallel.

EXERCISES

C. Oral

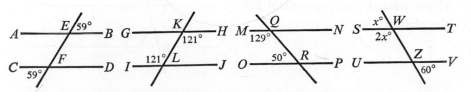

1. Which lines in the above figures are parallel? Why?

B. Written

2. Hyp. $AB \parallel CD$;
    EG bisects $\angle BEF$;
    HF bisects $\angle EFC$.
   Con. $EG \parallel HF$

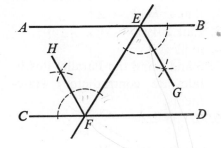

3. Hyp. RP bisects $\angle LPQ$;
    RQ bisects $\angle PQN$;
    $\angle 1 + \angle 2 =$ a rt. $\angle$
   Con. $KL \parallel MN$

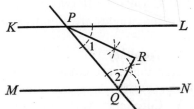

4. Hyp. GE bisects $\angle AEF$;
    FH bisects $\angle EFD$;
    $\angle 1 = \angle 2$
   Con. $AB \parallel CD$

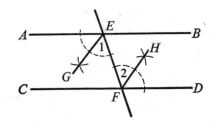

5. Hyp. $\triangle KLM \cong \triangle NPQ$
   Con. $KM \parallel NQ$; $LM \parallel PQ$

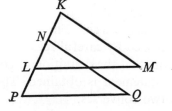

5-10 THEOREM If two parallel lines are cut by a transversal, the alternate interior angles are equal.

Hypothesis $l \parallel m$; transversal EF

Conclusion $\angle 1 = \angle 2$

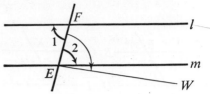

Proof

1. Assume $\angle 1 \neq \angle 2$

2. Draw $\overline{EW}$ distinct from m so that $\angle FEW = \angle 1$.
3. Line $EW \parallel l$
4. $m \parallel l$
5. 3 and 4 and the Parallel Postulate are contradictory statements.
6. $\angle 1 = \angle 2$

1. Added hypothesis, contradictory of conclusion
2. $\angle 1 \neq \angle 2$

3. Sec. 5–6
4. Given
5. Parallel Postulate

6. Sec. 4–8

5-11 Corollary If two parallel lines are cut by a transversal, the corresponding angles are equal. (Abbreviation: Cor. $\angle$s of $\parallel$ lines)

5-12 Corollary If two parallel lines are cut by a transversal, the alternate exterior angles are equal. (Abbreviation: Alt. ext. $\angle$s of $\parallel$ lines)

5-13 Corollary If two parallel lines are cut by a transversal, the consecutive interior angles are supplementary. (Abbreviation: Consec. int. $\angle$s of $\parallel$ lines)

5-14 Converse Theorem Compare the hypotheses of Sec. 5–6 and Sec. 5–10. Compare their conclusions. The theorem of Sec. 5–10 is a converse of the theorem of Sec. 5–6. A <u>converse</u> of a theorem is a theorem that is formed by interchanging one statement in the hypothesis of the given theorem with a statement in the conclusion. Note that the truth of the converse does not follow from the original theorem. Not all converse theorems are true. The truth of a converse theorem (if it is true) must be established by careful reasoning.

Note that the definition of converse above in effect tells how a converse of a statement is obtained. The following example illustrates a theorem and two converses.

Example: Consider the following.

Theorem: If a plane straight-line figure has three sides, if two of the sides are equal, and if a line bisects the angle included by the equal sides, then the angle bisector is perpendicular to the third side.

Hyp. (*a*) Straight-line figure *ABC*
            that has three sides.
     (*b*) $AB = AC$
     (*c*) *AD* is drawn so that
         $\angle BAD = \angle CAD$.
Con. (*z*) $AD \perp BC$

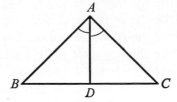

This theorem is like Ex. 7, page 82, and has been proved.

Now let us state two converses of this theorem and see whether they can be proved.

If we interchange (*b*) and (*z*) we have:

Hyp. (*a*) Straight-line figure *ABC* that has three sides.
     (*z*) $AD \perp BC$
     (*c*) $\angle BAD = \angle CAD$
Con. (*b*) $AB = AC$

These statements can be combined into:

Converse I If a plane straight-line figure has three sides, if a line is drawn through the point of intersection of two of these sides perpendicular to the third side, and if this perpendicular bisects the angle from whose vertex it is drawn, then the sides that meet at the point from which the perpendicular is drawn are equal.

If we interchange (*a*) and (*z*) in
the original theorem we have:

Hyp. (*z*) $AD \perp BC$
     (*b*) $AB = AC$
     (*c*) $\angle FAD = \angle EAD$
Con. (*a*) The figure has three sides.

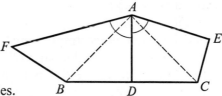

These statements can be combined into:

Converse II If a line is drawn from one vertex of a plane straight-line figure perpendicular to another side, if this line bisects the angle at this vertex, and if the lines that join the vertex to the end points of the side to which the perpendicular is drawn are equal, then the figure has three sides.

This converse cannot be proved. The figure illustrates why.

EXERCISES

1. Show that the theorem of Sec. 5–10 is a converse of the theorem of Sec. 5–6, and the theorem of Sec. 5–6 is a converse of the theorem of Sec. 5–10.
2. Write the converse of Sec. 5–7 and prove it. Compare Sec. 5–11.
3. Write the converse of Sec. 5–8 and prove it. Compare Sec. 5–12.
4. Write the converse of Sec. 5–9 and prove it. Compare Sec. 5–13.
5. Write the converse of this statement: If an animal is a horse, it has four legs. Is the converse true?
6. Write the converse of this statement: If an object is made of steel, it is made of metal. Is the converse true?
7. Write the converse of this statement: If an angle is a right angle, its sides are perpendicular to each other. Is the converse true?
8. Write the converse of this statement: If two lines are perpendicular to each other, they are not parallel. Is the converse true?

EXERCISES

C. Oral

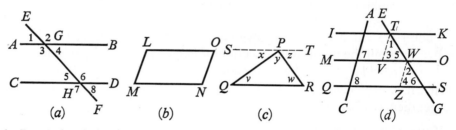

(a)	(b)	(c)	(d)

1. In each of the above figures, name (a) the transversals; (b) the pairs of alternate interior angles; (c) the pairs of alternate exterior angles; (d) the pairs of corresponding angles; (e) the pairs of consecutive interior angles; (f) the pairs of vertical angles.
2. In Figure (a), $AB \parallel CD$; in Figure (b), $LO \parallel MN$, and $LM \parallel NO$; in Figure (c), $ST \parallel QR$; in Figure (d), $IK \parallel MO \parallel QS$, $TV \parallel AC$, and $ZW \parallel AC$. In each of these figures, name all pairs of equal angles and give a reason for your statement in each case.

3. $AB \parallel CD$. Find the number of degrees in each angle of this figure.

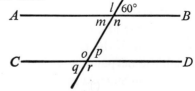

B. Written

4. Hyp. $AB \parallel CD$; $AD \parallel BC$;
     $\angle A =$ a rt. $\angle$
   Con. $CD \perp BC$

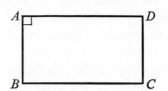

5. Hyp. $LO \parallel MN$; $LM \parallel NO$;
     $\angle LOP = 120°$
   Find the size of each $\angle$ in
   $LMNO$.

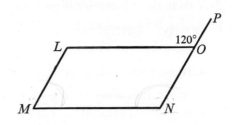

A.

6. Hyp. BD bisects $\angle ABC$;
     $EF \parallel BC$
   Con. $\triangle BEF$ is isosceles.

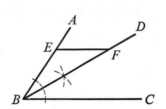

5–15 THEOREM If two lines are parallel to the same line, they are parallel to each other.

Hypothesis $AB \parallel EF$; $EF \parallel CD$

Conclusion $AB \parallel CD$

The plan is to show that AB and CD have equal corresponding angles when a transversal is drawn cutting all three lines.

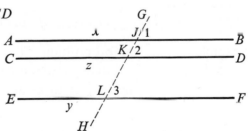

Construction. Draw GH cutting AB at J, CD at K, and EF at L.

Proof

1. $\angle 1 = \angle 3$ 1. Why?
2. $\angle 2 = \angle 3$ 2. Why?
3. $\angle 1 = \angle 2$ 3. Why?
4. $\therefore AB \parallel CD$ 4. By Sec. 5–6

5–16   If and Only If   A theorem and a converse of the theorem can frequently be stated as one proposition.   We shall give several illustrations, and frequently return to this use in the rest of this book.

In chapter 3 we proved that a triangle having two equal sides has two equal angles, and also if the triangle has two equal angles it has two equal sides.   We write this as the proposition:

A triangle is isosceles if and only if it has two equal angles.   (A)

If we write a part of this statement omitting the first *if and* and using *has two equal sides* for *is isosceles*, we obtain:

A triangle has two equal sides, *only if* it has two equal angles.   (B)

The clause following *only if* is to be interpreted as the conclusion we must establish.   Thus statement *B* is equivalent to:

If a triangle is isosceles, then it has two equal angles.   (Theorem)

If in the statement *A* we omit the words *and only if*, we obtain:

A triangle is isosceles *if* it has two equal angles.   (C)

This is an if-then statement with the if part placed second and is equivalent to:

If a triangle has two equal angles, it is isosceles.   (Converse)

Hence, an *if and only if* proposition can be written as two theorems. Using only the first *if* and omitting *and only if*, we get a theorem.   Omitting the first *if and* and using *only if*, we obtain the converse of the theorem.

Example: Write the proposition "Two lines are parallel if and only if a pair of alternate interior angles are equal" as two separate theorems.

Solution.   Using the *only if* to mean the conclusion we write the theorem:

If two lines are parallel, then a pair of alternate interior angles are equal.   (A)

Using the *if* (and omitting *and only if*) to mean the hypothesis, we write:

If a pair of alternate interior angles are equal, then the lines are parallel.   (B)

Remember that what follows *if* is hypothesis and that what follows *only if* is a conclusion.

WRITTEN EXERCISES

C.

Write each of the following propositions as a theorem and a converse (or a conditional statement and its converse).

1. Two lines are parallel if and only if they are perpendicular to the same line.
2. Two lines are parallel if and only if a pair of corresponding angles are equal.
3. Two triangles are congruent if and only if the sides of one equal the sides of the other.
4. Two angles are complementary if and only if their sum is a right angle.
5. A number is a factor if and only if it divides another number exactly.

B.

Express each of the following pairs of statements as a proposition in "if and only if" form.

6. (a) If a transversal to two lines makes two alternate exterior angles equal, then the lines are parallel.
   (b) If two lines are parallel and cut by a transversal, then the alternate exterior angles are equal.
7. (a) If two triangles are congruent, then corresponding two sides and the included angle of the triangles are equal.
   (b) If corresponding two sides and an included angle of two triangles are equal, the triangles are congruent.
8. (a) If a number is divisible by 2, it is an even number.
   (b) If a number is even, then it is divisible by 2.
9. (a) If a number cannot be divided without a remainder by any other whole number except 1, then it is prime.
   (b) If a number is prime, then it cannot be divided without a remainder by any other whole number except 1.
10. (a) If the three sides of a triangle are equal, then the three angles are equal.
    (b) If the three angles of a triangle are equal, then the three sides are equal.
11. Make two similar statements (see Ex. 8) about odd numbers, and write them as a single proposition.
12. Interpret the statement: You will go to the theater if and only if you finish your geometry assignment.

5–17   Discussion of the Relation "is parallel to"   In Sec. 5–1 we learned that a line is parallel to itself. If m denotes the line we write this as:

$$m \parallel m \qquad \text{(Reflexive)}$$

Any relation such that an element has the stated relation to itself is called reflexive. Thus *is equal to* is reflexive, since any measurable quantity is equal to itself. We write this: $a = a$. Again, *has the same color as* is a reflexive relation for an object has the same color as itself. However, *is perpendicular to* is not reflexive, for a line is not perpendicular to itself. To write $a \perp a$ is an error.

We also learned that if a line is parallel to a second line, this implies the second line is parallel to the first. If m and p denote the lines, we write this as:

$$m \parallel p \Rightarrow p \parallel m \qquad \text{(Symmetric)}$$

where the symbol $\Rightarrow$ is read "implies." Any relation that permits this symmetrical interchange of the elements is called symmetric. Thus *is equal to* is symmetric, for if $\frac{a}{b} = \frac{c}{d}$, then certainly $\frac{c}{d} = \frac{a}{b}$. The relation *is perpendicular to* is also symmetric for $a \perp b \Rightarrow b \perp a$. However, *is the father of* is not symmetric, since if Mr. A is the father of child B, certainly child B is not the father of Mr. A.

The theorem you have proved in 5–15 gives us another relation. Here we had three lines x, y, and z, and proved that $x \parallel y$ and $y \parallel z$ implies $x \parallel z$.

$$(x \parallel y \text{ and } y \parallel z) \Rightarrow x \parallel z \qquad \text{(Transitive)}$$

Any relation such that if a first element has this relation to the second, and then the second element has this relation to a third, then the first element must have the same relation to the third is called transitive, that is "carries over." The relation *is equal to* is transitive, since if for three fractions $\frac{a}{b} = \frac{c}{d}$ and $\frac{c}{d} = \frac{e}{f}$, then surely $\frac{a}{b} = \frac{e}{f}$. A postulate which says two things equal to the same thing are equal to each other is nothing more than the transitive property of equality. However *is perpendicular to* is not transitive, since if $a \perp b$ and $b \perp c$, we know that $a \not\perp c$, in fact $a \parallel c$. Why?

We have now seen that *is parallel to* is a relation that has all three properties: reflexive, symmetric, and transitive. Any relation that has all these three properties is called an equivalence relation.

Is parallel to is an equivalence relation.

WRITTEN EXERCISES

C.

1. Show that for fractions *is equal to* is an equivalence relation.
2. Show that for triangles *is congruent to* is an equivalence relation.
3. Show that for students in a high school *is in the same class as* is an equivalence relation.
4. Show that for positive and negative numbers *is greater than* is not an equivalence relation. What property does this relation have?
5. Show that for points on a horizontal line, *is to the right of* is not an equivalence relation.

B.

6. Consider the equivalence relation *is parallel to* and *all* the lines in a plane. Select one line in the plane. Apply the equivalence relation to this line and all the lines thus related to it. What can you say about all the lines thus selected?
7. Select a line not parallel to the line selected in Ex. 6. Apply the relation *is parallel to* to this line and all the lines related to it. What can you say about all the lines thus selected?
8. Are any of the lines selected in Ex. 6 in the set of lines selected in Ex. 7? Why or why not?

A.

9. Using the results of Ex. 6, 7, and 8 tell how the relation *is parallel to* separates all the lines of the plane into distinct sets of lines.
10. Show that *is equal to* is an equivalence relation that separates all common fractions into distinct sets. Consider $\frac{1}{2} = \frac{3}{6}$, etc.

DISCOVERY EXERCISE

PQ ∥ *ST*, *QR* ∥ *TV*. Can you prove that ∠*PQR* = ∠*STV*? If you need help, do these exercises.

1. Does ∠1 = ∠2? Why?
2. Does ∠2 = ∠3? Why?
3. Does ∠1 = ∠3? Why?

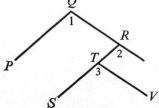

5–18 THEOREM If two angles have their sides parallel, initial side to initial side and terminal side to terminal side, the angles are equal.

Hypothesis $\angle ABC$ and $\angle DEF$; $BC \parallel EF$; $AB \parallel DE$

Conclusion $\angle ABC = \angle DEF$

Give the proof in detail. Review Sec. 0–11.

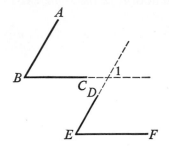 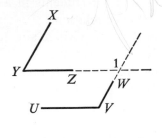

5–19 Corollary If two angles have their sides parallel, initial side to terminal side and terminal side to initial side, the angles are supplementary.

Prove $\angle Y + \angle V$ = a st. $\angle$.

Cloister arches, Palermo, Italy

Re-read Sec. 5–2, 5–6, 5–7, 5–8, 5–9. Note that these state conditions for parallel lines so that if two lines meet these conditions, the lines are parallel. If we wish to construct one line parallel to another, it is only necessary to make the constructed line meet one of the stated conditions.

Draw a line *AB* and place a point *C* above it. Construct a line through *C* parallel to *AB* by following the steps described in the problem below.

5–20 Problem Through a given point to construct a line parallel to a given line.

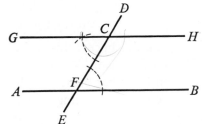

Given Point *C* not on *AB*.

Required To construct a line through *C* ∥ *AB*.

The plan is to make equal alternate interior angles.

Construction. (*a*) Draw any line through *C* cutting *AB* at *F*. (*b*) At *C* construct ∠*GCF* = ∠*CFB*, making ∠*GCF* and ∠*CFB* alternate interior angles. Then *GC* ∥ *AB*.

Give the proof.

Some General Characteristics of Geometric Reasoning: Summary

(*a*) We carefully state the meanings that we attach to definable terms, and we specifically list undefined terms.

(*b*) Only those statements are asserted as postulates that are consistent with other postulates and theorems in the system in which we are working.

(*c*) Hypotheses must be clearly and definitely stated.

(*d*) Any assertion can be accepted in proof if it has been specifically postulated, or if it has been proved.

(*e*) Reasons given for statements must be acceptable, and they must apply to the situation under consideration.

(*f*) No statement is accepted merely because a converse of it has been established.

(*g*) A statement is not accepted under all conditions merely because it is known to be acceptable for some particular case.

DISCUSSION EXERCISES

Nongeometric Problems

Answer the questions in the following exercises and give a reason from the list of characteristics of reasoning on page 125 for your answer.

1. If you find a cicada with a figure like a letter *W* on its wings, does it follow that there is to be a war?

Answer: No. See (*d*) above.

2. I read in a geography that cotton will not grow within the Arctic Circle. A friend owns some land in Mexico. Will it produce cotton?

Answer: I cannot tell. Knowing only that cotton will not grow within the Arctic Circle gives no information that will enable me to tell whether cotton will grow on my friend's farm in Mexico. See (*f*) above.

3. A child burned his hand. A woman blew her breath on the hand. The hand healed. When other people suffer burns, should they have the woman blow her breath on the burns and trust this to heal them?

4. A man was going down the street. A black cat crossed his path. The man fell and broke his arm. Does it follow that one will have bad luck if a black cat crosses his path?

5. Does kissing the Blarney stone in Blarney Castle in Ireland give one the gift of eloquence?

6. If one breaks a mirror, does it follow that he will have seven years of bad luck?

7. If a nation has a large army, is it certain that it will never have a war?

8. If a nation has no army, is it certain that it will never have a war?

9. A certain lady uses a particular kind of cold cream. She is beautiful. Does it follow that everyone that uses that kind of cold cream will be beautiful?

10. A certain man eats a particular kind of cereal for breakfast. He has good health. Does it follow that he would not have good health if he should eat another kind of cereal?

11. In a certain arid region, the ground water level is 60 feet below the surface of the ground. (*a*) Mr. X has a well that is 42 feet deep. Will it furnish a supply of water from the underground source? (*b*) Mr. Y has a well that is 71 feet deep. Does it have water in it? (*c*) Mr. Z has a well that furnishes a supply of water. What can be said of its depth?

12. One man is the only barber in a certain village. The barber shaves every man in the village that does not shave himself. Is the barber ever shaved?

13. In a certain state, every person over twenty-one years of age at the time of election is permitted to vote. (*a*) Mr. R is 35 years of age. Did he vote at the last election? (*b*) Mr. S voted at the last election. Is he past twenty-one years of age? (*c*) Miss Z did not vote at the last election. Is she past twenty-one years of age?

14. Every man in a certain regiment is over six feet tall. (*a*) J is in this regiment. What can be asserted with regard to his height? (*b*) K is not six feet tall. Is he in this regiment? (*c*) L is not in this regiment. Is he over six feet tall? (*d*) M is six feet tall. Is he in this regiment?

15. Every man living in Boon Township is a farmer. (*a*) Mr. X lives in Boon Township. Is he a farmer? (*b*) Mr. Y is a farmer. Does he live in Boon Township? (*c*) Mr. Z is not a farmer. Does he live in Boon Township? (*d*) Mr. W does not live in Boon Township. Is he a farmer?

16. Every graduating senior in Longvale High School is in roll room No. 127. (*a*) John Smith is a graduating senior in Longvale High School. Is he in roll room No. 127? (*b*) Sara Hart is in roll room No. 127 in Longvale High School. Is she a graduating senior? (*c*) Helen Dalton, a pupil in Longvale High School, is not a graduating senior. Is she in roll room No. 127? (*d*) Harry France, a pupil in Longvale High School, is not in roll room No. 127. Is he a graduating senior?

17. Mr. A and Mr. B were bitter enemies. On a very dark night on a lonely country road Mr. C saw two men beside the road as his car suddenly threw a light around the corner. One of the men was Mr. B, who was in the act of drawing out a long knife that had been plunged into Mr. A's heart. Mr. A was dead. Did Mr. B kill Mr. A? (These facts are essentially the same as those introduced in a famous murder trial.)

18. Three fourths of the wage earners in a certain town are employees of the X Mills. One winter when business was very bad, the mills closed down. Many people had little to eat. In the severest part of the winter, many houses were not warm. There was an epidemic of sickness. A candidate for public office made a speech in which he pointed out the sufferings of the people and asserted that if he were elected to office he would have a law passed to compel the owners of the mills to supply food, coal, clothes, homes, and medical service to former employees whether or not the mills were in operation. (*a*) Was the speaker sincere in his statement? (*b*) Was he merely trying to get votes so that he could be elected? (*c*) Does the problem furnish evidence to show what his motives were? (*d*) Should his election or defeat be determined by the nature of his motives or by the soundness of his ideas without regard to his motives?

C.

1. Hyp. $AP = PD$;
   $BP = PC$
   Con. $AB \parallel CD$

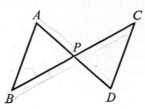

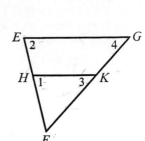

2. Hyp. $HK \parallel EG$
   Con. $\angle 1 + \angle 3 + \angle F$
   $= \angle 2 + \angle 4 + \angle F$

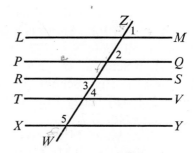

3. Hyp. $\angle 1 = \angle 2 = \angle 3 = \angle 4$;
   $\angle 4 + \angle 5 =$ a st. $\angle$
   Con. $LM \parallel PQ \parallel RS \parallel TV \parallel XY$

4. Hyp. $AO = OD$; $AB \parallel CD$
   Con. $AB = CD$

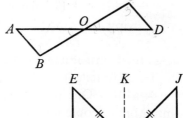

5. Hyp. $FG = GH$; $EG = GJ$;
   KG bisects $\angle EGJ$;
   $\angle F = \angle H =$ a rt. $\angle$
   Con. $KG \parallel EF$

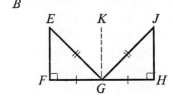

6. Hyp. $\angle 1 = \angle 2$;
   $\angle 3 = \angle 4$
   Con. $\angle A = \angle E$

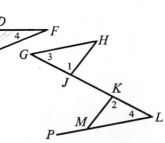

7. Hyp. $\angle 1 = \angle 2$;
   $\angle 3 = \angle 4$
   Con. $\angle H + \angle KMP =$ a st. $\angle$

8. Give all the tests by which one can tell whether two lines are parallel.
9. The exterior angles on the same side of a transversal cutting two parallel lines are $6x$ and $4x$. Find the number of degrees in each angle.
10. The alternate interior angles of two parallel lines cut by a transversal are $12x$ degrees and $(x^2 + 36)$ degrees. Find the angles.
11. The alternate exterior angles of two parallel lines cut by a transversal are $(x^2 + .0625)$ right angles and $.5x$ right angles. Find the angles.
12. The alternate exterior angles of two lines cut by a transversal are $(x + 1)(x - 1)$ degrees and $4 - (5 - x^2)$ degrees. Are the lines parallel?
13. Use the fact proved in Sec. 5-2 to construct a line through a given point parallel to a given line.
14. Use the fact proved in Sec. 5-6 to construct a line through a given point parallel to a given line.

OUTLINE OF CHAPTER 5

This chapter introduces the following terms:

transversal
interior angles of parallel lines
exterior angles of parallel lines
corresponding angles of parallel lines

alternate angles
consecutive angles
converse
if and only if
equivalence relation

REVIEW

1. What is the Parallel Postulate? Illustrate with a drawing.
2. What is a transversal? Illustrate.
3. Use the illustration for No. 2 and mark alternate interior angles a and b, c and d. Mark corresponding angles e and f, g and h, j and k, p and q.
4. Draw a pair of vertical parallel lines and a transversal, and indicate pairs of alternate exterior angles r and s, t and v.
5. Theorem. If two parallel lines are cut by a transversal, the alternate exterior angles are equal. Draw a figure and prove this theorem.
6. Theorem. If two parallel lines are cut by a transversal, the alternate interior angles are equal. State and prove the converse of this theorem.

7. Draw any line x. Now draw line y parallel to x, and draw line z parallel to x. What assertion can you make regarding the relation of y and z?

8. Theorem. If two angles have their sides parallel, initial to terminal and terminal to initial, the angles are supplementary. Give a demonstration of this theorem.

9. Draw a line AB. Let N be any point not on AB. Through N construct a line parallel to AB. Prove your construction.

10. If two lines are not parallel, can they have a transversal? Illustrate.

YES–NO TEST

Approximately 15 minutes

Copy on your paper the numbers of the following questions. If the answer to a question is *yes* under all conditions, place a plus sign ($+$) after its number. If the answer is *not yes* under all conditions, place a zero (0) after its number.

1. Are two lines parallel if they will not meet?

2. Are two lines parallel to each other if they are perpendicular to the same line?

3. Are two lines perpendicular to each other if they are parallel to the same line?

4. If line $x \perp$ line y, and line $y \parallel$ line z, is line $x \parallel$ line z?

5. If $\angle x$ and $\angle y$ are corresponding angles of two parallel lines cut by a transversal, and if $\angle x = 80°$, does $\angle y = 100°$?

6. If two lines are perpendicular, can they have a transversal?

7. If one angle of two parallel lines cut by a transversal is $60°$, can another angle be $100°$?

8. If two angles have their sides parallel, initial to terminal and terminal to initial, are the angles equal?

9. Can two lines be drawn through a given point parallel to a given line?

10. Does an interior angle of parallel lines cut by a transversal equal the exterior angle on the opposite side of the transversal with the other parallel line as a side?

COMPLETION TEST

Approximately 20 minutes

On your paper copy the numbers of the following statements and questions. After each number write a word, or letter, or number which if written in the blank or after a question would make the statement true or answer the question.

1. Two straight lines in the same plane that cannot meet however far they may be extended are ———— lines.

2. A line that intersects two or more lines is a ————.

3. Through a point not on a line ———— line can be drawn parallel ·to a given line.

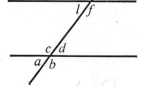

4. ∠*a* and ∠———— are corresponding ∠s.

5. ∠*c* and ∠———— are alternate interior ∠s.

6. ∠*q* and ∠———— are alternate exterior ∠s.

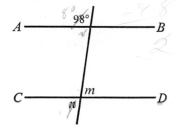

7. *AB* ∥ *CD*. ∠*m* = ————°

8. *AB* ∥ *CD*. ∠*n* = ————°

9. Is *XY* ∥ *ZW*?

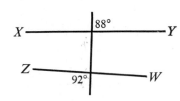

11. *ST* and *VW* are ————.

10. Is *AB* ∥ *CD*?

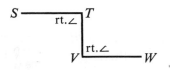

12. $MN \parallel BC.$ $\angle 2 = \angle$ _____ .

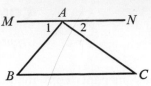

13. $RS \parallel XY;$ $ST \parallel YZ$
$\angle Y$ contains _____ degrees.

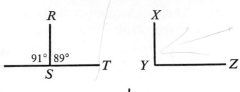

14. AB is $\parallel$ to _____ .

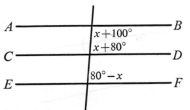

SUPPLEMENTARY EXERCISES

C.

1. Hyp. $AB \parallel CD$
    Con. $\angle 1 = \angle 2;$ $\angle 3 = \angle 4;$
          $\angle 5 = \angle 6$

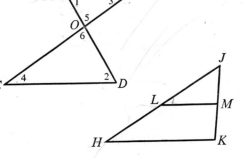

2. Hyp. $LM \parallel HK$
    Con. $\angle JLM = \angle JHK;$
          $\angle JML = \angle JKH$

3. Hyp. $\angle 1 + \angle 2 = $ a st. $\angle;$
          $\angle 2 = \angle 3 = \angle 4 = \angle 5$
    Con. $NO \parallel PQ \parallel RS \parallel TV \parallel XY$

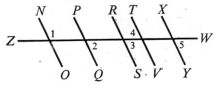

4. Hyp. $AB = CD;$ $AB \parallel CD$
    Con. AD and BC bisect each
          other.

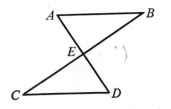

5. Hyp.   ∠G and ∠K are
right ∠s.
Con.   ∠J = ∠H

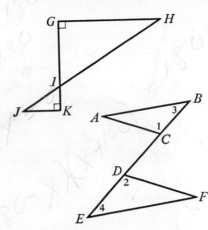

B.

6. Hyp.   ∠1 = ∠2; ∠3 = ∠4
Con.   ∠A = ∠F

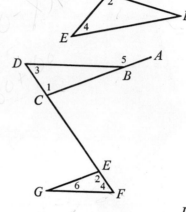

7. Hyp.   ∠1 = ∠2; ∠3 = ∠4
Con.   ∠5 and ∠6 are supplementary.

8. Hyp.   LK ∥ HI; HK ∥ IJ
Find   ∠H, ∠I, ∠J, and
∠HKJ.

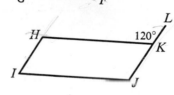

9. Hyp.   AB = EF; AC = DE;
DB = FC
Con.   AC ∥ DE

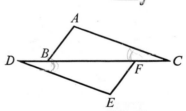

10. Corresponding angles of two parallel lines cut by a transversal are $70° - x°$ and $3x° - 90°$. Find each angle.

11. Interior angles on the same side of a transversal which cuts two parallel lines are $5a° - 42°$ and $7a° + 30°$. Find each angle.

A.

12. Alternate interior angles of two parallel lines cut by a transversal are $(x^2 + 20)°$ and $(9x)°$. Find each angle.

CHAPTER | 6

ANGLES OF POLYGONS

IF you examine the designs in tile, linoleum, drapes, rugs, or wallpaper where the same geometric figure is repeated many times, you will realize that the artist who worked out the designs is quite limited as to the kinds of regular geometric forms that he can use. A study of a great many patterns will disclose that equilateral triangles, squares, and regular hexagons are much more common in these designs than other geometric figures. There is a reason why this is true. It is because of the relationship between the angles in the various figures. Any merchant who deals in linoleum will give you a folder that shows various geometric figures. Get this and study the various combinations of forms.

This chapter presents facts that control the making of designs based upon regular geometric figures as well as facts frequently used in proofs that follow in the remainder of the book.

6–1 Polygons A polygon is a closed broken line, lying in a plane, that has three or more segments.

Each of the segments that make a polygon is called a side.

Each of the end points of the segments is called a vertex.

The angle formed at each vertex is called an angle of the polygon.

Polygons are named according to the number of sides, or vertices, or angles they contain. The number of angles or vertices of a given polygon is always the same as its number of sides. Verify this, using the figures below.

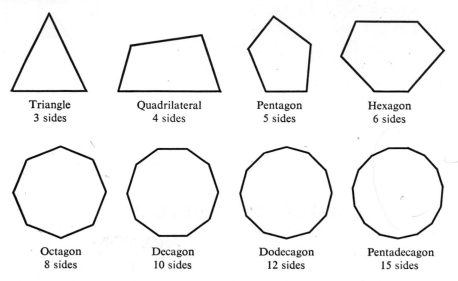

| Triangle | Quadrilateral | Pentagon | Hexagon |
| 3 sides | 4 sides | 5 sides | 6 sides |

| Octagon | Decagon | Dodecagon | Pentadecagon |
| 8 sides | 10 sides | 12 sides | 15 sides |

It will help you to remember the names if you know that *gon* is derived from the Greek word meaning corner or angle, and *lateral* from the Latin word for side.

6–2 Types of Polygons A polygon divides a plane into two regions. The region that is common to the interior of *all* the angles of the polygon is called the interior of the polygon. The set of points in the plane, not on the polygon or in its interior is called the exterior of the polygon.

A convex polygon has no angle that is greater than a straight angle. It can be cut by a straight line in two and only two points.

A concave polygon is one that has at least one angle greater than a straight angle. It can be cut by a straight line in more than two points.

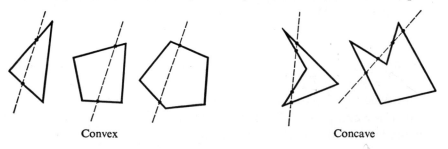

Convex   Concave

In this book we shall always mean convex polygon when the word *polygon* is used, unless otherwise specified.

There is a special type of angle studied in connection with the polygon. It is given the name *exterior angle* to distinguish it from an *angle of the polygon*. (See also Sec. 4–2.)

An <u>exterior angle</u> of a polygon is an angle that is formed at a vertex by extending one side through this vertex. It is supplementary to the angle of the polygon at this vertex. In the figure, ∠*ADE* is an exterior angle of the polygon *ABCD*.

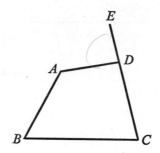

EXERCISES

1. Define a hexagon; an octagon; a decagon; a dodecagon.
2. What is a trigon? A tetragon? Each of the figures defined in Ex. 1?
3. What is a trilateral? An octalateral?
4. Draw figures to illustrate a convex and a concave hexagon.
5. How many angles greater than 180° can a concave quadrilateral have?
6. How many angles greater than 180° can a concave pentagon have? Draw a figure to illustrate your answer.
7. Can a triangle be concave? Explain.
8. Using the diagram shown where *a*, *b*, *c* are sides, define each type of triangle as determined by the sides.

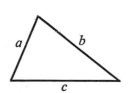

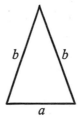

9. Polygon *ABCD* above can have eight exterior angles. Draw a quadrilateral and show its eight exterior angles. On your drawing point out angles that are neither exterior nor interior.
10. Draw △*RST*. Let *W* be a point between *S* and *T* and draw *RW*. What interior angle of △*RWS* is an exterior angle of △*RWT*?

11. Using the diagram, where x is an acute angle, y is a right angle, and z is an obtuse angle, define each type of triangle as determined by their angles.

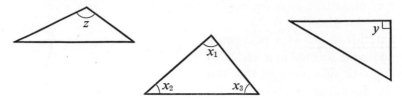

12. Show that at a given vertex of a polygon, the exterior angle is the same size no matter which side is extended through the vertex.

AN EXPERIMENT

Draw a triangle XYZ having any size or shape. Mark P and Q, the mid-points of XY and XZ respectively. Draw PQ. Draw PR and QS each perpendicular to YZ. Cut out the triangle and fold on PQ, PR, and QS. You will have a figure like the second one shown with the vertices of the given triangle at the same point. What seems to be the sum of the three angles?

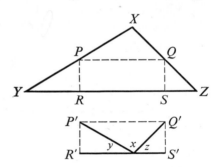

DISCOVERY EXERCISE

Draw a triangle ABC. Draw a line MN through A parallel to BC. What angle of the triangle equals $\angle MAB$? What angle of the triangle equals $\angle CAN$? What is the sum of angles MAB, BAC, and CAN? What is the sum of the angles of the triangle? State a theorem based upon this exercise. Compare your theorem with that of Sec. 6–3.

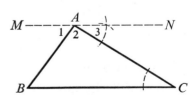

6–3 THEOREM The sum of the angles of a triangle is a straight angle.

Hypothesis $\triangle ABC$

Conclusion $\angle 2 + \angle B + \angle C =$ a st. $\angle$

The plan is to construct a line through one vertex parallel to the opposite side and show that the sum of the angles at this vertex on one side of the line equals the sum of the angles of the triangle. See Discovery Exercise.

Proof

1. Through A construct $MN \parallel BC$ 1. Give reason.
2. $\angle 1 = \angle B$ 2. Why?
3. $\angle 2 = \angle 2$ 3. By identity
4. $\angle 3 = \angle C$ 4. Why?
5. $\angle 1 + \angle 2 + \angle 3$ 5. Why?
   $= \angle 2 + \angle B + \angle C$
6. But $\angle 1 + \angle 2 + \angle 3 =$ a   6. Post. 1
   st. $\angle$
7. $\angle 2 + \angle B + \angle C =$ a st. $\angle$ 7. Why?

6–4 Corollary An exterior angle of a triangle equals the sum of the interior angles that are not adjacent to it.

Prove. $\angle XZW = \angle X + \angle Y.$

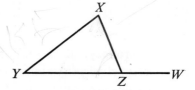

6–5 POSTULATE 19 If unequal quantities are subtracted from equal quantities, the differences are unequal in opposite order.

Here the expression *opposite order* means that the sign showing the relation of the differences is the opposite of the sign showing the relation of the subtrahends.

Illustration. Suppose that $AB = CD$ and $AH < CK$. If AH is subtracted from AB, and CK is subtracted from CD, then $HB > KD$. We can write:

$$AB = CD$$
$$AH < CK$$
$$HB > KD$$

Give several other illustrations of this postulate using numbers; start with $8 = 8$ and $3 < 5$.

6–6 Another proof of Sec. 4–3. Refer to the figure of Sec. 6–4.

1. $\angle XZW = \angle X + \angle Y$	1. Sec. 6–4
2. $\qquad 0 < \qquad\quad \angle Y$	2. Why?
3. $\angle XZW > \angle X$	3. Post. 19

6–7 Corollary If one angle of a triangle is a right angle, the other two are acute.

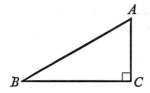

$$\angle A + \angle B + \angle C = \text{a st. } \angle$$
$$\underline{\qquad\qquad\quad \angle C = \text{a rt. } \angle}$$
$$\angle A + \angle B \qquad\quad = \text{a rt. } \angle$$
$$\underline{\qquad\qquad \angle B \qquad > 0}$$
$$\angle A \qquad\qquad\quad < \text{a rt. } \angle$$

Prove $\angle B <$ a rt $\angle$.

6–8 Corollary The acute angles of a right triangle are complementary.

6–9 Corollary If one angle of a triangle is obtuse, the other two are acute.

6–10 Corollary If two triangles have two angles of one equal respectively to two angles of the other, the third angles are equal.

6–11 Corollary If two triangles have a side and any two angles of one equal respectively to a side and the corresponding angles of the other, the triangles are congruent. (s a a)

A special case of this corollary is for right triangles with any side and acute angle of one triangle equal to corresponding parts of the other.

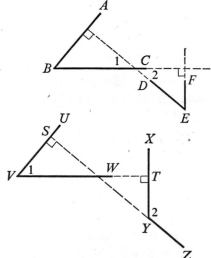

6–12 Corollary If two angles have their sides perpendicular, initial side to initial side and terminal side to terminal side, the angles are equal.

Prove $\angle B = \angle E$.

6–13 Corollary If two angles have their sides perpendicular, initial side to terminal side and terminal side to initial side, the angles are supplementary.

Prove $\angle 1 + \angle 2 = $ a st. $\angle$.

EXERCISES

C. Oral

1. Find the number of degrees in each angle of these triangles.

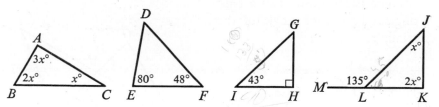

B. Written

2. Prove the theorem of Sec. 6–3 by methods suggested by each of these figures.

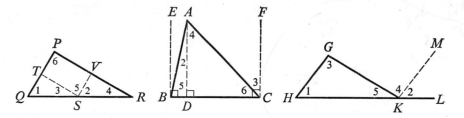

3. Hyp.   △*ABC* is isosceles;
   ∠*A* = 64°   Find ∠*B*.

4. Hyp.   *EG* = *FG*;   ∠*E* = 30°,
   DF ⊥ *EF*

   v = _____°   x = _____°
   y = _____°   z = _____°
   w = _____°

   Compare *GD*, *GF*, and *DF*.

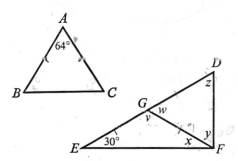

5. Prove: Each angle of an equilateral triangle is 60°.
6. Construct a 60° angle.
7. Construct a 30° angle.
8. Construct a 15° angle.
9. Construct an angle of 22½°.

10. Is *AB* ∥ *CD*?

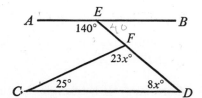

11. Trisect a straight angle. (To *trisect* means to divide into three equal parts.)
12. Trisect a right angle.
13. The vertex angle of an isosceles triangle is 30° more than a base angle. Find each angle of the triangle.

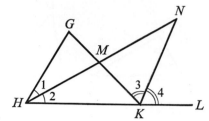

A.

14. Hyp. $\angle 1 = \angle 2$; $\angle 3 = \angle 4$
    Con. $\angle G = 2\angle N$

15. Prove: If one of the equal sides of an isosceles triangle is extended through the vertex by its own length, the line that joins its end point to the nearer end of the base is perpendicular to the base.
16. Prove: The angle formed at the intersection of the bisectors of the equal angles of an isosceles triangle equals an exterior angle at the base.

DISCOVERY EXERCISE

Draw a line segment *BC*. At *B* draw an acute angle. At *C* construct an angle equal to $\angle B$. Let the sides of the angles intersect at *A* forming $\triangle ABC$. Do you think $AC = AB$? Try to prove it. *Suggestion.* Draw a line through *A* dividing $\triangle ABC$ into two triangles which you think you can prove congruent. Consider carefully how this line should be drawn.

6–14 THEOREM If two angles of a triangle are equal, the sides opposite them are equal. (Second Proof. See Sec. 3–19.)

Hypothesis $\triangle ABC$; $\angle B = \angle C$

Conclusion $AB = AC$

The plan is to bisect the third angle of the triangle and prove the resulting triangles congruent.

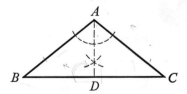

Construction. Bisect $\angle A$.

Let the pupil give the proof in detail. *Suggestion.* Use Sec. 6–11 to prove $\triangle ABD = \triangle ACD$.

6–15 Corollary If a triangle is equiangular, it is equilateral.

C. Oral

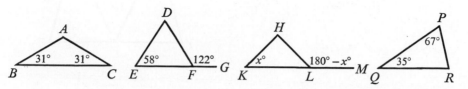

1. Which of the above triangles are isosceles? Why?
2. Of what theorem is Sec. 6–14 the converse?
3. $XY =$ _____ Why?

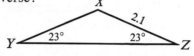

4. $AC =$ _____ Why?

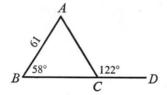

5. $PQ =$ _____ Why?

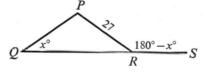

B. Written

6. Hyp. $AB = AC$;
   $\angle ABC = 39°$;
   $BD = 2.4$ Find DC.
   Give a complete
   demonstration.

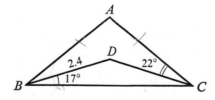

7. Hyp. $EF = EG$; $FH = KG$
   Con. $\angle 1 = \angle 2$
8. Hyp. $\angle 1 = \angle 2$; $FH = KG$
   Con. $\angle 3 = \angle 4$

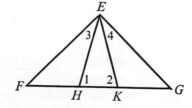

9. Hyp. $XY = ZW$; $YV = VZ$;
$\angle c = \angle d$
   Con. $\angle a = \angle b$

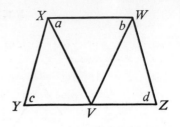

10. Hyp. $XY = ZW$; $YV = VZ$;
$\angle a = \angle b$
    Con. $\angle c = \angle d$

11. Hyp. $MN \parallel ST$; $\angle 1 = \angle 2$;
$RS = 11$

    Find RT. Give a complete demonstration.

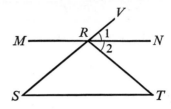

12. Hyp. $AB = AC$; $DE = EF$;
$AC = EF$
    Find DF. Show your work in detail.

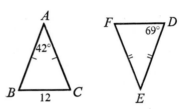

13. Hyp. $PQ = PR$; $RS = RT$;
$\angle S = 32°$
    Find $\angle P$.

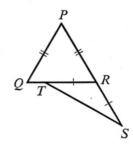

A.

14. Prove: If a line is parallel to the base of an isosceles triangle and intersects the other two sides, it forms another isosceles triangle.
15. The sum of two angles of a triangle is 110° and their difference is 40°. Find each angle of the triangle.
16. The sum of two angles of a triangle is 96° and one is twice the other. Find each angle of the triangle.

6–16 Diagonal A diagonal of a polygon is a line segment that connects any two nonconsecutive vertices.

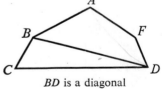

BD is a diagonal

DISCOVERY EXERCISES

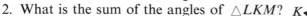

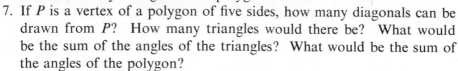

1. What is the sum of the angles of △HKM?
2. What is the sum of the angles of △LKM?
3. What is the sum of the angles of HKLM?
4. How many sides has this polygon?
5. How many diagonals has it at one vertex?
6. Into how many triangles is the polygon divided?
7. If P is a vertex of a polygon of five sides, how many diagonals can be drawn from P? How many triangles would there be? What would be the sum of the angles of the triangles? What would be the sum of the angles of the polygon?
8. If Q is a vertex of a polygon of s sides, how many diagonals can be drawn from Q? How many triangles would be formed? What would be the sum of the angles of the triangles? What would be the sum of the angles of the polygon?

6–17 THEOREM The sum of the angles of a polygon of *n* sides is (*n* − 2) straight angles.

Hypothesis ABCDEF, a polygon of *n* sides.
Conclusion The sum of the angles is (*n* − 2) straight angles.

The plan is to divide the polygon into triangles and find the sum of the angles.

Construction. From one vertex draw all possible diagonals.

Proof

1. Each side of the polygon except AB and BC is the base of a triangle the vertex of which is at B. Hence the polygon contains (*n* − 2) △s.
2. The sum of the interior angles of each triangle is 1 st. ∠. Why?
3. The sum of the interior angles of the (*n* − 2) △s is (*n* − 2) st. ∠s.
4. But the sum of the interior angles of the triangles is the sum of the interior angles of the polygon.
5. ∴ The sum of the interior ∠s of ABCDEF is (*n* − 2) st. ∠s.

A polygon of any number of sides, *n*, can only be illustrated by the omission of some sides as shown in the figure. The dotted lines indicate that only a part of the figure is shown. Repeat the above proof using this figure.

DISCOVERY EXERCISES

What is the sum of exterior angles 1, 2, 3, 4, 5? If you cannot give the answer immediately, consider angles a, b, c, d, e about a point. They are formed by drawing lines from the point parallel to the sides of the polygon.

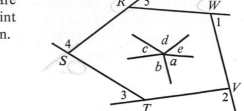

1. $\angle a = \angle 1$ Why?
2. $\angle b = \angle$_____ Why?
3. $\angle$_____ $= \angle 3$ Why?
4. $\angle$_____ $= \angle 4$ Why?
5. $\angle e = \angle$_____ Why?
6. $\angle a + \angle b + \angle c + \angle d + \angle e =$ _____° Why?
7. $\angle 1 + \angle 2 + \angle 3 + \angle 4 + \angle 5 =$ _____° Why?

6–18   THEOREM   The sum of the exterior angles of a polygon, one at each vertex, is two straight angles.

Hypothesis $ABCDE$ . . . is a polygon of n sides with one exterior angle at each vertex made by extending each side in clockwise order.

Conclusion The sum of the exterior angles is two straight angles.

The plan is to subtract the sum of the interior angles from the sum of the interior and exterior angles.

Proof At each vertex the sum of the interior and the exterior angle is one straight angle. Then the sum of the interior and exterior angles of the entire polygon is n straight angles. (Why?) We have already proved that the sum of the interior angles of the polygon is $(n - 2)$ straight angles. Hence the sum of the exterior angles is 2 straight angles. (Why?)

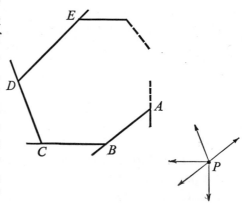

Alternate Proof Select a point in the plane outside the polygon of n sides. Using this point as a vertex construct rays parallel to AB, BC, CD, . . . in order. Show that each angle thus constructed is equal to an exterior angle of the polygon. Show that these angles do not overlap, that is, have any interior in common. What is the sum of the angles about point P?

WRITTEN EXERCISES

C.

1. What is the sum of the interior angles of a quadrilateral? A pentagon? A hexagon? An octagon? A decagon?

B.

2. How many degrees in ∠*x*? Why?

3. How many degrees in ∠*y*? Why?

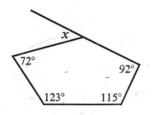

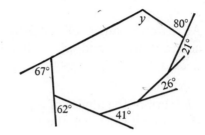

4. Find the number of degrees in each angle of this hexagon.

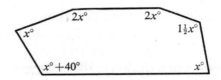

5. How many degrees are there in each exterior angle of a pentagon if the angles are all equal?

6. How many degrees are there in each exterior angle of an octagon if the angles are all equal?

A.

7. How many sides has a polygon if the sum of its angles is 18 straight angles?

8. How many sides has a polygon if the sum of its angles is 34 right angles?

9. How many sides has a polygon if each of its angles is 150°?

10. How many sides has a polygon if each of its angles is 156°?

11. Gauss proved that it is possible to construct geometrically a polygon that has 257 equal angles and 257 equal sides. (He did not show how this could be done.) How many degrees would each angle of such a polygon have? (Compare Ex. 40 on page 155.)

MISCELLANEOUS WRITTEN EXERCISES

B.

1. The angles *A*, *B*, and *C* of a triangle are $5x°$, $4x°$, and $3x°$. Find each angle.
2. Each base angle of an isosceles triangle is 4 times the vertex angle. Find each of the three angles.
3. An exterior angle at the base of an isosceles triangle is 140°. Find each angle of the triangle.
4. What is the sum of the angles of a square? Of a polygon of 11 sides? Of a pentadecagon?
5. An exterior angle of a triangle is 120°. The interior angles not adjacent are $x°$ and $\frac{1}{3}x°$. Find each angle of the triangle.

A.

6. The sum of the angles of a polygon is 900°. The angles are all equal. How many sides has the polygon? How many degrees are there in each exterior angle?
7. How many sides has a polygon if the sum of its angles is 2520°?
8. How many sides has a polygon if the sum of its interior angles equals five times the sum of its exterior angles?
9. Can a tile floor be laid using only tiles that are equilateral triangles? Make a drawing. Must any tiles be cut? Where?
10. Can a tile floor be laid using only squares? Make a drawing.
11. Can a floor be covered using only hexagons the sides of which are equal and the angles of which are equal? Make a drawing.
12. Can a floor be covered using only pentagons of which the angles are all equal and the sides are all equal? Make a drawing.
13. Can a floor be covered by using only tiles that have eight equal sides and equal angles? Make a drawing.
14. From Ex. 9–13 you discovered that certain figures can be used in tiles and others cannot if only one shape is used. However, a designer often combines different forms. By means of drawings show how pentagons (Ex. 12) can be combined with other forms to make a tile floor.
15. A tile floor pattern can be made using squares and octagons. Make a drawing to show how they would be arranged. Prove that in this pattern there will be no spaces between the tiles and no overlapping. *Hint.* The squares will have sides equal in length to the sides of the octagon.

OUTLINE OF CHAPTER 6

This chapter introduces the following terms:

polygon	pentadecagon
quadrilateral	angle of a polygon
pentagon	interior, exterior angles of a polygon
hexagon	trisect
octagon	diagonal
decagon	convex polygon
dodecagon	concave polygon

This chapter presents information concerning:

1. The sum of the angles of a triangle. Page 139
2. The relation between an exterior angle of a triangle and the non-adjacent interior angles. Page 139
3. The relation between the acute angles of a right triangle. Page 140
4. The relation between two triangles that have a side and any two angles of one equal to a side and the corresponding angles of the other. Page 140
5. The relation between angles whose sides are perpendicular. Page 140
6. The relation between the sides opposite equal angles of a triangle. Page 142
7. The sum of the angles of a polygon. Page 145
8. The sum of the exterior angles of a polygon. Page 146

REVIEW

1. What is a polygon? Name two kinds of polygons.
2. What is an interior angle of a polygon? An exterior angle? Illustrate.
3. Theorem. The sum of the angles of a triangle is a straight angle. Give a complete demonstration.
4. What is the sum of the angles of a quadrilateral? Of a pentagon? Of a hexagon? Of a polygon that has seven sides?
5. What is the sum of the exterior angles of a triangle? Of a quadrilateral? Of a pentagon?

6. $\angle x$ is an exterior angle of $\triangle ABC$ at A. What can you say of the relation of $\angle x$ and $\angle C$?

7. $\angle C$ of $\triangle ABC$ is a right angle. $\angle B$ has $32°$. How large is $\angle A$?

8. The angles of a quadrilateral are $x°$, $2x°$, $3x°$, and $4x°$. Find the number of degrees in each angle.

9. Construct an angle that has $45°$. Construct an angle that has $15°$.

10. The sum of angles of a polygon is $540°$. How many sides has it?

11. All of the angles of a polygon are equal. One exterior angle has $45°$. How many sides has the polygon?

12. An exterior angle at A of $\triangle ABC$ has $52°$. An exterior angle at B has $137°$. How many degrees has each interior angle of the triangle?

YES–NO TEST

Approximately 10 minutes

Copy on your paper the numbers of the following questions. If the answer is *yes* under all conditions, place a plus sign (+) after its number. If the answer is *not yes* under all conditions, place a zero (0) after its number.

1. Is a triangle a polygon?

2. Is an exterior angle of a polygon equal to its adjacent interior angle?

3. Is the sum of the interior angles of a triangle two right angles?

4. Is the sum of the interior angles of a square two straight angles?

5. Is the sum of the exterior angles of a square two straight angles?

6. Is the sum of the interior angles of a pentagon equal to the sum of the exterior angles?

7. If the sum of the angles of a polygon is $720°$, does it have 6 sides?

8. If the sum of the interior angles of a polygon is 8 straight angles, does it have 8 sides?

9. Is an exterior angle of a triangle greater than an interior angle that is not adjacent?

10. Are the acute angles of a right triangle supplementary?

11. If two angles have their sides perpendicular, initial side to initial side and terminal side to terminal side, are the angles right angles?

12. Does the sum of the exterior angles of a triangle equal the sum of the exterior angles of a quadrilateral?

COMPLETION TEST

Approximately 20 minutes

Copy on your paper the numbers of the following statements. After each number write a word, or letters, or number, or an expression which if written in the blank would complete the statement and make it true.

1. An angle that is formed by two sides of a polygon and lies inside the polygon is an _____ angle.

2. An angle that is formed by one side of a polygon and an adjacent side extended through the vertex is an _____ angle of the polygon.

3. $\angle A + \angle B + \angle C + \angle D + \angle E =$ _____ degrees

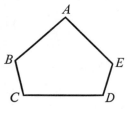

4. $\angle 1 + \angle 2 + \angle 3 + \angle 4 + \angle 5 + \angle 6 =$ _____ °

5. $\angle x =$ _____ degrees

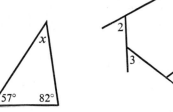

6. The angles of polygon P are equal. $\angle n =$ _____ degrees

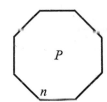

7. The sum of the angles of a polygon is 1080°. The polygon has _____ sides.

8. $\angle A =$ _____ degrees

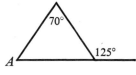

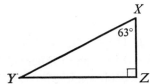

9. $XZ \perp YZ$. $\angle Y =$ _____ °

10. $\angle P = \angle C$; $\angle Q = \angle A$

$\angle B = $ _____ degrees

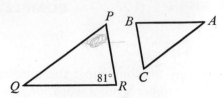

The sum of the angles of a triangle is a straight angle.

Hyp. $\triangle ABC$

Con. $\angle A + \angle B + \angle ACB = $ a st. $\angle$

Construction. Extend BC any distance to D. Construct $CE \parallel AB$.

Proof.

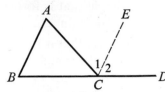

11. $\angle 1 = $ _____

12. $\angle 2 = $ _____

13. $\angle 1 + \angle 2 + \angle ACB = $ a st. $\angle$

14. $\angle A + \angle B + \angle ACB = $ a st. $\angle$

11. Alt. int. $\angle$s of $\parallel$ lines

12. Corresponding $\angle$s of $\parallel$ lines

13. _____

14. _____

SUPPLEMENTARY EXERCISES

1. Find the number of degrees in each angle of $\triangle ABC$.

C.

2. Find the number of degrees in each angle of $\triangle DEF$ if it is not given.

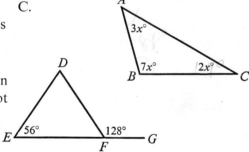

3. Find the number of degrees in each angle of $\triangle GHK$.

4. Hyp. $OP = PQ$
Find the number of degrees in each angle of $\triangle OPQ$.

5. Find $\angle A$ of $\triangle ABC$ given:
   (a) $\angle B = 27°$, and $\angle C = 81°$
   (b) $\angle B = 54°$, and $\angle A = \angle C$
   (c) $\angle A = \angle B + \angle C$
   (d) $\angle A + \angle B = 89°$, and $\angle A + \angle C = 114°$

6. The vertex angle of an isosceles triangle is 49°. How large is each base angle?

7. One of the base angles of an isosceles triangle is 51° 12'. What is the size of the vertex angle?

8. Two exterior angles of a triangle are 31° and 163°. Find each interior angle.

9. One acute angle of a right triangle is 27° 31'. Find the other acute angle.

10. One angle of a triangle is $\frac{2}{3}$ of a right angle and another is $\frac{5}{6}$ of a right angle. How many degrees are there in the third angle?

11. One angle of a triangle is $\frac{1}{4}$ of a straight angle and another is $\frac{5}{6}$ of a right angle. How large is the third angle of the triangle?

12. The vertex angle of an isosceles triangle is 50°. How many degrees are there in the angle formed by the bisectors of the base angles?

13. Given two angles of a triangle to construct the third angle.

14. Prove: The exterior angles formed at each vertex of the base of an isosceles triangle are equal.

B.

15. The altitudes BE and CD of $\triangle ABC$ are drawn. Prove $\angle ABE = \angle ACD$.

16. Two angles of a triangle are 40° and 60°. What is the size of the angle formed by their bisectors?

17. One angle of a triangle is 34°. What is the size of the angle formed by the bisectors of the other two angles?

18. One angle of a triangle contains 48° and another contains 64°. What is the size of the angle formed by the bisectors of the two largest angles?

19. Prove: If an exterior angle of an isosceles triangle is $\frac{2}{3}$ of a straight angle, the triangle is equilateral.

20. Prove: If two angles of a triangle are respectively $\frac{5}{9}$ of a straight angle and $\frac{2}{9}$ of a straight angle, the triangle is isosceles.

21. Prove: If two angles of a triangle are respectively $\frac{4}{9}$ of a straight angle and $\frac{2}{9}$ of a right angle, the triangle is isosceles.

22. Prove: If the bisector of an exterior angle of a triangle is parallel to a side of the triangle, the triangle is isosceles.

23. Prove: If the vertex angle of an isosceles triangle is $\frac{1}{3}$ of a straight angle, the triangle is equilateral.

24. Prove: If the bisectors of two angles of a given triangle form with the included side an isosceles triangle, the given triangle is isosceles.

25. Prove: The altitude on the hypotenuse of an isosceles right triangle divides it into two isosceles right triangles.

26. Prove: The angle formed by the bisector of an angle of a triangle and the altitude from the same vertex equals one half the difference of the other two angles of the triangle.

27. Hyp. $AB = AC$; $BD = CF$
    Con. $DE = EF$

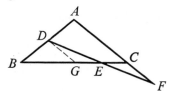

28. Prove: The angle formed by the bisectors of two angles of a triangle is an obtuse angle.

29. One interior angle of a triangle is 34°; one exterior angle is 134°. Find the number of degrees in each of the interior angles not given.

30. The sum of two angles of a triangle is 138° and their difference is 18°. Find each angle of the triangle.

31. $\angle a = $ _____ degrees.

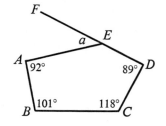

32. $\angle b = $ _____ degrees.

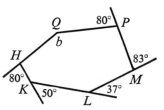

33. Find the number of degrees in each angle of this polygon.

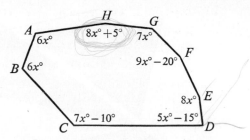

34. The sum of the interior angles of a polygon is 2340°. How many sides has it?

35. The sum of the interior angles of a polygon is 1440°. Find the number of degrees in each interior angle if they are all equal.

36. The sum of the interior angles of a polygon is 2520°. Find each exterior angle if the interior angles are all equal.

37. A polygon has 7 sides. Six of the exterior angles are 42°, 35°, 59°, 63°, 47°, and 33° respectively. Find the number of degrees in each interior angle of the polygon.

38. How many degrees are there in the sum of the interior angles of a polygon of 192 sides?

39. If the sum of the interior angles of a polygon is 35,640°, how many sides has it?

40. Gauss, a great German mathematician, discovered a method for constructing a polygon having 17 equal sides and angles. How many degrees are there in each interior angle of this polygon?

41. The interior angles of a polygon are all equal. Each interior angle is three times as large as its adjacent exterior angle. How many sides has the polygon?

42. The exterior angles of a polygon are all equal. Each exterior angle is twice as large as its adjacent interior angle. How many sides has the polygon?

CHAPTER 7

PARALLELOGRAMS

You have seen that one of the very useful properties of the triangle is that its shape — that is, the sizes of its angles — cannot be changed without changing the length of one or more of its sides. Now, it often happens that mechanical needs are such that flexibility and movement rather than rigidity are required. To meet these needs, the parallelogram is frequently employed. Its properties are such as to fit it quite well to these requirements.

No doubt you have seen a variety of objects which make use of the flexibility of the parallelogram. Fruit crates are often made collapsible to save space in shipment; this is done by hinging the sides to make parallelogram sections. Telephone racks are often made with a connected series of parallelograms so that the telephone can be pulled out for convenience. Elevator gates are sometimes made with a series of parallelograms so that they will fold out of the way.

You can recall other similar devices based upon the parallelogram. The first well-known device for constructing a geometric straight line, Peaucellier's cell, is based upon the parallelogram. Read about this instrument in an encyclopedia. You can easily make one.

In this chapter, we are to study the properties of a parallelogram.

7–1 Types of Quadrilaterals

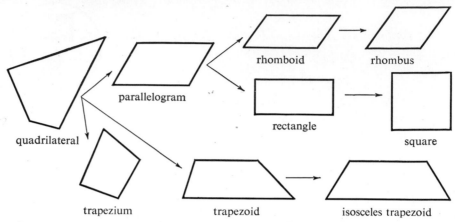

rhomboid   rhombus

parallelogram

rectangle

quadrilateral   square

trapezium   trapezoid   isosceles trapezoid

Recall that a good definition puts the word to be defined in its nearest or smallest class, and then gives characteristics that distinguish it from the other members of the class. In the diagrams shown above, the quadrilaterals are first divided into three classes which differ in the number of pairs of parallel sides they have. Define each of these classes, using parallelism as the distinguishing characteristic.

The parallelograms are further classified into those that have right angles and those that have oblique angles. Define each type of parallelogram. Finally, the trapezoids, rhomboids, and rectangles each have a special class characterized by equality of sides. Define these special classes. Consult the dictionary.

EXERCISES

Write your definition for each of the quadrilaterals shown above. Keep these definitions and compare them with those given in this chapter.

7–2 Parallelogram A parallelogram is a quadrilateral that has two pairs of parallel sides.

The symbol for parallelogram is $\square$.

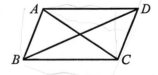

In parallelogram $ABCD$, AB and DC are a pair of parallel sides; AD and BC are a second pair of parallel sides; $\angle A$ and $\angle C$ (and $\angle B$ and $\angle D$) are opposite angles. $\angle A$ and $\angle B$, $\angle B$ and $\angle C$, etc., are consecutive angles; AC and BD are diagonals. An altitude of a $\square$ is a $\perp$ to any side from any point in the opposite side.

7-3 THEOREM **Any two consecutive angles of a parallelogram are supplementary.** Give the proof of this theorem. Apply Sec. 5-13.

7-4 THEOREM **The opposite sides of a parallelogram are equal.**

Hypothesis $\square RSTV$

Conclusion $RS = VT$; $RV = ST$

Suggestion. Draw RT. What pairs of angles may be proved equal? Give the rest of the proof.

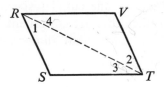

7-5 THEOREM **The opposite angles of a parallelogram are equal.**

Using the figure for Sec. 7-4, supply the proof.
Suggestion. Why does $\angle S = \angle V$? How can you prove $\angle R = \angle T$?

7-6 THEOREM **The diagonals of a parallelogram bisect each other.**

Hypothesis $\square ABCD$ with diagonals AC, BD, meeting at M

Conclusion $AM = MC$; $BM = MD$

Supply the complete proof.

Suggestion. Prove $\triangle AMD \cong \triangle BMC$.

Exercise. State and prove the converse of this theorem.

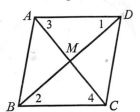

Congruent Polygons If two polygons are congruent, then by using translation, rotation, and reflection we can transform one polygon into the other so that all the corresponding sides coincide (and are equal) and all the corresponding angles are equal. If we do not know whether two triangles are congruent, it is not necessary to make translations; we need only determine if they have three corresponding sides, or two sides and an included angle, or two angles and a side respectively equal. We shall use the converse of the above statement about congruent polygons, namely, that if two polygons have the corresponding sides of one equal to those of the other, and the corresponding angles of one equal to those of the other, then one polygon can be transformed into the other and the polygons are congruent.

POSTULATE 20 **Two polygons are congruent if they have all corresponding sides and angles equal.**

EXERCISES

1. Prove: A diagonal divides a parallelogram into two congruent triangles.

2. Prove: Two parallelograms that have two sides and the included angle of one equal respectively to two sides and the included angle of the other are congruent.

    Hint. Show that all corresponding sides and angles are equal.

3. *ABCD* is a □.
    ∠*C* = _____ °
    CD = _____
    Why?

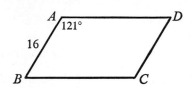

4. In the figure *R*, *S*, *T*, and *V* are the mid-points of the sides of □*JHKL*.
    Prove: *HS* = *LV*; *RL* = *TH*

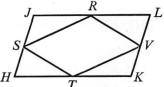

5. In □*ABCD*, *AE* ⊥ *BD* and *CF* ⊥ *BD*
    Prove: *AE* = *CF*; *DF* = *EB*

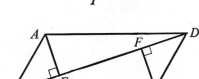

6. In △*GHK*, *ML* ∥ *GK* and *LQ* ∥ *HG*. Prove the broken line *HMLQK* is equal to *HG* + *GK*.

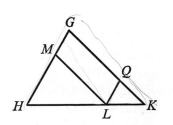

7. *ABCD* is a □.
    ∠*C* = _____ °
    ∠*D* = _____ °
    AD = _____
    DC = _____
    Why?

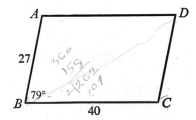

8. $PQRS$ is a ⌀.
   $\angle R =$ _____°

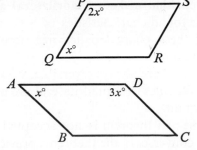

9. $ABCD$ is a ⌀.
   $\angle B =$ _____°
   $\angle C =$ _____°
   Why?

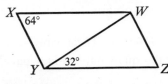

10. $XYZW$ is a ⌀. Find the number of degrees in $\angle XYW$.

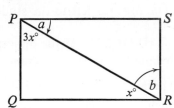

11. $PQRS$ is a rectangle.
    $\angle a =$ _____°
    $\angle b =$ _____°

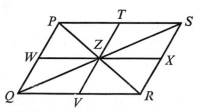

12. Hyp. $PQRS$ is a ⌀;
          $TV \parallel PQ$; $WX \parallel QR$;
          Z is mid-point of PR.
    Con. ⌀$PWZT \cong$ ⌀$VRXZ$

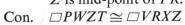

13. List the properties of a parallelogram, writing after each property whether it was obtained by definition or by demonstration.

14. Write the converse of each of the definitions and theorems of Sec. 7–2 to Sec. 7–6.

15. $ABCD$ is a rectangle. AC and BD are diagonals intersecting at P. $\angle ACB = 30°$. How large is $\angle DBC$? Why?

16. Refer to Ex. 5 on page 160. Copy the figure and draw AF and CE. Prove $AECF$ is a parallelogram.

17. Side AD of parallelogram $ABCD$ is extended to E making $DE = DC$. CE is drawn. $\angle E = 29°$. Find each angle of ⌀$ABCD$.

18. $PQRS$ is a parallelogram in which $\angle Q = 26°$. PS is extended to T and $\angle RST$ is bisected. QR is extended and intersects the bisector at V, thus forming $\triangle RSV$. Find each angle of $\triangle RSV$.

7–7   Conditions that make a quadrilateral a parallelogram   In Sec. 7–2 to Sec. 7–6 we found characteristics of a parallelogram. We now investigate whether these characteristics are necessary for a quadrilateral to be a parallelogram.

Since definitions are always reversible, we know by Sec. 7–2 that if both pairs of opposite sides of a quadrilateral are parallel, then the quadrilateral is a parallelogram.

The converse of a theorem is not accepted until it is proved. However, if we take the converses of the theorems previously established about parallelograms, we obtain the following new theorems.

7–8   THEOREM   If the consecutive angles of a quadrilateral are supplementary, the quadrilateral is a parallelogram.

The proof is left to the student.

7–9   THEOREM   If the opposite sides of a quadrilateral are equal, the quadrilateral is a parallelogram.

Hypothesis   Quadrilateral $ABCD$; $AB = DC$; $AD = BC$

Conclusion $ABCD$ is a parallelogram.

Proof   Draw AC.   Use congruent triangles and alternate interior angles. Complete the proof.

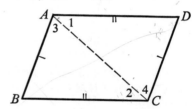

7–10   THEOREM   If the opposite angles of a quadrilateral are equal, the quadrilateral is a parallelogram.

Write out the proof in full. Recall that the sum of the interior angles of a quadrilateral is 360°.

7–11   THEOREM   If the diagonals of a quadrilateral bisect each other, the quadrilateral is a parallelogram.

Hypothesis   Quadrilateral $ABCD$; diagonals AC and BD intersecting at M; $AM = MC$; $BM = MD$

Conclusion $ABCD$ is a parallelogram.

Hint. Use $\cong \triangle$s and refer to Sec. 7–9.

Give the proof.

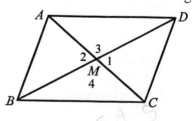

We could state other theorems about the parallelogram. For example:
In a parallelogram, a pair of opposite sides are both equal and parallel.
The proof of this is very easy. Give the proof. We can now write a con-
verse o this theorem which is very useful in later work in geometry.

**7–12   THEOREM   If two sides of a quadrilateral are both parallel and
equal, then the quadrilateral is a parallelogram.**

Hypothesis   Quadrilateral *ABCD*;
$$AB = CD; \quad AB \parallel CD$$
Conclusion   *ABCD* is a parallelogram.
   Proof   Draw *AC*. Prove that the tri-
angles are congruent; then prove *AD* ∥ *BC*.

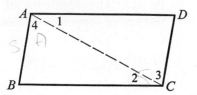

EXERCISES

Oral

1. ∠*A* = _____°   ∠*D* = _____°
    Prove your answer.

2. *PQ* ∥ *RS*. *QR* = _____
    ∠*R* = _____°   ∠*S* = _____°
    Prove your answer.
    Draw any needed lines.

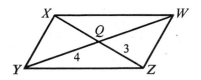

3. *XYZW* is a ▱.
    QX = _____   *QW* = _____
    Why?

4. *ABCD* is a ▱; *BO* = 32; *AC* = 52
    DO = _____   *AO* = _____
    Prove your answer.

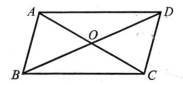

PARALLELOGRAMS   **163**

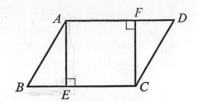

5. Prove: The altitudes of a parallelogram drawn from opposite vertices are equal.

6. Prove: The segments of bisectors of opposite angles of a parallelogram terminated by a diagonal are equal.

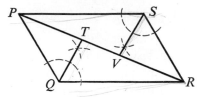

7. Construct a parallelogram having adjacent sides 1 in. and 1.5 in. and the included angle 30°. Do not use the protractor.
8. Construct a parallelogram having adjacent sides 2 in. and 3 in. and the included angle 120°. Do not use the protractor.
9. Construct a parallelogram having adjacent sides 2 in. and 2.5 in. and the included angle 135°. Do not use the protractor.

10. Hyp.   □PQRS with
         PS = PQ
    Con.   PR is the ⊥ bisector of QS.
11. In the figure for Ex. 10, prove △PXS ≅ △RXS.

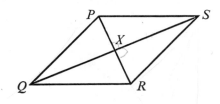

12. Hyp.   □ ABCD with
         AD = DC
    Con.   △ABD is equilateral.

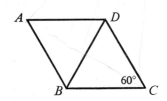

13. Given: LO = NO;
    MO = PO; ∠LMN = 135°
    Find NP, ∠LPN, and
    ∠MNP.
    Prove your answers.

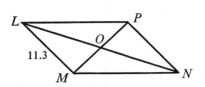

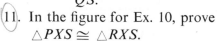

7–13 Rectangle. Square A rectangle is a parallelogram that has one right angle. A square is a rectangle that has two adjacent sides equal.

Show, from the above definitions, that all the angles of a rectangle are right angles, and that all sides of a square are equal.

7–14 THEOREM The diagonals of a rectangle are equal.

Hypothesis $ABCD$ is a rectangle having diagonals AC and BD.

Conclusion $AC = BD$

Give the proof.

Suggestion. Prove $\triangle ABC \cong \triangle BCD$.

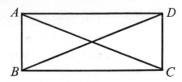

7–15 THEOREM The diagonals of a square are perpendicular to each other.

Hypothesis Square $ABCD$; diagonals AC, BD

Conclusion $AC \perp BD$

Give the proof.

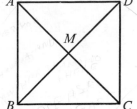

7–16 THEOREM Parallel lines are everywhere equally distant.

In the figure $AB \parallel CD$. E and F are any two points on AB. Drop perpendiculars from E and F to CD. Are these perpendiculars parallel? Write out the entire proof.

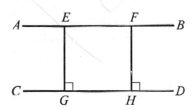

EXERCISES

1. The converse of Sec. 7–14 is: If the diagonals of a parallelogram are equal, the parallelogram is a rectangle. Prove this.
2. Write the converse of Sec. 7–15 and prove it. Recall that a square is a rectangle.
3. Write the converse of Sec. 7–16 and prove it.
4. $ABCD$ is a $\square$. Prove it is a square.

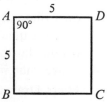

5. *PQRS* is a ▱.
   Prove it is a rectangle.

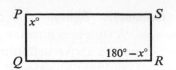

6. Town A is 5 miles due east of town B. Town C is 11 miles due south of A. Town D is 11 miles due south of B. What is the distance from C to D? Prove your answer.

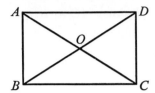

7. Hyp.   *ABCD* is a ▱; △*AOD* is isosceles.
   Con.   *ABCD* is a rectangle.

8. Hyp.   Rectangle *ABCD* with *AD* extended so that *AD = DE*
   Con.   *BCED* is a parallelogram.

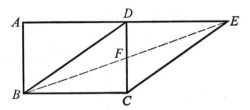

9. In the figure for Exercise 8 with the same data, prove *BE* bisects *DC*.

10. In parallelogram *ABCD*, diagonal *DB* is divided into three equal parts by the points *E* and *F*. Prove *AECF* is a parallelogram.

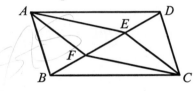

11. In parallelogram *ABCD*, *E* is the mid-point of *AB*; *F* is the mid-point of *DC*. *AF* meets *DB* at *M*, and *CE* meets *DB* at *N*.
    Prove: *MENF* is a parallelogram.

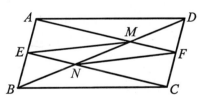

12. Prove: If the diagonals of a quadrilateral are perpendicular to each other and bisect each other, and if the diagonals are also equal, the quadrilateral is a square.

13. Draw a quadrilateral in which the diagonals are equal and are perpendicular to each other, yet the quadrilateral is not a square.

14. Prove that in a kite one pair of opposite angles are equal.
    Hint. Draw a diagonal. See the definition in Sec. 3–19.

7–17 Rhomboid. Rhombus A rhomboid is a parallelogram that has an oblique angle. A rhombus is a rhomboid that has two adjacent sides equal. Show from these definitions that all angles of the rhomboid are oblique. Show that for either figure there are two acute angles and two obtuse angles.

Use the definition and prove that all sides of a rhombus are equal.

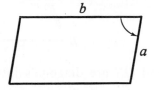

7–18 THEOREM The diagonals of a rhomboid are unequal.

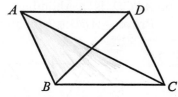

Hypothesis Rhomboid $ABCD$;
diagonals AC and BD;
$\angle ADC$ is oblique.

Conclusion $AC \neq BD$

Proof

1. Suppose $AC = BD$.
2. Then $ABCD$ is a rectangle.
3. Then $\angle ADC$ is a right angle.

4. This is impossible.

5. Then $AC \neq BD$

1. Either $AC = BD$ or $AC \neq BD$
2. See Ex. 1, page 165.
3. All angles of a rectangle are right $\angle$s.
4. Since it is given that $\angle ADC$ is oblique.
5. Since the contradictory assumption is false.

NOTE: In Chapter 9 we shall prove that the greater diagonal is opposite the obtuse angle.

7–19 THEOREM The diagonals of a rhombus are perpendicular to each other.

Write the complete proof.

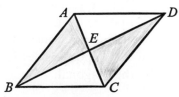

1. State the converse of theorem 7–18. Recall that a rhomboid is a parallelogram. Prove this converse using the indirect method.
2. State the converse of theorem 7–19. Recall that a rhombus is a particular rhomboid. Prove this converse by a direct method.
3. $ABCD$ is a $\square$; $BO = 32$; $AC = 52$;
   $OO' = 46$.
   $DO' = \underline{\hspace{1cm}}$ $AO = \underline{\hspace{1cm}}$
   Prove your answers.

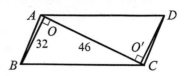

4. $PQRS$ is a rhombus. PR and QS are diagonals intersecting at X. Prove PR is the $\perp$ bisector of QS.
5. In the figure for Ex. 4, prove $\triangle PXS \cong \triangle RXS$.

6. $ABCD$ is a rhombus. $\angle C = 60°$
   Prove $\triangle ABD$ is equilateral.

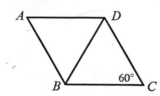

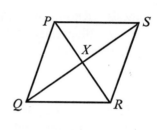

7. Hyp. $LO = NO$; $MO = PO$; $\angle LMN = 135°$.
   Find $\angle MNP$.
   Prove your conclusion.

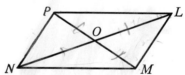

8. Prove: The bisectors of two consecutive angles of a parallelogram are perpendicular to each other.
9. Prove: A diagonal of a rhombus bisects the opposite angles.
10. Prove: A segment through the mid-point of a diagonal of a parallelogram and terminated on the opposite sides is bisected by the diagonal.

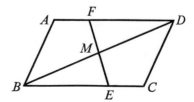

11. Prove: Lines drawn from two opposite vertices of a parallelogram to the mid-points of two opposite sides are equal.

12. Prove: The lines joining the mid-points of the four sides of a parallelogram in clockwise order form another parallelogram.

13. An altitude of a parallelogram is the distance between a pair of opposite sides.
Prove: If two nonparallel altitudes of a parallelogram are drawn, they form angles equal to the angles of the parallelogram.

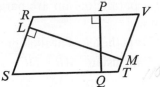

14. Prove: Bisectors of opposite angles of a parallelogram are parallel.

15. This is one form of parallel ruler often used for drawing parallel lines. Show how it is constructed, and explain how it can be used to draw a line through a point parallel to a given line.

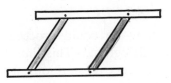

How can it be used to test two given lines to see whether they are parallel?

7–20 Optional. **A Mathematical System**   In a mathematical system we have:

(1) *Undefined terms*, which we accept as primitive or understood
(2) *Defined terms*, which are explained in terms of other classes and terms
(3) *Postulates*, which are statements we accept without proof
(4) *Logic*, which is a method of reasoning from assumed and proved statements to conclusions

We use these four essentials to demonstrate or establish the truth of theorems, which are statements not included in (2) and (3).

When a theorem is proved (or its truth is demonstrated), the theorem thenceforth can be used to demonstrate new theorems. Thus the proof of new theorems (original exercises included) goes on and on.

The student may wonder how we decide what to define, what to postulate, and what to state as theorems. This is a difficult question to answer, but in general it does not matter which statement we take as a definition or postulate and which we regard as a theorem so long as *we reason logically and arrive at no contradiction*. To illustrate this we shall use a previous theorem as a definition, and then show how the previous definition becomes a theorem in our new system.

Suppose we ignore (for the time being only) the definition of parallelogram that you learned in the first part of this chapter and give a new definition as follows: A parallelogram is a quadrilateral that has the opposite sides equal. (Recall that this was a theorem in the early part of the chapter.) Now we shall prove this theorem: The opposite sides of a parallelogram are parallel. (Recall that this was our original definition.)

Hypothesis   Parallelogram $ABCD$

Conclusion $AB \parallel DC$; $AD \parallel BC$

Proof   Draw AC. Then $AD = BC$; $AB = DC$ (Our new definition of parallelogram)

Hence, $\triangle ADC \cong \triangle ABC$ (s s s); $\angle 1 = \angle 2$, and $AD \parallel BC$; $\angle 3 = \angle 4$, and $AB \parallel DC$.

Now we could proceed to prove all the other theorems about the parallelogram. This illustrates the fact that we have choice in selecting statements to start our study which we call definitions and postulates. Other properties we prove as theorems.

We introduced this alternate definition of a parallelogram only to illustrate the fact that we have choice. In all future work in this course, we shall use the original definition given in Sec. 7–2.

EXERCISES

1. Using the definition that a rectangle is a parallelogram with equal diagonals, prove that the angles of a rectangle are right angles.
2. Using as a definition the statement that a parallelogram is a quadrilateral with two sides equal and parallel, prove that the opposite sides of a parallelogram are parallel.
3. Using as a postulate that two lines are parallel if a transversal makes a pair of alternate interior angles equal, prove that through a point outside a line only one line can be drawn parallel to the given line.
4. Using as a definition the statement that a square is a rectangle with perpendicular diagonals, prove that the sides of a square are equal.
5. Using as a definition the statement that an isosceles triangle is a triangle with two equal angles, prove that in an isosceles triangle the opposite sides are equal. (*Hint.* Bisect the equal angles.)
6. Using the definition that parallel lines are lines in the same plane that are everywhere equally distant, prove that they do not intersect.

OUTLINE OF CHAPTER 7

The following terms have been defined, illustrated, or explained:

trapezium	trapezoid	parallelogram	rhomboid
rhombus	rectangle	square	
altitude of a parallelogram		mathematical system	

In this chapter you learned the following relations:

1. If a quadrilateral is a parallelogram (*a*) its opposite sides are parallel, (*b*) its opposite sides are equal, (*c*) two sides are both parallel and equal, (*d*) the opposite angles are equal, (*e*) the consecutive angles are supplementary, and (*f*) the diagonals bisect each other. Pages 158–159, 163

2. If any of the conditions (*a*) to (*f*) exists for a quadrilateral, then it is a parallelogram. Pages 158, 162, 163

3. If a parallelogram is a rectangle, its diagonals are equal, and conversely. Page 165

4. In a square or rhombus the diagonals are perpendicular to each other. Pages 165, 167

5. If a parallelogram is a rhomboid, the diagonals are unequal, and conversely. Page 167

6. Parallel lines are everywhere equally distant. Page 165

REVIEW

1. Define (*a*) quadrilateral, (*b*) parallelogram, (*c*) rectangle, (*d*) rhombus.

2. State six conditions under which a quadrilateral is a parallelogram.

3. State two conditions under which a rectangle is a square.

4. Prove the theorem: In a parallelogram opposite sides and opposite angles are equal.

5. Prove the theorem: If two sides of a quadrilateral are equal and parallel, the quadrilateral is a parallelogram.

6. If a quadrilateral is a parallelogram, state six properties about the parts of the parallelogram.

7. If a rhomboid is a rhombus, state two properties about its diagonals.

8. Are all the properties proved for a parallelogram also true for a rhombus? Explain.

9. Are the properties proved for a square always true for any parallelogram? Explain.

10. In a parallelogram a line is drawn from a vertex to the mid-point of an opposite side and continued until it meets the other opposite side extended. Prove that this line is bisected by the side to whose mid-point it is drawn.

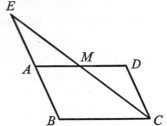

11. Prove: Segments of two parallel lines included between two other parallel lines are equal.

12. If in parallelogram *ABCD*, altitudes are drawn from *A* and *C*, prove that the triangles formed are congruent.

13. In the parallelogram shown, *M* is the mid-point of *BC*. *N* is the mid-point of *AD*. *DB* and *AC* are diagonals.
Prove: (*a*) *SE* = *ER*; (*b*) *DS* = *RB*

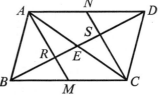

14. Prove the theorem: If a pair of opposite sides of a quadrilateral are equal and parallel the quadrilateral is a parallelogram.

15. State and prove a converse of the following statement. If in a quadrilateral one pair of opposite angles are equal and one pair of opposite sides are equal, the quadrilateral is a parallelogram.

16. In the figure *E*, *F*, *G*, and *H* are the mid-points of the sides of the parallelogram *ABCD*. Prove that the lines *BH*, *DF*, *CE*, and *AG* form a parallelogram *RSVT*.

17. *HJKL* is a quadrilateral. Diagonal *HK* divides it into two equilateral triangles. Prove *HJKL* is a rhombus.

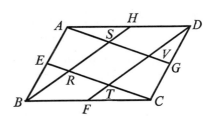

18. *RS* and *TV* are line segments that bisect each other at right angles. *RT*, *TS*, *SV*, *VR* are drawn. Prove *RTSV* is a rhombus.

19. *ABCD* is a parallelogram in which ∠*A* = 126°. *AD* is extended indefinitely to *E*. *BC* is extended through *C*. At *D* angle *CDF* is constructed = 72°, thus forming △*CDF*. Prove △*CDF* is isosceles.

COMPLETION TEST

Approximately 20 minutes

Copy on your paper the numbers of the following statements. After each number write a word, or letters, or number, or expression which, if written in the blank, would complete the statement and make it true, or would answer the question.

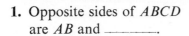

1. Opposite sides of *ABCD* are *AB* and ―――――.

2. The definition of a parallelogram states that a quadrilateral is a parallelogram if the opposite sides are ―――――.

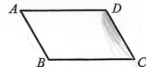

3. Is *EFGH* a parallelogram? ―――――

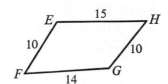

4. *PQ* ∥ *RS*. Must *PQRS* be a parallelogram? ―――――

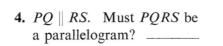

5. Is *ABCD* a parallelogram? ―――――

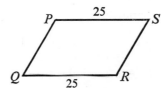

6. ∠*H* = ―――――- degrees.
7. ∠*E* = ―――――- degrees.

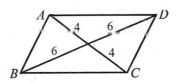

8. *XYZW* is a parallelogram. *OZ* = ―――――

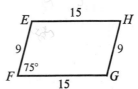

YES-NO TEST

Approximately 15 minutes

Copy on your paper the numbers of the following questions. If the answer to a question is *yes* under all conditions, place a plus sign (+) after its number. If the answer is *not yes* under all conditions, place a zero (0) after its number.

1. Is a diagonal of a polygon a line that connects any two vertices?
2. Is a parallelogram a rectangle?
3. Is a square a rhombus?
4. Are the adjacent sides of a parallelogram equal?
5. Are the opposite sides of a rectangle equal?
6. Does one diagonal of a rectangle bisect the other?
7. Can four lines the lengths of which are 5, 6, 6, and 5 be put together so as to form a parallelogram?
8. If a quadrilateral is composed of two congruent triangles, is it a parallelogram?
9. Are the diagonals of a parallelogram equal?
10. Are the diagonals of a rectangle perpendicular to each other?
11. Are the sides of a rhombus equal?
12. Do the diagonals of a rhombus bisect each other?
13. If the adjacent sides of a parallelogram are equal, are the diagonals equal?
14. Is a rhombus a square?
15. If two opposite sides of a quadrilateral are equal, is it a parallelogram?
16. If two parallelograms have two sides and the included angle of one equal respectively to two sides and the included angle of the other, are they congruent?

SUPPLEMENTARY EXERCISES

1. Given: *ABCD* is a □. Is △*ABD* ≅ △*BCD*? Why?

2. Given: *EFGH* is a □.   *HG* = _____
   FG = _____   Why?

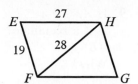

3. Given: *JKLM* is a □.
   ∠*x* = _____°   ∠*y* = _____°
   ∠*z* = _____°   ∠*L* = _____°

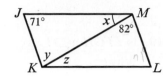

4. Given: *OPQR* is a rectangle.
   ∠*a* = _____°   ∠*b* = _____°
   ∠*c* = _____°   ∠*P* = _____°
   ∠*R* = _____°   *OR* = _____
   OP = _____

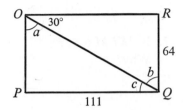

5. Given: *ABCD* is a rectangle.
   ∠*x* = _____°   ∠*y* = _____°
   ∠*z* = _____°   ∠*A* = _____°
   ∠*C* = _____°   *BC* = _____
   DC = _____

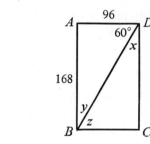

6. Given: *EFGH* is a square
   EH = _____   *FG* = _____
   ∠*G* = _____°   ∠*H* = _____°
   Why?

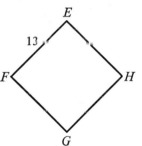

7. Given: *JKLM* is a □.
   Is it a square? Why?

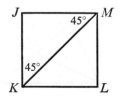

8. Given: *OPQR* is a □.
   Is it a square? Why?

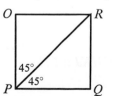

9. Is *ABCD* a □?
Is it a rectangle?
AB = _____   *BC* = _____
Why?

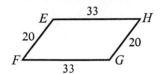

10. Is *EFGH* a □?
Why?

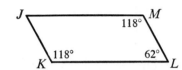

11. Is *JKLM* a □?
Why?

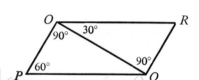

12. Is *OPQR* a □?
Why?

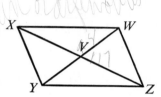

13. Given: *XYZW* is a □.
     XZ = 117; *YW* = 98
XV = _____   *VW* = _____
Why?

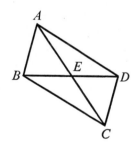

14. Given: *ABCD* is a □.
     BE = 11; *AC* = 26
EC = _____   *BD* = _____
Why?

15. Is *GHKJ* a □?
Why?

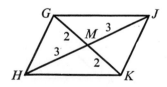

16. $OP =$ _____ $\angle QOP =$ _____°
Why?

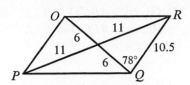

17. $KL =$ _____ $LM =$ _____
Why?

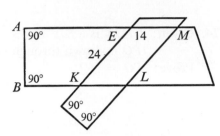

18. Given: $OPQR$ is a rectangle.
$OQ =$ _____ Why?

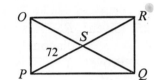

19. Is $XYZW$ a rhombus?
Why?

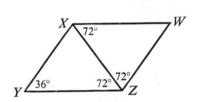

20. Given: $ABCD$ is a rhombus.
$\angle x =$ _____° Why?

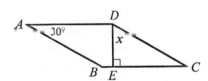

21. Given: $FGHJ$ is a $\square$;
    $FL = LK = KH$
Prove: $JK = GL$

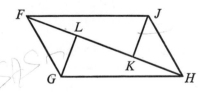

22. Given: $PQRS$ is a $\square$; PS and QR are
    bisected at T and V respectively.
Prove: $TQVS$ is a $\square$.

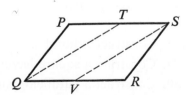

23. Given: *ABCD* is a ▱; *DF* = *BE*.
Prove: *AFCE* is a ▱.

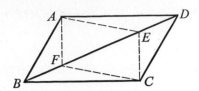

24. Given: *GHJK* is a ▱; *HN* = *KL*;
PQ is drawn through *O*.
Prove: *PO* = *OQ*.

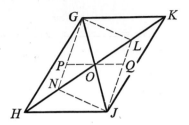

25. Given: *RSTV* is a ▱; *X*, *Y*, *Z*, and *W* are the mid-points of the half-diagonals.
Prove: *XYZW* is a ▱.

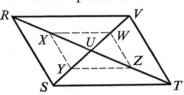

26. Given: *ABCD* is a ▱; *E*, *F*, *G*, and *H* are the mid-points of the sides; *AH*, *BE*, *CF*, and *DG* intersect the diagonals at *M*, *J*, *K*, *L*.
Prove: *JKLM* is a ▱.

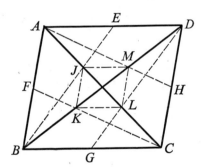

27. Given: *PQRS* is a ▱; *PV* and *RT* bisect ∠s *QPS* and *QRS* respectively.
Prove: *PVRT* is a ▱.

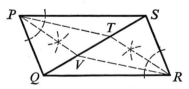

28. Construct a rhombus having one side 1.5 inches long and one angle 60°.

29. Construct a square having each side 2.25 inches.

30. Construct a parallelogram congruent to a given parallelogram.

31. Construct a rectangle having one side equal to half a diagonal.
32. Construct a rhombus having one exterior angle 120° and one side 1.75 inches.
33. Prove: The line that connects the mid-points of two opposite sides of a parallelogram bisects either diagonal.
34. Prove: The diagonals of a rhombus bisect each other at right angles.
35. Prove: If the diagonals of a parallelogram are perpendicular to each other, the parallelogram is a rhombus.
36. One side of a rectangle is half the length of a diagonal. What is the size of each angle made by the diagonal with a side?
37. Construct a rhombus, the diagonals of which are $\frac{3}{4}$ inch and $1\frac{1}{4}$ inches.
38. Construct a square, one diagonal of which is $1\frac{3}{4}$ inches.
39. Two sides and the included angle of one parallelogram are respectively 2 inches, 3 inches, and 60°. Two sides and the included angle of another parallelogram are respectively 3 inches, 2 inches, and 120°. Prove the parallelograms are congruent.
40. Prove: If two sides of a quadrilateral are equal and parallel, the other two sides are equal.
41. Prove: If a diagonal of a parallelogram bisects one angle, it bisects the opposite angle.

42. A lunchroom has seats which fold against the wall when not in use. If *ABCD* is a parallelogram, and *BE* = *CF*, prove that when the seat is in use, *AE* will be vertical and *AD* will be horizontal.

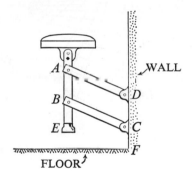

WALL

FLOOR

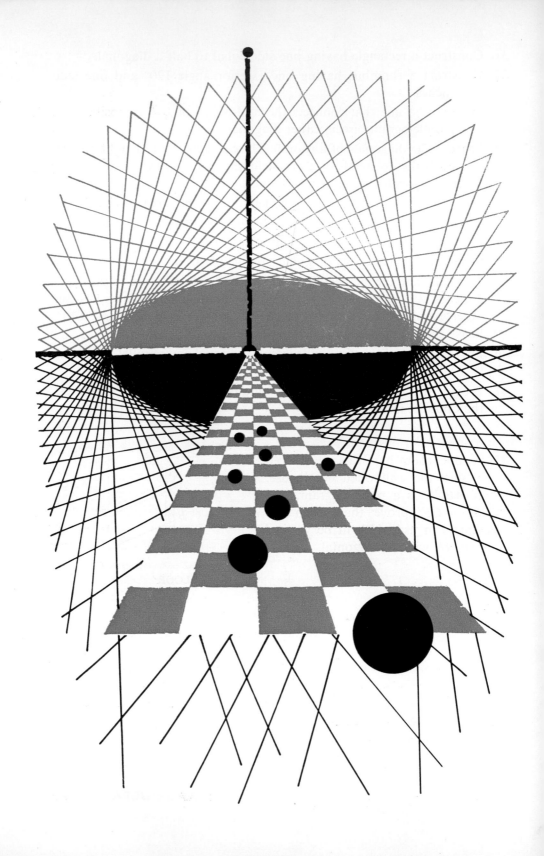

CHAPTER | 8

DISTANCE

In all stages of cultural development, from the lowest to the highest, one of the fundamental needs of men is measurement of length and distance. In ancient times "a day's journey" was a common unit for measuring distance. The length of the forearm, the cubit, was used in many lands. The distance from the nose to the finger tips of the out-stretched arm, the yard, had wide use. In some places "a whoop and a holler" is still a unit of distance measure. In contrast to these crude means of measure we have the modern micrometer calipers, the vernier calipers, and the Johannsen gages, which are some of the most accurate measuring devices ever constructed.

But before any measuring can be done, certain fundamental concepts of length and distance must be understood. What is meant by the distance between two points? What is meant by the distance from a point to a line? Under what conditions is a point equally distant from two points, or from two lines? What is the relation between length and distance? Under what conditions can we speak of the distance between two lines?

In this chapter we are to study some of the fundamental geometric concepts of distance. Study them well, since they provide a basis for much of the geometry of this course as well as for analytic geometry to be studied later.

8–1 Intercept To intercept means to cut off, or limit. Thus, the lines *AB* and *CD* intercept the arcs *EF* and *GH*. The lines *XY* and *ZW* intercept the segment *MN*.

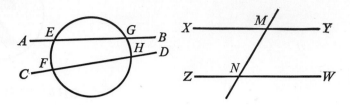

EXERCISE

Name all arcs and straight-line segments intercepted by *AB* and *CD*, and by *CD* and *EF*.

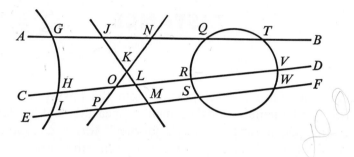

DISCOVERY EXERCISES

In this figure *ST*, *VW*, and *XY* are parallel lines. *SV* = *VX*. Does *TW* = *WY*? If you cannot answer this question and prove your answer, consider the following questions.

PV ‖ *TY*, and *RX* ‖ *TY*

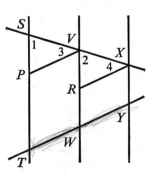

1. Does ∠1 = ∠2? Why?
2. Does ∠3 = ∠4? Why?
3. Is △*SVP* ≅ △*VXR*? Why?
4. Does *PV* = *RX*? Why?
5. What kind of figure is *PVWT*? *RXYW*? Why?
6. Does *PV* = *TW*? Does *RX* = *WY*? Why?
7. Does *TW* = *WY*? Why?

8-2 THEOREM If a number of parallel lines intercept equal segments on one transversal, they intercept equal segments on any other transversal.

Hypothesis Parallel lines AE, BF, and CG. Transversal l intersecting parallels at A, B, C. Transversal m intersecting parallels at E, F, G. $AB = BC$

Conclusion $EF = FG$

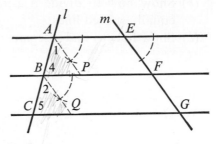

The plan is to construct segments through the points of intersection on one transversal parallel to the other transversal and prove these segments are equal to each other and to the segments intercepted on the second transversal.

Construction. Construct $AP \parallel EF$, $BQ \parallel FG$.

Proof

1. $AP \parallel BQ$	1. Sec. 5–15
2. $\angle 1 = \angle 2$; $\angle 4 = \angle 5$	2. Why?
3. $AB = BC$	3. Why?
4. $\triangle ABP \cong \triangle BCQ$	4. Why?
5. $AP = BQ$	5. Why?
6. $EF = AP$; $FG = BQ$	6. Sec. 7–4
7. $EF = FG$	7. Post. 2

8-3 Corollary If a line is drawn through the mid-point of one side of a triangle and is parallel to a second side, it bisects the third side.

Hypothesis $AD = DB$; $DE \parallel BC$
Conclusion $AE = EC$
Construction. Construct $AF \parallel DE$.
Give the complete proof.

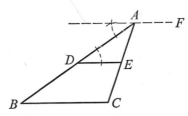

8-4 Equally Spaced Lines

The theorem 8–2 enables us to speak of a series of parallel lines that intercept equal segments on a transversal as equally spaced lines; for the theorem says that the segments intercepted on any other transversal by these same parallels will be equal. In particular, a transversal perpendicular to these parallel lines is also divided into equal segments. The length of one of these segments is the distance between two consecutive lines of the set.

C.

1. (*a*) Show how to use equally spaced parallel lines to divide a 1-inch segment into 3 equal parts.

   (*b*) Show how to divide a 2-inch segment into 5 equal parts using equally spaced lines.

   (*c*) Show how to find a segment $\frac{3}{7}$ inch long.

2. *x* = _____   *y* = _____
   Why?

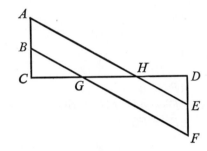

B.

3. A thousand years ago the construction suggested by this figure was used for dividing a line segment (*CD*) into three equal parts. Show how to make the construction, and prove *CG* = *GH* = *HD*. Show how to divide a line segment into any given number of equal parts by a similar construction.

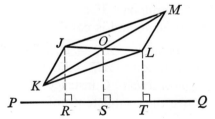

4. *JKLM* is a parallelogram and *PQ* is any line. *JR*, *OS*, and *LT* are perpendicular to *PQ*. Prove *RS* = *ST*.

5. *BD* is a median of △*ABC*. *EF* is any line. *AG*, *DH*, and *CI* are perpendicular to *EF*. Prove *GH* = *HI*.

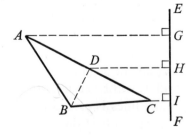

6. *JKLM* is a □. *P* is the mid-point of *JM*, and *Q* is the midpoint of *KL*. *RS* is any line that intersects *JK* and *LM*. Prove: *RT* = *TS*.

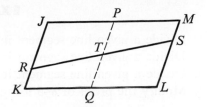

7. *AC* = _____ Why? Quote each theorem that enters into justification of your conclusion.

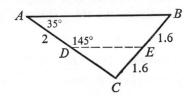

A.

8. Hyp. *GH* = *GI*;
   GJ bisects ∠*HGI*.
   Con. *GK* = *KI*

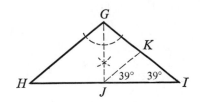

8–5 Problem   To divide a given line segment into a given number of equal parts.

Given   Segment *AB*
Required   To divide *AB* into 3 equal parts.

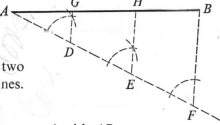

The plan is to make *AB* one of two transversals intersected by parallel lines.

Construction.

1. Draw *AC* making any angle (not a st. ∠) with *AB*.
2. With any convenient radius, mark off on *AC*, *AD* = *DE* = *EF*.
3. Draw *BF*.
4. At *D* and *E* construct *DG* ∥ *BF*, and *EH* ∥ *BF*.
   Then *AG* = *GH* = *HB*.

Proof

1. *AG* = *GH*	1. Sec. 8–3
2. *GH* = *HB*	2. Sec. 8–2
3. ∴ *AG* = *HB*	3. Why?

EXERCISES

1. Divide a given line segment into 5 equal parts.
2. Divide a given line segment into 6 equal parts.
3. Divide a given line segment into 7 equal parts.
4. Modify the proof of 8–5 using n parts instead of a given number.

8–6 THEOREM If a line joins the mid-points of two sides of a triangle, it is parallel to the third side and equal to one half its length.

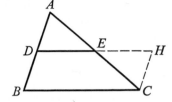

Hypothesis $AD = DB$; $AE = EC$

Conclusion $DE \parallel BC$; $DE = \frac{1}{2} BC$

Construction. Extend DE to H, making $EH = DE$. Draw HC.

Proof

1. $\triangle ECH \cong \triangle ADE$
2. $\angle ADE = \angle EHC$
3. $HC \parallel DB$
4. $HC = DB$
5. $DBHC$ is a $\square$.
6. $DE \parallel BC$
7. $DH = BC$
8. $DE = \frac{1}{2} BC$

1. Give the details.
2. Why?
3. Sec. 5–6
4. Why?
5. Sec. 7–12
6. Why?
7. Why?
8. Explain.

8–7 Trapezoid. Isosceles Trapezoid. Bases of Trapezoid A trapezoid is a quadrilateral that has one pair of parallel sides and one pair of non-parallel sides.

Trapezoid

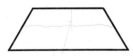

Isosceles Trapezoid

An isosceles trapezoid is one in which the nonparallel sides are equal. The parallel sides of a trapezoid are the bases.

8–8 Corollary If a line is parallel to the bases of a trapezoid and bisects one of the nonparallel sides, it bisects the other also.

8–9 Median of a Trapezoid The median of a trapezoid is the line segment that joins the mid-points of its nonparallel sides.

EXERCISES

C.

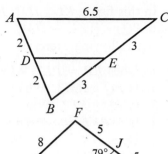

1. Is $DE \parallel AC$? Why?
2. $DE =$ _____ Why?

3. $\angle G =$ _____ ° Why?
4. $JK =$ _____ Why?

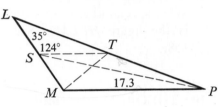

5. MT and PS are medians of $\triangle LMP$.
   $\angle MPT =$ _____ ° Why?
6. $ST =$ _____ Why?

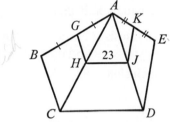

7. Hyp. $AG = GB$; $AK = KE$;
          $GH \parallel BC$; $JK \parallel DE$
   Con. $HJ \parallel CD$
8. $CD =$ _____ Why?

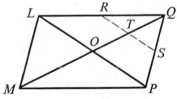

9. Hyp. $LMPQ$ is a $\square$;
          $LR = RQ$; $QS = SP$
   Con. $RS = OP$
10. Prove: $QT = \frac{1}{2}OM$

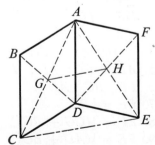

A.

11. Hyp. $ABCD$ and $ADEF$ are $\square$s.
    Con. $GH = \frac{1}{2}CE$
    Suggestions. What are the segments AC, BD, AE, DF?

In this figure $KL \parallel HM$, $HP = PK$, $MQ = QL$. Show that $PQ \parallel HM$, and $PQ = \frac{1}{2}(KL + HM)$. If you need help, follow the steps indicated in the following exercises.

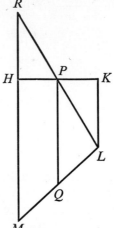

1. Does $RP = PL$? Why?
2. Is $PQ \parallel RM$? Why?
3. Is $PQ \parallel KL$? Why?
4. Is $\triangle PKL \cong \triangle PHR$? Prove this.
5. Does $HR = KL$? Why?
6. Does $PQ = \frac{1}{2}RM$? Why?
7. Does $RM = KL + HM$? Why?
8. Does $PQ = \frac{1}{2}(KL + HM)$? Why?
9. What special kind of quadrilateral is the figure $HKLM$? See page 158.

8–10 THEOREM The median of a trapezoid is parallel to the bases and equals half their sum.

Hypothesis Trapezoid $ABCD$ and its median EF

Conclusion $EF \parallel BC \parallel AD$; $EF = \frac{1}{2}(AD + BC)$

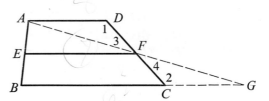

The plan is to draw AF and extend AF and BC to meet at G, prove $EF = \frac{1}{2}BG$, and prove $CG + BC = AD + BC$.

Construction. Draw AF and extend AF and BC to meet at G.

Proof

1. $\angle 1 = \angle 2$	1. Why?
2. $DF = FC$	2. Why?
3. $\angle 3 = \angle 4$	3. Why?
4. $\triangle ADF \cong \triangle FCG$	4. Why?
5. $AD = CG$; $AF = FG$	5. Why?
6. $EF \parallel BC \parallel AD$	6. Sec. 8–6, Sec. 5–15
7. $EF = \frac{1}{2}BG$	7. Sec. 8–6
8. $EF = \frac{1}{2}(CG + BC)$	8. Why?
9. $EF = \frac{1}{2}(AD + BC)$	9. Why?

EXERCISES

C.

1. Construct a trapezoid of three congruent equilateral triangles with common sides as shown. Cut out, fold, and fasten to form the second figure. This is a pyramid.

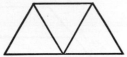

2. Construct four congruent isosceles trapezoids with common sides as shown. Cut out, fold, and fasten to form the second figure. This is a frustum of a pyramid.

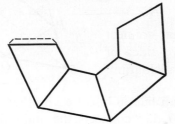 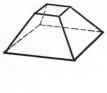

3. $DE \parallel BC$; $AC = 9$
   $AE =$ _____ Why?

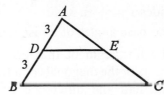

4. Prove $JK \parallel GH$.
   $GH =$ _____ Why?

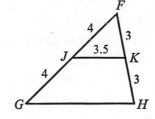

5. $ABCD$ is a trapezoid.
   $EF =$ _____

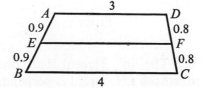

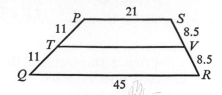

B.

6. *PQRS* is a trapezoid.
   Prove *TV* ∥ *PS*.
   TV = _____ Why?

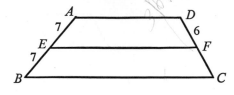

7. *ABCD* is a trapezoid.
   EF ∥ *BC*. *CF* = _____
   Why?

8. Construct a segment $\frac{3}{5}$ in. long.
   ($\frac{3}{5}$ in. = $\frac{1}{5}$ of 3 in.)

9. Construct a segment $\frac{4}{7}$ in. long.

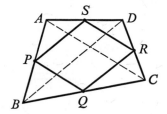

A.

10. Prove: The line segments that connect
    the mid-points of consecutive sides of
    any quadrilateral form a parallelogram.

11. Prove: The medians of a quadrilateral bisect each other. (A *median
    of a quadrilateral* is a segment that connects the mid-points of non-
    adjacent sides.)

12. Prove: The base angles of an isosceles trapezoid are equal.

13. Prove: The line segment that connects
    the mid-points of the diagonals of a trape-
    zoid equals half the difference of the
    bases.

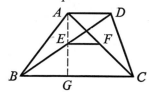

14. Prove: The opposite angles of an isosceles trapezoid are supple-
    mentary.

15. Prove: The line segment that connects
    the mid-points of the bases of an isosceles
    trapezoid is perpendicular to the bases.
    Suggestion.   Prove   △*ABF* ≅ △*DCF*.
    Then *AF* = *DF*. Prove △*AEF* ≅ △*DEF*.

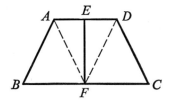

16. Prove: The line segment that connects the mid-points of the bases
    of an isosceles trapezoid is perpendicular to the median.

8–11 THEOREM Any point on the perpendicular bisector of a line segment is equally distant from the ends of the segment.

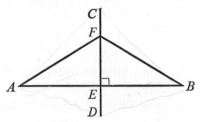

Hypothesis $CD \perp AB$; $AE = EB$;
  F is any point on CD.

Conclusion $AF = BF$

Give the complete proof.

Suggestion. Prove $\triangle AFE \cong \triangle BFE$.

8–12 THEOREM (a converse of 8–11) Any point equally distant from the ends of a line segment is on the perpendicular bisector of the segment.

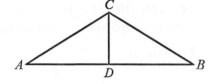

Hypothesis $AC = BC$

Conclusion C is on the perpendicular bisector of AB.

The plan is to draw a line from C to the mid-point of AB and prove the triangles congruent.

Construction. Bisect AB at D. Draw CD.

Proof

1. _____ = _____
2. $AD = BD$
3. _____ = _____
4. $\triangle ACD \cong \triangle BCD$
5. $\angle ADC = \angle BDC$
6. $\angle ADC$ = a rt. $\angle$
7. $\therefore CD \perp AB$, and C is on the perpendicular bisector of AB.

1. Given
2. By construction
3. By identity
4. Why?
5. Why?
6. Sec. 0–16
7. Sec. 0–16

The theorems of Sec. 8–11 and Sec. 8–12 can be written as one proposition as follows: A point is on the perpendicular bisector of a line segment if and only if it is equidistant from the end points of the segment.

8–13 Corollary Two points, each equally distant from the ends of a segment, determine the perpendicular bisector of the segment.

Give the proof.

Suggestion. How many lines can be drawn through two points? Post. 16.

DISCOVERY EXERCISES

In this figure $\angle 1 = \angle 2$; $WX \perp RS$; $WY \perp ST$. Does $WX = WY$? Can you prove it? If not, consider the steps indicated by the following exercises.

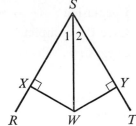

1. What kind of triangle is $\triangle SXW$?
   $\triangle SYW$? Why?
2. Is $\triangle SXW \cong \triangle SYW$? Why?
3. Does $XW = YW$? Why?

8–14 THEOREM Any point on the bisector of an angle is equally distant from the sides of the angle.

Hypothesis $\angle ABC$; $\angle ABD = \angle DBC$;
   E is any point on BD;
   $EF \perp AB$; $EG \perp BC$

Conclusion $EF = EG$

What plan can be used?

Proof

1. ———— $\perp$ ————; and ———— $\perp$ ————	1. Given
2. $\angle BFE = \angle BGE$	2. Why?
3. $\angle 3 = \angle 4$	3. Why?
4. $BE = BE$	4. By identity
5. $\triangle BEF \cong \triangle BEG$	5. Sec. 6–11
6. $\therefore EF = EG$	6. Why?

Beginning of Geometry More than 5000 years ago, the Babylonians, the Egyptians, and perhaps other peoples began the study of geometry. However, their interest was in its practical uses, surveying, measuring, and building. About 600 B.C. the Greeks began to study geometry as a science, developing and proving general theorems much as we do. They stated postulates and worked out systematic proofs. Some of the Greek scholars were Thales, Eratosthenes, Archimedes, Hero, Euclid, and Pythagoras. These men did not all live at the same time nor in the same place, of course. It was Euclid who collected and organized the geometrical knowledge of his time. This was about 300 B.C.

8-15 THEOREM (a converse of 8-14) **Any point equally distant from the sides of an angle is on the bisector of the angle.**

Hypothesis $\angle ABC$; $EF \perp AB$ and $EG \perp BC$;
$EF = EG$

Conclusion $\angle FBE = \angle EBG$

What plan can be used?

Proof

1. ——— $\perp$ ———;   1. Given
   ——— $\perp$ ———
2. $\triangle BEF$ and $\triangle BEG$ are rt. $\triangle$s.   2. Why?
3. ——— = ———   3. By identity
4. $EF = EG$ 4. Why?
5. $\triangle BEF \cong \triangle BEG$ 5. Why?
6. $\therefore \angle EBF = \angle EBG$, or E is on   6. Why?
   the bisector of $\angle ABC$.

State the theorems of Sec. 8-14 and Sec. 8-15 as one proposition in "if and only if" form. See Sec. 5-16.

Theorems about angle bisectors find great use in navigation.
Shown here is the Navy's first atomic submarine.

$\triangle LMP$ is a right triangle; $LQ = QP$; $QR \perp LM$. Try to prove $QM = QP$. If you do the following exercises, the steps in the proof will be made clear.

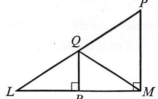

1. Is $QR \parallel PM$? Why?
2. Does $LR = RM$? Why?
3. Is RQ the perpendicular bisector of LM? Why?
4. Does $QM = QP$? Why?

8–16 THEOREM The mid-point of the hypotenuse of a right triangle is equally distant from the three vertices.

Hypothesis $\triangle ABC$; $\angle ACB$ is a rt. $\angle$; $AD = BD$

Conclusion $AD = DC$; $BD = DC$

The plan is to construct a line through D and perpendicular to BC, and prove the resulting triangles congruent.

Construction. From D construct $DE \perp BC$ at E. (Sec. 1–7)

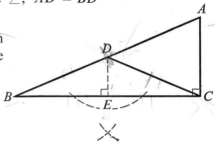

Proof

1. $DE \parallel AC$	1. Sec. 5–2
2. $BE = EC$	2. Sec. 8–3
3. DE is the $\perp$ bisector of BC.	3. By def.
4. $\therefore BD = DC$	4. Sec. 8–11
5. $AD = DC$	5. Why?

8–17 Corollary The side opposite the 30° angle of a 30°-60° right triangle equals half the hypotenuse. (A 30°-60° right triangle is a right triangle that has a 30° angle and a 60° angle.)

Hypothesis $\triangle ABC$; $\angle ACB = 90°$; $\angle B = 30°$; $\angle A = 60°$

Conclusion $AC = \frac{1}{2}AB$

Construction. Construct $\angle 1 = \angle B$.
Complete the proof.

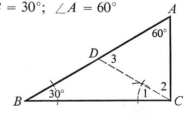

Suggestions. $\angle 1 =$ how many degrees? $\angle 2 =$ how many degrees? Compare BD and CD. Compare AD and CD. Compare AD and AC. Compare AC and AB.

EXERCISES

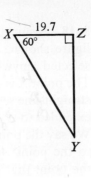

C. Oral

1. $XY = $ _____ Why?

2. $AC = $ _____ Why?

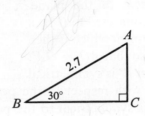

3. What is the length of the hypotenuse of a 30°-60° right triangle if the side opposite the 30° angle is 17.5?

4. What is the length of the side opposite the 30° angle of a 30°-60° right triangle if the hypotenuse is 1728?

5. Find the altitude AD of this triangle.

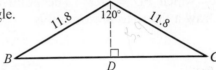

B. Written

6. In the figure determine the value of x and the sides PQ and PR. What reason can you use in setting up an equation?

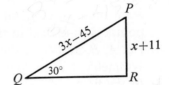

7. Find the angles of this triangle.
$AB = $ _____ $AC = $ _____

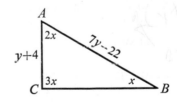

8. A ship is sailing along the course ST. At S the navigator sights a lighthouse 30° to the left of his course. He observes L until at T the lighthouse bears 60° to the left of his course. His chart gives the distance ST as 4 miles. Find the distance from the ship to the lighthouse when the ship is at T.

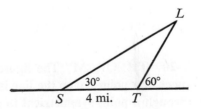

8–18 Symmetry. Symmetry with Respect to a Point in a Plane In the figure shown, O is a fixed point in a plane. Then another point A is selected anywhere in the plane. The point A is connected to O by a straight-line segment which is then extended to A' so that $AO = OA'$. We say the point A' is symmetrical

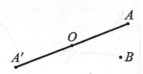

to the point A with respect to the point O. Explain how you can find the point that is symmetrical to the point B with respect to the point O. Is there more than one point in the plane symmetrical to point B with respect to the point O? Explain.

Definition. The symmetrical point to a point P in a plane with respect to a fixed point O in the plane is the point Q on the extended line PO for which $PO = OQ$. The point O is called the center of symmetry. Draw a figure to illustrate this.

EXERCISES

1. Locate three points at random in a plane. Select a point O distinct from these three points. Using O as a center of symmetry find the points symmetrical to the three random points.
2. Let A, B, and O be the vertices of a triangle. Using O as a center of symmetry, find the points symmetrical to A and B.
3. In the figure of Ex. 2, let X be any point on line AB. Find the point symmetrical to X with respect to O.
4. In Ex. 2 and 3 draw the line that connects the two points symmetrical to A and B. Is the symmetrical point to X on this line? Prove your answer.

8–19 *Definition.* The figure symmetrical to a given figure with respect to a given point is the set of points symmetrical to the points of the given figure.

Exercises 3 and 4 above prove the following theorem. No further proof of this theorem is needed.

8–20 THEOREM The figure symmetrical to a line in a plane with respect to a point not on the line is a line parallel to the given line and passing through a point symmetrical to a point on the given line.

EXERCISES

1. Write out the proof of Theorem 8–20.
2. Prove: A line and its symmetrical line are the same distance from the center of symmetry.
3. Using any two points on a 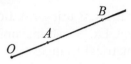 line, show how to construct the line symmetrical to *CD* with respect to point *O*.
4. Find the segment symmetrical with respect to point *O* to the line segment *CD* in Ex. 3.
5. Prove: The opposite sides of a parallelogram are symmetric with respect to the intersection of the diagonals.
6. If the center of symmetry *O* is in line *AB*, what is the symmetrical line to line *AB*? What segment is symmetrical to segment *AB*?
7. Draw an acute angle *ABC* and select a point *O* inside the angle. Construct and describe the figure that is symmetrical to the angle with respect to *O*.
8. Repeat Ex. 7 with point *O* selected outside the angle *ABC*.
9. Repeat Ex. 7 with point *O* in one of the sides of the angle *ABC*.
10. Draw any angle *RST*. Let *S* be the point of symmetry and construct the figure which is symmetrical to ∠*RST* with respect to *S*.
11. Draw a circle with center *Q*. Let *T* be a point between the circle and *Q*. Construct the figure which is symmetrical to ⊙*Q* with respect to *T*. Let *T'* be a point outside ⊙*Q*. Construct the figure which is symmetrical to ⊙*Q* with respect to *T'*.

8–21 You have already seen how an angle can be formed by rotating a ray or half-line about its initial point. We can use this idea of turning or rotating in a plane to find a point symmetrical to a given point. In the figure, given points *O* and *A*, we draw the line *AOY*. Using *O* as a center and *OA* as a radius we rotate *OA* through an angle of 180°. Then *AOA'* is a straight angle and *A'* is on the line *AOY*. The point *A'* is thus symmetrical to point *A* with respect to *O*.

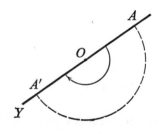

EXERCISES

1. Draw a triangle *ABO* and obtain the point symmetrical to *A* with respect to *O* by rotation.   Do the same for point *B*.

2. By the use of rotation explain how to find the segment symmetrical to a given segment *AB* (*a*) with respect to point *O* on extended *AB*; (*b*) with respect to a point *O* not on *AB*.

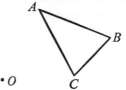

3. Copy the figure shown and construct the triangle symmetrical to triangle *ABC* with respect to *O* by using the points symmetrical to *A*, *B*, and *C* through *O*.

4. Repeat Ex. 3 using rotation or turning of the figure about *O*.

5. Repeat Ex. 3 making only a freehand sketch of the position of the symmetrical triangle.

6. Repeat Ex. 5 using differently shaped triangles and differently placed centers of symmetry.

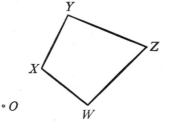

7. Repeat exercises 3 to 6 replacing triangle *ABC* by quadrilateral *XYZW*.

8. Prove: Two triangles that are symmetrical to each other with respect to a given point are congruent.

9. Prove: Two quadrilaterals symmetrical to each other with respect to a given point are congruent.

10. Construct a triangle symmetric to a given equilateral triangle with respect to the point of intersection of the perpendicular bisectors of two sides.

11. Prove that the vertices of the two triangles of Ex. 10 are the vertices of a regular hexagon. (Remember that regular polygons have equal sides and equal angles. How many equal sides and equal angles does a regular hexagon have?)

12. Prove: A square and its symmetrical square with respect to the center of the square coincide. Is this statement true if "square" is replaced by "circle"? Can you draw another figure of which this is true?

13. Construct the square symmetrical to a given square with respect to one vertex as center of symmetry.

14. Construct the pentagon symmetrical to a regular pentagon with respect to the point of intersection of the perpendicular bisectors of two sides. (The two pentagons have vertices that form a regular decagon.)

15. The triangles shown are congruent. Show by experiment that if $\triangle A'B'C'$ remains in the plane but is allowed to take various positions in the plane by translation only, there is no point for which it will be symmetrical to $\triangle ABC$.

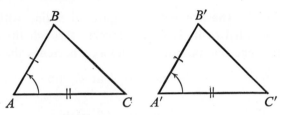

16. Bring to class illustrations of symmetry with respect to a point that you find in drawings, design, or sculpture.

8–22 Symmetry with Respect to a Line Let l be a fixed line in a plane and A a point not on the line. Draw $AP \perp l$ and extend it to A' so that $AP = PA'$. Then A' is symmetric to A with respect to the line l. The line l is called the <u>axis of symmetry</u>.

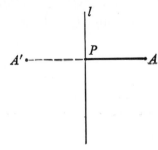

EXERCISES

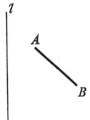

1. Let A and B be any two points on one side of a line l. Find the points A' and B' which are symmetrical to A and B with respect to l as an axis.

2. In Ex. 1 connect A and B by a line. Select any point P on AB and find its symmetrical point P' with respect to line l.

3. In Ex. 2 prove that P' is on line $A'B'$. (Use isosceles trapezoids.)

4. In Ex. 2 and 3, if AB and $A'B'$
are extended to meet the axis l,
will they meet it at the same
point?
Prove your answer.

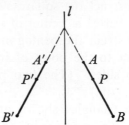

5. Using the results of Ex. 3 and 4 state a theorem concerning the line symmetrical to a given line with respect to a given axis.

8–23 THEOREM The symmetrical figure to a line with respect to a given axis, not parallel to it, is a line passing through the point of intersection of the line and the axis so that the axis becomes the angle bisector.

 Hypothesis Axis l, line AB meeting l at C, line $CA'B'$
      with $\angle B'CD = \angle DCB$

 Conclusion $A'B'$ is symmetrical to AB with
      respect to line l.

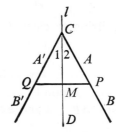

 Proof Let P be any point on AB. Draw
$PM \perp l$ and extend it to meet $A'B'$ at Q. Then
right triangles CMQ and CMP are $\cong$. (Why?)
$QM = MP$, and Q is symmetrical to P with respect to l.

EXERCISES

1. Prove: An angle bisector is an axis of
symmetry of the sides of an angle.

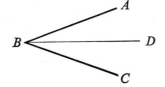

2. Prove: A circle is symmetrical
about any diameter.

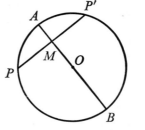

3. Prove: If a line is perpendicular to an axis, it is symmetrical to itself.
This means any segment of the line has its symmetrical segment also
on the line.

4. Prove: An altitude of an equilateral triangle is an axis of symmetry of the triangle.
5. Are all the altitudes of an isosceles triangle axes of symmetry of the triangle?
6. Prove: A diagonal of a square is an axis of symmetry.
7. In an isosceles triangle the bisectors of the base angles are drawn. Name three pairs of symmetric triangles thus formed and the axis of symmetry in each case. Prove your statement.

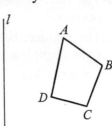

8. Copy the figure shown and construct the figure symmetrical to *ABCD* with respect to *l*.
9. Show how to construct the figure symmetrical to a given figure by folding along the axis of symmetry.
10. Bring to class photographs or drawings showing axial symmetry in nature, in architecture, and in engineering designs. Bring actual specimens of leaves, insects, or moths.

OUTLINE OF CHAPTER 8

This chapter introduces or defines the following terms:

intercept   30°-60° right triangle
isosceles trapezoid   point symmetry
median of a trapezoid   line symmetry
bases of a trapezoid   axis of symmetry

This chapter presents information concerning:

1. The relation between the segments on a transversal intercepted by parallels that cut off equal segments on another transversal. Page 183
2. The relation between the segments intercepted on one side of a triangle by a line that bisects another side and is parallel to the third side of the triangle. Page 183
3. The method of dividing a segment into any number of equal parts. Page 185
4. The relation between a side of a triangle and the line that joins the mid-points of the other two sides. Page 186
5. The relation between the median and bases of a trapezoid. Page 188

6. The location of any point equally distant from the sides of an angle. Pages 192–193

7. The location of any point equally distant from the ends of a segment. Page 191

8. The relation between the distances from the mid-point of the hypotenuse of a right triangle to the vertices. Page 194

9. The relation between the side opposite the 30° angle of a 30°-60° right triangle and the hypotenuse. Page 194

10. Construction of symmetrical figures. Pages 196–199

REVIEW

1. What is the meaning of intercept? Illustrate.

2. Show how to use ruled writing paper to divide a two-inch line segment into three equal parts. Prove geometrically that the three parts are equal.

3. In $\triangle ABC$ a line connects the mid-points of sides AB and AC. How long is this segment if $BC = 3$ inches?

4. In $\triangle RST$, $\angle R = 73°$, $\angle S = 58°$. V is the mid-point of RS, and W is the mid-point of RT. How many degrees are in $\angle RWV$? Show the steps by which you reason to your conclusion and give a reason for each step.

5. The bases of a trapezoid are 1.7 inches and 2.3 inches respectively. What is the length of the median? Tell how you arrive at your result.

6. AB and CD are the bases of a trapezoid and EF is the median. $AB = 32$ cm., $EF = 44$ cm. What is the length of CD?

7. Theorem. Any point that is on the perpendicular bisector of a line segment is equally distant from the ends of the segment. Give a complete demonstration of this theorem.

8. Right $\triangle HJK$ has a 30° angle at H and a right angle at J. $HK = 21$ cm. How long is JK?

9. The vertex angle of isosceles $\triangle ABC$ is $\angle A$ and has 120°. $AB = 2.5$ inches. Find the length of altitude AD of the triangle.

10. By construction divide a line segment into five equal parts.

11. Draw $\angle XYZ$ and a line t. Construct an angle symmetrical to $\angle XYZ$ with respect to t.

YES–NO TEST

Approximately 15 minutes

Copy on your paper the numbers of the following questions. If the answer to a question is *yes* under all conditions, place a plus sign (+) after its number. If the answer is *not yes* under all conditions, place a zero (0) after its number.

1. Does intercept mean to divide into two equal parts?
2. If a number of parallels cut off segments 2 inches long on one transversal do they cut off segments 2 inches long on another transversal?
3. If a line is drawn through the mid-point of one side of a triangle, does it bisect another side?
4. If a line is parallel to the base of a triangle, does it bisect the other two sides?
5. If a line bisects two sides of a triangle is it parallel to the third side?
6. If a line is parallel to the bases of a trapezoid and bisects one of the nonparallel sides, does it bisect the diagonals?
7. Can a line segment be trisected?
8. If a point is the same distance from each of two points on a circle, is it on the perpendicular bisector of the line segment connecting the two points?
9. Does every point that is on the line that bisects an angle lie in the interior of the angle?
10. If a point is 6 inches from one line and 7 inches from another, is it on the bisector of the angles formed by the lines?
11. If the hypotenuse of a right triangle is 14 inches, is its mid-point 14 inches from the vertex of the right angle?
12. If two angles of a triangle are 30° and 90° and the hypotenuse is 8, is the smallest side 4?
13. If the bases of a trapezoid are 22 and 28, is the median 26?
14. Does the median of a trapezoid bisect both diagonals?
15. Circle *O* has radius *r*. Circle *Q* is symmetric to *O*. Is *r* the radius of *Q*?
16. *ABCD* is a square. *AC* is a diagonal. Is the figure symmetrical to *ABCD* with respect to *AC* the same square?

COMPLETION TEST

Approximately 30 minutes

Copy on your paper the numbers of the following statements. After each number write a word, or letters, or number, or expression which, if written in the blank, would complete the statement and make it true.

1. When we speak of the distance between two points, we mean the length of the ———— that joins them.

2. When we speak of the distance from a point to a line, we mean the length of the ———— from the point to the line.

3. $AB \parallel CD \parallel EF$
   $x =$ ————

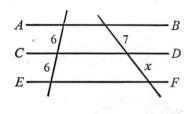

4. $YZ =$ ————

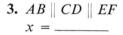
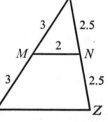

5. $PQ =$ ————

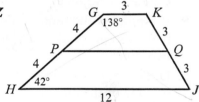

6. $RW \perp ST$
   $RT =$ ————

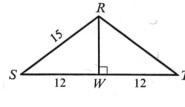

7. $\angle 1 = \angle 2$; $DA \perp AB$;
   $DC \perp BC$. $AD =$ ————

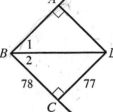

204 GEOMETRY

8. $XZ \perp YZ$

$WZ =$ _____

9. $AB \perp BC$

$AB =$ _____

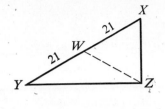

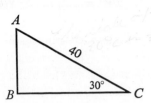

To divide a given line segment into any number of equal parts.

Given.   Line segment AB.

Required.   To divide AB into

3 equal parts.

Construction.

10. Draw any line _____ through A.

11. On AC mark off 3 _____ lengths, AD, DE, and EF.

12. Draw _____.

13. Construct EG and DH each $\parallel$ _____.

14. Then $AH = HG =$ _____.

Proof.

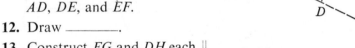

15. $AH = HG =$ _____ because if two parallels intercept equal segments on one transversal, they intercept equal segments on any other transversal.

SUPPLEMENTARY EXERCISES

C.

1. $ABCD$ is a trapezoid.

$DC = 17$

$CF =$ _____ Why?

$EF =$ _____ Why?

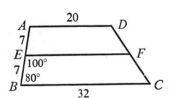

2. $JK =$ _____ Why?

$LM =$ _____ Why?

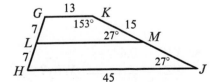

DISTANCE   **205**

3. TS = _____
QR = _____ Why?
TV = _____ Why?

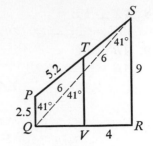

4. YZ = _____ Why?

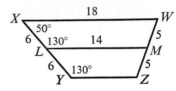

5. $ABCD$ is a trapezoid.
$AE = EB$; $DF = FC$
AD = _____
BC = _____

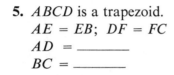

6. LM is the median of trapezoid $GHJK$.
$\angle MLH$ = _____°
HJ = _____

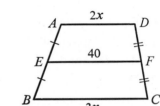

7. $\angle Q$ = _____° Why?

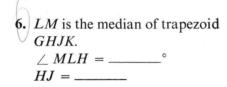

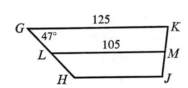

8. $XW = 0.4$
XZ = _____ Why?

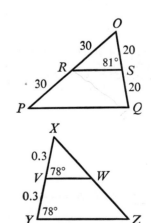

9. $AB = 22$
$CD =$ _____ Why?

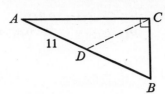

B.

10. Hyp. $EG \perp FH$; $EJ = JF$;
          $EK = KH$; $FG = GH$
   Con. $JG = KG$

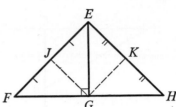

11. Hyp. $\angle ORQ =$ a rt. $\angle$;
          $\angle OPQ =$ a rt. $\angle$;
          $OS = SQ$
   Con. $SR = SP$

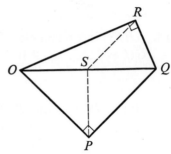

12. $XZ =$ _____ Why?

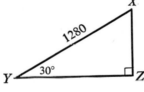

13. $BC =$ _____ Why?

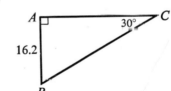

14. $DE =$ _____ Why?

15. GL bisects $\angle HGK$.
   $KL =$ _____ Why?

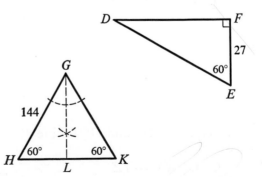

16. *RS* bisects ∠*PRQ*.
   RQ = _____ Why?

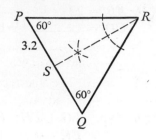

17. *AB* = _____ Why?

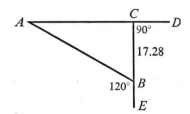

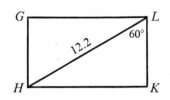

18. *GHKL* is a rectangle.
   GH = _____ Why?

19. Hyp.   *PQRV* and *RSTV* are squares; *XZ* is any line; *QX*, *RY*, and *SZ* are perpendicular to *XZ*.
   Con.   *XY* = *YZ*

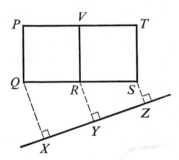

20. Hyp.   *ABCF* and *CDEF* are rhombuses; *GK* is any line.
   Con.   *GH* = *HK*

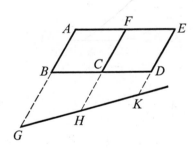

21. Hyp.   *PQSO* and *OQRS* are ▱s.
   Con.   *XY* = *YZ*

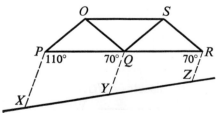

208   GEOMETRY

22. Prove: The line segments that connect in order the mid-points of the sides of a parallelogram form a parallelogram.

23. Prove: The line segments that connect in order the mid-points of the sides of a rhombus form a rectangle.

24. Prove: The line segments that connect in order the mid-points of the sides of a square form a square.

25. The vertex angle of an isosceles triangle is 120°. Find the length of the median to the base if each of the equal sides of the triangle is 11 inches.

26. Prove: The line segments that connect the mid-points of the three sides of a triangle divide it into four congruent triangles.

A.

27. Prove: The line segment that connects the mid-points of two sides of a triangle bisects the median to the third side.

28. Prove: The line segment that connects the mid-points of two sides of a triangle bisects the altitude to the third side.

29. Prove: The line segments that connect the mid-points of the opposite sides of a rhombus are equal.

30. Prove: If the mid-point of one side of an equilateral triangle is connected to the mid-point of each of the other two sides, a rhombus is formed.

31. Prove: Any point unequally distant from the sides of an angle is not on the bisector of the angle.

32. Prove: Any point that is not on the bisector of an angle is unequally distant from the sides of the angle.

33. Prove: If a line is parallel to the bases of a trapezoid and bisects one of the nonparallel sides, it bisects the second of the nonparallel sides.

34. Prove: The segment of the median of a trapezoid intercepted by the diagonals equals half the difference of the bases.

35. Prove: If one of the nonparallel sides of a trapezoid is perpendicular to the bases, its ends are equally distant from either end-point of the median.

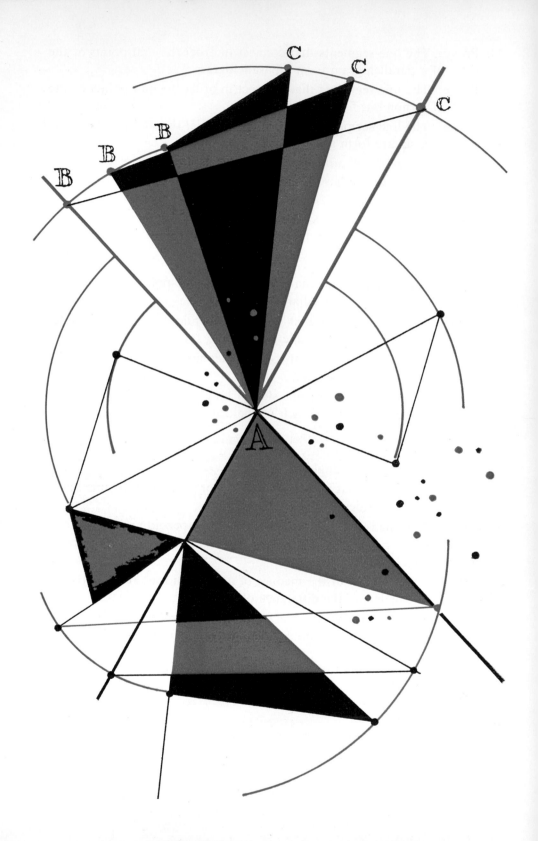

CHAPTER 9

INEQUALITIES

MUCH of geometry is concerned with the study of equal quantities, equal lines, equal angles, equal areas, equal circles. Often, however, an important question concerns which of two unequal things is larger. In this chapter we are to investigate unequal angles and lines in triangles. The facts established here will be found useful in a number of geometric situations.

9–1 Variable Angle of a Triangle You have learned a number of ways to prove two angles equal, two line segments equal, and two triangles congruent. You have also learned some tests for comparing unequal line segments. (See Sec. 8–6, 8–10, 8–17, etc.) Also you know that if two angles have the same initial side but one has its terminal side in the interior of the other angle, then the angle whose terminal side is within the other is smaller, since it is one of the parts of the other angle. Draw a figure to illustrate this.

Let us see what change takes place in a side of a triangle when the angle opposite it is made larger and larger, two vertices of the triangle remaining fixed. Starting with $\triangle ABC$, let $\angle B$ be increased by rotating BC clockwise. Consider the figure and try to answer the following questions. You are not required to give reasons for your answers.

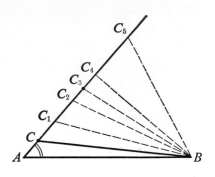

1. As $\angle B$ increases, what change takes place in side AC?
2. As $\angle B$ increases, what change takes place in side BC?
3. Under what conditions does side BC equal side AC?
4. Under what conditions is side BC greater than side AC?
5. Under what conditions is side BC less than side AC?

In this chapter we shall learn how to prove the correct answers to these questions. We shall study the relations of angles and sides in a given triangle, and we shall study the relations of parts in two triangles that are not congruent. A fundamental inequality that we shall use in this study is the relation of an exterior angle of a triangle and a remote interior angle. (See Sec. 4–3.) Also Postulate 19 is very important in the present chapter (Sec. 6–5). Review and illustrate it by using numbers, angles, and arc segments.

9–2 POSTULATE 21 A straight-line segment is the shortest distance between two points.

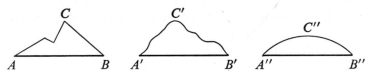

Thus, $AB < ACB$, $A'B' < A'C'B'$, $A''C'' < A''C''B''$.

Optional Discussion Postulate 21 applies only to the geometry of plane figures, of course. The shortest distance on a sphere between two points is an arc of a great circle of the sphere. Thus, the shortest distance between New York and Paris is on the arc of the great circle which runs northeast from New York

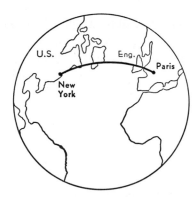

through Nova Scotia, curves eastward, then southeast, and passes over Newfoundland, Ireland, and England to Paris. This is the Lindbergh circle.

9–3 Corollary The sum of two sides of a triangle is greater than the third side.

$AC + CB > AB$ since AB is a straight-line segment joining A and B, and ACB is a broken-line segment.

9–4 Inequality Postulates In comparing the measures of unequal quantities, such as the lengths of segments and sizes of angles, it is frequently necessary to add and subtract these measures. In doing these operations we make use of postulates, of which postulate 19 (Sec. 6–5) is a very important one. Review it now. Here we examine a few more relations of equalities and inequalities.

Quantities are said to be ordered when their measures can be put into a sequence of increasing size or decreasing size. We use the symbols $>$ and $<$ to indicate this order. If $a < b$ and $c < d$ we say the inequalities are of the same order; similarly, $m > n$ and $p > q$ are of the same order. But $a < b$ and $d > e$ are said to be of opposite order.

POSTULATE 22 If unequal quantities are added to unequal quantities of the same order, the sums are unequal in the same order.

Thus, $9 < 10$ and $6 < 8$, then $9 + 6 < 10 + 8$, or $15 < 18$. Also if $8 < 10$ is combined by addition with $9 < 10$ we obtain $17 < 20$.

POSTULATE 23 If equal quantities are subtracted from unequal quantities, the differences are unequal in the same order.

Thus, $18 > 12$; if 6 is subtracted from each member, we have $12 > 6$.

NOTE WELL: If unequal quantities are subtracted from unequal quantities of the same order, no definite order exists for the differences. Consider the following examples to see why.

$9 < 11$	$8 < 11$	$8 < 11$
$3 < 10$	$7 < 9$	$5 < 8$
$6 > 1$	$1 < 2$	$3 = 3$

If opposite order relations are added, again no conclusion of definite order exists. Show this using the following examples.

Add			
	$16 > 9$	$16 > 10$	$16 > 14$
	$7 < 14$	$7 < 23$	$14 < 16$

The following postulate is more difficult to see, but you should verify it by numerical and geometrical examples as well as by reasoning about sizes of quantities.

POSTULATE 24 **If unequals are subtracted from unequals of the opposite order, the differences are unequal in the same order as the minuends.**

$$
\begin{array}{ccc}
8 > 4 & 7 < 10 & \underline{} > \underline{} \\
2 < 3 & 4 > 1 & \underline{} < \underline{} \\
\hline
6 > 1 & 3 < 9 & \underline{} > \underline{}
\end{array}
$$

Use the above postulates to prove:

Corollary Any side of a triangle is greater than the difference of the other two sides.

From Sec. 9–3 $AB + AC > BC$

Subtract. $\underline{AC = AC}$

            $AB > BC - AC$

NOTE: In this corollary we assume that $BC > AC$ or $BC = AC$. If $BC < AC$, then $BC - AC$ does not represent a line segment. What length is represented by $BC - AC$ if $BC = AC$?

9–5 POSTULATE 25 **If the first of three quantities is greater than the second and the second is greater than the third, then the first is greater than the third.**

Thus, if $x > y$, and $y > z$, then we can assert that $x > z$.

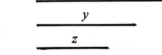

EXERCISES

1. Hyp. $ABCD$ is a quadrilateral.
     Con. $AB + BC + CD > AD$.

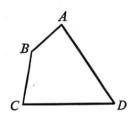

2. Hyp. $AB = BD$; ABC is a
            straight line.
     Con. $AC > CD$
     Suggestion.   Start with
     $CB + BD$.

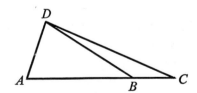

9–6 THEOREM If two sides of a triangle are unequal, the angles opposite them are unequal, and the greater angle is opposite the greater side.

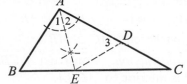

Hypothesis $\triangle ABC$; $AC > AB$

Conclusion $\angle B > \angle C$

Construction. Mark off $AD = AB$. Construct AE bisecting $\angle BAC$. Draw DE.

Proof

1. $AD =$ _____	1. By construction
2. $\angle$ _____ $= \angle 2$	2. By construction
3. _____ $=$ _____	3. By identity
4. $\triangle ABE \cong \triangle ADE$	4. s a a
5. $\angle B = \angle 3$	5. c p c t e
6. $\angle 3 > \angle C$	6. Sec. 6–6
7. $\angle B > \angle C$.	7. Why?

EXERCISES

1. Prove Sec. 9–6 by using this figure. (First, there is a point X between A and C such that $AX = AB$. Then consider the marked angles.)

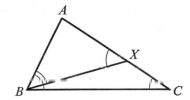

2. Prove: If the base of an isosceles triangle is greater than one of the equal sides, then the vertex angle is greater than a base angle.
3. In a triangle XYZ if the bisector XW of $\angle X$ is greater than XY, then $\angle Y > \angle Z$.
4. Prove: The bisector of an acute angle of an obtuse triangle is greater than one side of the triangle.

9–7 POSTULATE 26 If unequal quantities are added to equal quantities of the same kind, the sums are unequal in the same order.

Example: $2 + 3 = 5$
  Add: $\underline{\quad\ 4 > 1}$
    $2 + 7 > 6$

9–8 THEOREM If two angles of a triangle are unequal, the sides opposite them are unequal and the greater side is opposite the greater angle.

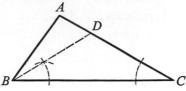

Hypothesis △ABC; ∠ABC > ∠C

Conclusion $AC > AB$

Construction. Construct ∠CBD = ∠C. BD is interior to ∠CBA.

Proof

1. $DC = BD$	1. Why?
2. $AD + DB > AB$	2. Post. 21
3. $AD + DC > AB$, or	3. Post. 2
4. $AC > AB$	4. Post. 1 and 2

9–9 Corollary The perpendicular is shorter than any other line segment drawn from a point to a line.

Prove $PR < PQ$. Compare ∠Q and ∠R.

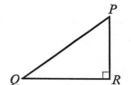

9–10 Corollary If two oblique line segments drawn from a point on a perpendicular cut off unequal distances from the foot of the perpendicular, the more remote is the greater.

Suggestions. What kind of angle is ∠1? Then what kind of angle is ∠2? Now consider △ADE. What kind of angle is ∠3? Use Sec. 6–9.

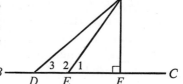

EXERCISES

C. Oral

1. Name the angles of this triangle in the order of their size, naming the largest first.

2. Name the sides of this triangle in the order of their length, naming the largest first.

3. What is the longest side of any right triangle?

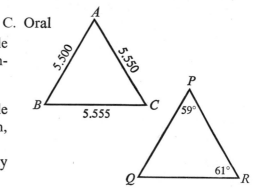

B. Written

4. Name the sides of this triangle in the order of their length, naming the longest first.

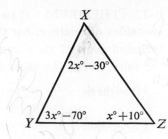

5. Hyp.   △*ABC* is isosceles; *E* is between *A* and *B*; *B* is between *E* and *D*.
   Con.   *CE* < *CB* < *CD*

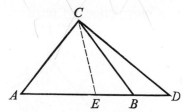

6. Hyp.   *BC* > *AC*; *AE* bisects ∠*BAC*; *BE* bisects ∠*ABC*.
   Con.   *BE* > *AE*

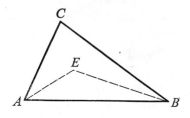

7. Hyp.   *ABCD* is a quadrilateral; ∠*ABC* = ∠*ADC*; *AB* > *AD*.
   Con.   *BC* < *CD*

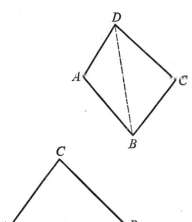

8. Hyp.   *AB* > *BC* > *AC*
   Con.   ∠*C* > 60° > ∠*B*
   Suggestion.   Compare ∠*A* + ∠*B* + ∠*C* with ∠*C* + ∠*C* + ∠*C*, etc.

9–11   POSTULATE 27   Of two like quantities, the first is greater than, equal to, or less than the second.

Example: If *X* and *Y* are angles, then either ∠*X* > ∠*Y*, or ∠*X* = ∠*Y*, or ∠*X* < ∠*Y*.

9–12 THEOREM If two sides of one triangle are equal respectively to two sides of another, but the included angle of the first is greater than the included angle of the second, then the third side of the first is greater than the third side of the second.

Hypothesis $\triangle ABC$ and $\triangle DEF$; $AB = DE$; $AC = DF$; $\angle BAC > \angle D$

Conclusion $BC > EF$

Construction. Construct $\triangle ABF' \cong \triangle DEF$. Let the bisector of $\angle CAF'$ meet BC at G. Draw GF'.

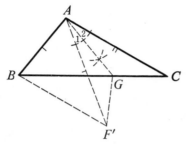 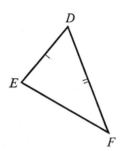

Proof

1. $\triangle AGF' \cong \triangle AGC$
2. $GF' = GC$
3. $BG + GF' > BF'$
4. $\therefore BG + GC > EF$
5. $BC > EF$

    1. Give the proof in detail.
    2. Why?
    3. Why?
    4. Post. 2
    5. Post. 2

9–13 THEOREM If two sides of one triangle are equal respectively to two sides of another, but the third side of the first is greater than the third side of the second, then the angle opposite the third side of the first triangle is greater than the angle opposite the third side of the second triangle.

Hypothesis $\triangle ABC$ and $\triangle DEF$; $AB = DE$; $AC = DF$; $BC > EF$

Conclusion $\angle A > \angle D$

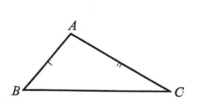 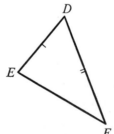

The plan is to use the indirect method. See 4–8.

Proof

1. $\angle A > \angle D$, or $\angle A = \angle D$, or $\angle A < \angle D$
2. If $\angle A = \angle D$, then $\triangle ABC \cong \triangle DEF$, and $BC = EF$
3. But $BC \neq EF$
4. $\therefore \angle A \neq \angle D$
5. If $\angle A < \angle D$, then $BC < EF$.
6. But BC is not less than EF, and hence $\angle A$ is not less than $\angle D$.
7. $\therefore \angle A > \angle D$

1. The stated conclusion and alternate conclusions
2. s a s, c p c t e

3. Given

5. Sec. 9–12

EXERCISES

C. Oral

1. Is $\angle H = \angle L$, or $< \angle L$, or $> \angle L$? Why?

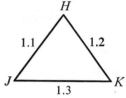

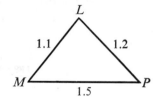

B.

2. Is $SV = PR$, or $< PR$, or $> PR$? Why?

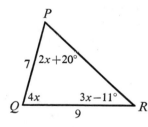

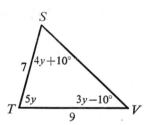

A.

3. $XY = YW$; $YZ = ZW$;
   $XZ = XW$
   Prove $XY > XZ$.

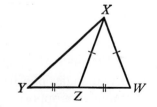

OUTLINE OF CHAPTER 9

This chapter presents information concerning the relation between angles opposite unequal sides and sides opposite unequal angles of a triangle. It also presents information concerning parts opposite unequal parts of two triangles.

Pages 215, 216, 218

REVIEW

1. In $\triangle ABC$, $AB = 5$ inches, $AC = 6$ inches, and $BC = 7$ inches. Which is the largest angle? Which angle is smallest? Give reasons for your answers.

2. In $\triangle XYZ$, $\angle X = 59°$, $\angle Y = 60°$. Which side is longest? Which side is smallest? Give reasons for your answers.

3. In $\triangle RST$ and $\triangle R'S'T'$, $RS = 5$ cm. $= R'S'$; $RT = 7$ cm. $= R'T'$; $ST = 5$ cm.; $S'T' = 6$ cm. Which angle is larger, $\angle R$ or $\angle R'$? Give a reason for your answer.

4. In $\triangle ABC$ and $\triangle A'B'C'$, $AB = 3$ inches $= A'B'$; $AC = 4$ inches $= A'C'$; $\angle A = 49°$, $\angle A' = 51°$. Which side is longer, BC or $B'C'$? Give a reason for your answer.

5. Theorem: The perpendicular is the shortest distance from a point to a line. Give a complete demonstration of this theorem.

YES–NO TEST

Approximately 15 minutes

Copy on your paper the numbers of the following questions. If the answer to a question is *yes* under all conditions, place a plus sign (+) after its number. If the answer is *not yes* under all conditions, place a zero (0) after its number.

1. Can a triangle have sides the lengths of which are 123, 138, and 251?

2. If the sides of a triangle are 11, 12, and 13, is the largest angle included by the sides whose lengths are 11 and 12?

3. If two angles of a triangle are 54° and 31°, does the longest side of the triangle lie opposite the 54° angle?

4. If two angles of a triangle are 30° and 90°, does the shortest side lie opposite the 30° angle?

5. Is the shortest distance from a point to a line measured on the perpendicular from the point to the line?

6. If two sides and the included angle of one triangle are respectively 11 inches, 15 inches, and 39°, and if two sides and the included angle of a second triangle are respectively 11 inches, 15 inches, and 41°, is the third side of the second triangle greater than the third side of the first?

7. If the sides of a triangle are 7, 8, and 9 and the sides of a second triangle are 9, 6, and 8, is the angle included by the sides whose lengths are 8 and 9 in the first triangle equal to the angle included by the sides whose lengths are 8 and 9 in the second triangle?

COMPLETION TEST

Approximately 20 minutes

Copy on your paper the numbers of the following statements. After each number write a word, or letters, or number, or expression which, if written in the blank, would complete the statement and make it true.

1. If equal quantities are added to unequal quantities, the results are unequal in the ————— order.

2. If the first of three quantities is greater than the second and the second is greater than the third, then the first is ————— the third.

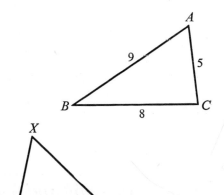

3. The largest angle of △ABC is ∠—————.

4. The smallest angle of △ABC is ∠—————.

5. The longest side of △XYZ is —————.

6. The shortest side of △XYZ is —————.

7. $AD \perp BC$

AC is _____ than AB.

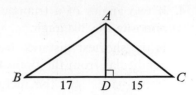

8. The shortest side of $\triangle PQR$ is

_____.

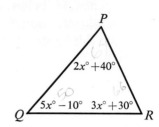

9. BC is longer than _____.

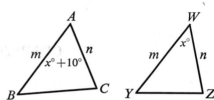

10. In $\triangle GHK$, $\angle$_____ is larger than $\angle D$.

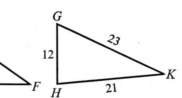

11. The longest side of $\triangle ABC$ is

_____.

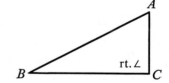

12. Hyp. $AB = AD$; ADC is a straight line.

Con. $\angle 1$ is _____ than $\angle C$.

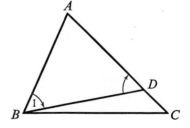

THEOREM If two sides of a triangle are unequal, the angles opposite them are unequal, and the greater angle is opposite the greater side.

Hypothesis $\triangle ABC$; $AC > AB$

Conclusion $\angle ABC > \angle C$.

Construction. On AC, mark off $AD = AB$. Draw BD.

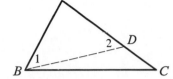

Proof

13. $\angle 1 = \angle$_____, because angles opposite the equal sides of an isosceles triangle are equal.

14. $\angle$_____ $> \angle C$, because an exterior angle of a triangle is greater than either interior angle that is not adjacent.

15. $\angle 1 > \angle$_____, because in any equation or inequality, equals may be substituted for equals.

16. $\angle ABC > \angle$_____, because the whole is greater than the part.

17. $\angle ABC > \angle$_____, because if the first of three quantities is greater than the second, and the second is greater than the third, then the first is greater than the third.

SUPPLEMENTARY EXERCISES

C.

1. Name the sides of $\triangle ABC$ in the order of their length, naming the longest first.

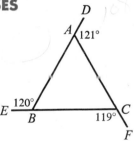

2. Name the sides of this triangle in the order of their length, naming the longest first.

3. Is $OQ > RS$, $OQ < RS$, or $OQ = RS$? Why?

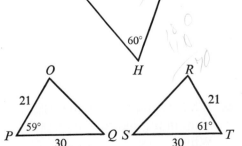

4. $AC = YZ$, and $BC = XY$. Is $AB > XZ$, $AB < XZ$, or $AB = XZ$? Why?

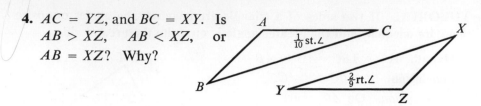

5. Name the angles of $\triangle DEF$ in the order of their size, naming the largest first.

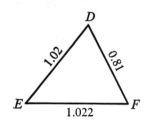

6. Name the angles of $\triangle GHK$ in the order of their size, naming the largest first.

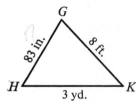

B.

7. Which is the longest line segment PQ, PR, PS, or QR? Why?

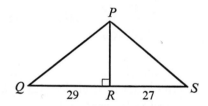

8. What is the longest line segment in this figure? Why?

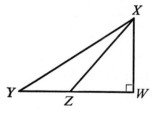

9. What is the longest line segment in this figure? Shortest? Why?

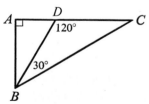

A.

10. Hyp. $EG = HG$
       Con. $EF < HF$

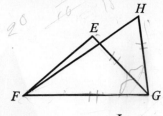

11. Hyp. $KL = LM$;
                $\angle JLM$ is acute.
       Con. $JK > JM$

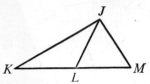

12. Hyp. S is the mid-point of
                PR; $QR > PQ$.
       Con. $\angle RSQ$ is obtuse.

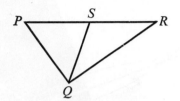

13. Hyp. $XYZW$ is a rhombus.
       Con. $XY > TY$

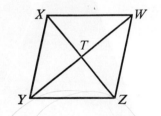

14. Hyp. $ABCD$ is a rhombus;
                AC is the longer diag-
                onal.
       Con. $\angle ADC$ is obtuse.

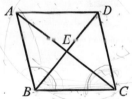

CHAPTER | 10

CONCURRENT LINES

TAKE three straight pieces of stiff wire or thin sticks to represent straight lines and toss them, one by one, onto a table, trying to make them all fall on a selected spot. Usually they will cross each other two by two, but you will find it very difficult to make the three cross each other at one point. This is an illustration of what usually happens when three independent lines are drawn on a piece of paper, each one according to its own conditions. It is very unusual to find three such lines passing through the same point. This makes it all the more interesting when we discover that certain sets of three lines always pass through a common point. In the first part of this chapter we are to study some of these line triplets. Those selected for study are connected with triangles but in this chapter we shall not study all known triplets of such lines connected with triangles.

Closely related to the points of intersection of two of the triplets of lines connected with a triangle is a famous special circle called the nine-point circle. Read about this in a good encyclopedia and construct and study it.

10–1 Concurrent Lines Concurrent lines are three or more lines that pass through a point.

10–2 THEOREM The bisectors of the angles of a triangle are concurrent at a point which is equally distant from the sides of the triangle.

Hypothesis △*ABC*; *AD* bisects ∠*BAC*; *BE* bisects ∠*ABC*; *CF* bisects ∠*ACB*.

Conclusion *AD*, *BE*, and *CF* are concurrent at a point equally distant from *AB*, *AC*, and *BC*.

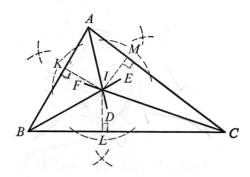

Proof

1. Let *AD* and *BE* intersect at *I*. | 1. Give reasons.
   Construct *IK* ⊥ *AB*, *IM* ⊥ *AC*,
   IL ⊥ *BC*.
2. *IK* = *IM* | 2. Sec. 8–14
3. *IK* = *IL* | 3. Why?
4. ∴ *IM* = *IL* | 4. Post. 2
5. ∴ *I* is on *CF*. | 5. Sec. 8–15
6. *AD*, *BE*, and *CF* are | 6. All pass through *I*.
   concurrent.

NOTE: The point *I* is called the <u>incenter</u> of the triangle.

WRITTEN EXERCISES

1. In the figure for Sec. 10–2, prove *AD* and *BE* are not parallel.
   Suggestion. Can ∠*ABE* + ∠*BAD* = a st. ∠?
2. Prove: The bisector of an interior angle of a triangle and the bisectors of the exterior angles at the other vertices of the triangle are concurrent. Their point of intersection is called the <u>excenter</u> of the triangle. How many excenters are there for any triangle? Draw a scalene triangle and construct all of its excenters.

10–3 THEOREM The perpendicular bisectors of the sides of a triangle are concurrent at a point which is equally distant from the vertices of the triangle.

Hypothesis $\triangle ABC$; DG is the $\perp$ bisector of BC; EH is the $\perp$ bisector of AC; FI is the $\perp$ bisector of AB.

Conclusion DG, EH, and FI are concurrent at a point equally distant from A, B, and C.

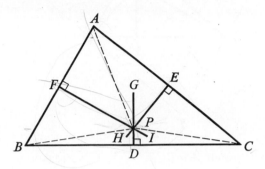

Proof

1. Let DG and FI intersect at P. Draw AP, BP, and CP.	1. Give reason.
2. $AP = BP$	2. Sec. 8–11
3. $BP = CP$	3. Why?
4. $AP = CP$	4. Why?
5. $AP = BP = CP$	5. Why?
6. $\therefore EH$ passes through P.	6. Sec. 8–12
7. DG, EH, and FI are concurrent.	7. All pass through P.

NOTE: The point P is called the circumcenter of the triangle. It is the center of the circle passing through the three vertices.

10–4 Corollary The circumcenter of a right triangle is the mid-point of the hypotenuse.

WRITTEN EXERCISES

1. In the figure for Sec. 10–3, prove DG and FI are not parallel.
   Suggestion. Draw DF. Can $\angle IFD + \angle GDF =$ a st. $\angle$?

2. Draw an acute triangle and construct its circumcenter. Construct the circumcenter of an obtuse triangle. Consider these figures in connection with Sec. 10–4. Can you suggest a general conclusion as to the location of the circumcenter?

10–5 · THEOREM   The altitudes of a triangle are concurrent.

Hypothesis $\triangle ABC$; AD, BE, and CF are altitudes.

Conclusion AD, BE, and CF are concurrent.

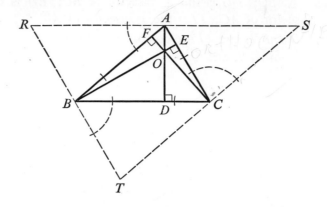

Proof

1. Construct RS through $A \parallel BC$, RT through $B \parallel AC$, and ST through $C \parallel AB$.
    1. Give reasons.

2. $RACB$, $SABC$, and $TBAC$ are $\square$s.
    2. By def. of $\square$

3. $RA = BC$; $AS = BC$
    3. Sec. 7–4

4. $RA = AS$
    4. Why?

5. $AD \perp BC$
    5. Why?

6. $AD \perp RS$
    6. Why?

7. AD is the $\perp$ bisector of RS.
    7. By def.

In like manner it can be proved that BE is the $\perp$ bisector of RT, and CF is the $\perp$ bisector of ST.

8. $\therefore$ AD, BE, and CF are concurrent.
    8. Sec. 10–3

NOTE: The point O where the altitudes of a triangle meet is called the orthocenter of the triangle. It is the point of intersection of lines that are orthogonal, or perpendicular, to the sides of the triangle and pass through the vertices.

WRITTEN EXERCISE

Construct a right triangle and construct its orthocenter. Where is this point? Construct the orthocenter of an obtuse triangle. Where does it lie?

10–6   THEOREM   The medians of a triangle are concurrent at a point which is two thirds the distance from each vertex to the mid-point of the opposite side.

Hypothesis $\triangle ABC$; AD, BE, and CF are the medians.

Conclusion AD, BE, and CF are concurrent at some point M;
$AM = \frac{2}{3}AD$; $BM = \frac{2}{3}BE$; $CM = \frac{2}{3}CF$.

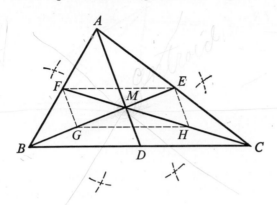

Proof

1. Let BE and CF intersect at M. Bisect BM at G and CM at H. Draw GH, FG, EH, and EF.	1. Give reason.
2. In $\triangle ABD$, $FE \parallel BC$, and $FE = \frac{1}{2}BC$	2. Sec. 8–6
3. In $\triangle MBC$, $GH \parallel BC$, and $GH = \frac{1}{2}BC$	3. Why?
4. $\therefore FE = GH$	4. Why?
5. $FE \parallel GH$	5. Why?
6. $\therefore EFGH$ is a ▱.	6. Why?
7. $\therefore GM = ME$	7. Why?
8. $BG = GM$	8. Why?
9. $BG + GM + ME = BE$	9. Why?
10. $\therefore 3BG = BE$	10. Post. 2
11. $\therefore BG = \frac{1}{3}BE$	11. Why?
12. $\therefore BM = \frac{2}{3}BE$	12. Explain.

Now, having shown that CF intersects BE at its two-thirds point, we can likewise show that AD intersects BE at its two-thirds point, which is M. Also it can be shown as above that $CM = \frac{2}{3}CF$, and $AM = \frac{2}{3}AD$. Since the medians all pass through M, they are concurrent.

NOTE: The point M is called the centroid of the triangle.

C. Oral

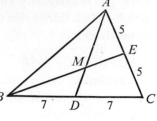

1. $BE = 15$ $BM = $ _____
   Why?

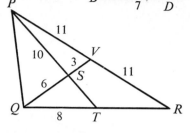

2. $QR = 16$ $TR = $ _____
   $ST = $ _____ Why?

A. Written

3. Prove: If from a vertex of a parallelogram line segments are drawn to the mid-points of the nonadjacent sides, these segments trisect a diagonal of the parallelogram.

Constructions In making constructions which involve any considerable difficulty, some systematic plan of attack is necessary. Such a plan is here given in detail. Study it carefully as a guide in making all constructions.

Illustrative Exercise. Construct a triangle, given a segment equal to the sum of its sides and given two of its angles.

First step. *Suppose the construction has been made. Make a sketch to illustrate the figure as completed.* This figure may not be at all like the figure as finally constructed, but is intended only to be studied for suggestions for making the required construction.

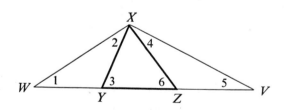

Let $\triangle XYZ$ illustrate the constructed figure, $\angle XYZ$ and $\angle XZY$ being the given angles.

Second step. *Draw any lines on this figure that may suggest ways of making the required construction.*

Since the sum of the sides is a straight-line segment, extend YZ and mark off $YW = XY$ and $ZV = XZ$. Connect the points X and W, X and V.

Third step. *Study the sketch for any relations of parts that might suggest ways of making the required construction.*

Since $XY = YW$, $\angle 1 = \angle 2$. Likewise, $\angle 4 = \angle 5$. Also, $\angle 3 = 2\angle 1$, and $\angle 6 = 2\angle 5$.

Fourth step. *Try to make the required construction, using the data given in the exercise and following the suggestions gained from studying the sketch.*

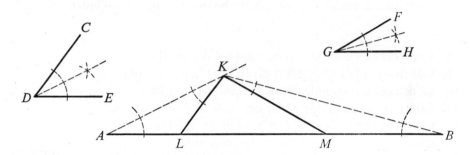

Let AB be the given line segment and $\angle CDE$ and $\angle FGH$ be the given angles. (*a*) Bisect each of the given angles. (*b*) At A construct $\angle BAK = \frac{1}{2}\angle CDE$. (*c*) At B construct $\angle ABK = \frac{1}{2}\angle FGH$. (*d*) Construct $\angle AKL = \frac{1}{2}\angle CDE$. (*e*) Construct $\angle BKM = \frac{1}{2}\angle FGH$. Then $\triangle KLM$ is the required triangle.

Fifth step. *Prove that the figure constructed fulfills the given requirements.*

Proof.

1. $KL = AL$ 1. Why?
2. $KM = BM$ 2. Why?
3. $KL + LM + KM = AB$ 3. Why?
4. $\angle KLM = 2\angle A = \angle CDE$ 4. Why?
5. $\angle KML = 2\angle B = \angle FGH$ 5. Why?

Sixth step. *Investigate and discuss possible constructions other than the one made.*

Sometimes the pupil will find it possible to omit the first three steps above and proceed at once to make the construction.

MISCELLANEOUS CONSTRUCTIONS

C.

1. Construct an equilateral triangle given a line segment equal to the sum of the three sides.
2. Construct an isosceles triangle given the base and the altitude on the base.
3. Construct a triangle given a side, an adjacent angle, and the angle opposite the side.
4. Construct a square given one side.
5. Construct a square given a line segment equal to the sum of the sides.
6. Construct a square given a diagonal.
7. Construct a parallelogram given two sides and the included angle.

B.

8. Construct a rhombus given the two diagonals.
9. Construct a parallelogram given the diagonals and a side.
10. Construct a rectangle given two adjacent sides.
11. Construct a rectangle given one side and a diagonal.
12. Construct an isosceles trapezoid given the bases and one angle.
13. Construct a trapezoid given the four sides.
14. Construct an isosceles trapezoid given the two bases and a diagonal.
15. Construct an equilateral triangle given an altitude.
16. Construct a triangle given two sides and the angle opposite one of them. Under what conditions will there be one triangle? Two triangles? No triangle?
17. Construct a parallelogram given the diagonals and an angle formed by them.
18. Construct a parallelogram given one side, one angle, and one diagonal.
19. Construct a trapezoid given the bases and the altitude.
20. Construct an isosceles trapezoid given the bases and perimeter.
21. Construct an isosceles trapezoid given the bases and the altitude.
22. Construct a triangle given the mid-points of the three sides.
23. Through a given point draw a line making a given angle with a given line.
24. Construct a right triangle given an arm and the hypotenuse.
25. Construct a right triangle given an arm and the opposite acute angle.
26. Construct a rectangle given a diagonal and the sum of two sides.
27. Construct a trapezoid given the two bases and the two diagonals.
28. Construct a triangle given the three medians.

Optional. **Geometry in Three-Space** As you know, plane geometry deals with figures that lie wholly in one plane. This geometry is sometimes called two-space geometry. However, there are many figures we need to study that do not lie in one plane. Illustrations of such figures are a milk container, a water pipe, a football, or a lamp shade. The relations of lines, planes, and curved surfaces that are situated in three-space are important. Three-space geometry, or solid geometry, deals with figures which have three dimensions — length, width, and height.

10–7 Geometry of Solid Figures Since we assume that all figures of plane geometry lie in one plane, we do not often mention this plane. In solid geometry we must consider more than one plane. Any one of these planes may contain points, lines, circles, and other figures that are considered in plane geometry.

A plane, like a straight line, is unbounded. A sheet of paper lying flat on the desk represents a portion of a plane. In drawing a portion of a plane we think of the drawing as representing what we see in the space about us. If the top surface of a desk represents a portion of a plane, we usually see this as a parallelogram. Hence on a sheet of paper or a blackboard we draw a portion of a plane as the parallelogram we see.

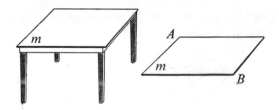

Think of a table as it appears in a picture; then think of the legs in the picture as being removed. The remaining figure represents a portion of a plane. We name a plane by using a single letter at one corner or by two capital letters at opposite corners. In the figure the plane is *m* or *AB*.

10–8 Properties of a Plane A plane is a set of points. These points have the property that the line determined by any two of them has all its points in the plane; that is, the line lies entirely in the plane.

To determine a plane means to designate its position in space. Since two points determine a line, to have a plane there must be at least one other point outside the line to determine a plane.

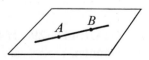

POSTULATE 28   Three noncollinear points determine a plane.

If two thumbtacks, points up, are placed on a table, they will not support a windowpane. But a third, noncollinear tack placed point up will form a basis for fixing the plane in one position. The 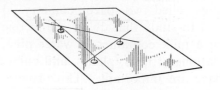 points of the tacks represent points in space. The lower surface of the glass represents a plane in space determined by these three points. Hence we can designate a plane by designating three of its noncollinear points.

Using postulate 28, we can now prove:

Corollary I.   A plane is determined by a line and a point not on the line.
Corollary II.   A plane is determ'ned by two intersecting lines.

Since parallel lines are already defined as lines in the same plane, we also have:

Corollary III.   Two parallel lines determine a plane.

10–9   Intersections of Lines and Planes   Recall that by the intersection of two geometric figures we mean the set of points common to both when not all points are in common. If all points are in common, we say the figures coincide, or are identical.

If a line has two points in common with a plane, it lies entirely in the plane. If a line has only one point in common with the plane, it is not in the plane and we say it intersects the plane. The point of intersection is called the <u>foot</u> of the line.

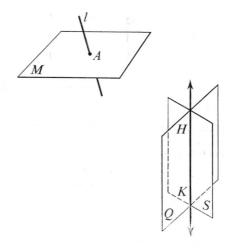

If two planes intersect, what kind of geometrical figure will this intersection be? Can we prove that the intersection is a straight line? Only if we accept the following:

POSTULATE 29   If two planes intersect, they have at least two points in common.

10–10   THEOREM   The intersection of two planes is a straight line.

Hypothesis   Intersecting planes S and Q.

Conclusion   The intersection is a straight line.

Proof   Let H and K be two points on the intersection.   (Post. 29)
Draw the straight line determined by H and K.   This line lies in
plane Q since both H and K are in Q.   Likewise, this line lies in plane S.
Hence HK is on the intersection of Q and S.   To prove the planes have no
intersection other than HK we assume that there is a point common to
both planes but not on the line HK.   This assumption leads to a contradiction: the planes would then coincide and not intersect.

10–11   Parallel Planes   If two planes do not intersect, they are parallel.
V and W represent parallel planes.

**POSTULATE 30   Through a point
P outside a plane W there is one
and only one plane that is parallel
to W.**

Compare this assumption with the postulate of parallel lines.

**POSTULATE 31   A straight line and a plane are parallel to each other
if they do not intersect.**

Hence, any line in plane V that passes through P is parallel to W.
Also, any line that passes through P and is parallel to W lies in plane V.
Note that a straight line can intersect a plane, or be parallel to it, or lie
wholly in the plane.

**10–12   THEOREM   If parallel planes are intersected by a third plane,
the lines of intersection are parallel.**

Hypothesis   Plane C and plane D are parallel; plane P intersects C in
RS and intersects D in TV.

Conclusion $RS \parallel TV$

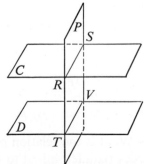

Proof RS and TV are both in P by Sec.
10–9. RS and TV cannot intersect because
they are in parallel planes.   Hence, $RS \parallel TV$ by
Sec. 5–1.

10–13 THEOREM If a line is parallel to a plane, any plane that contains the given line either is parallel to the given plane or intersects it in a line that is parallel to the given line.

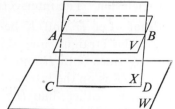

Hypothesis   Line *AB* is parallel to plane *W*; plane *V* contains *AB*.

Conclusion   *V* is parallel to *W*, or *V* intersects *W* in a line *CD* which is parallel to *AB*.

Proof (1) By Sec. 10–11 there is a plane that passes through point *A* and is parallel to *W*, and this plane contains *AB*. (2) Let *C* be any point in plane *W*. Then *C* and *AB* determine a plane *X* by Corollary I of Sec. 10–8. Let this plane intersect *W* in *CD*. (Sec. 10–10) Then by Sec. 10–12 *CD* ∥ *AB*.

10–14 THEOREM If two angles that are not in the same plane have their sides parallel, initial side to initial side, and terminal side to terminal side, the angles are equal.

Hypothesis   ∠*ABC* and ∠*DEF* with *AB* ∥ *DE*, *BC* ∥ *EF*

Conclusion   ∠*ABC* = ∠*DEF*

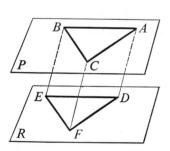

Construction. Let *AB* be any definite length and measure *DE* = *AB*. Likewise measure *EF* = *BC*. Now, *AB* and *DE* determine a plane, and *BC* and *EF* determine a plane. (Sec. 10–8, Corollary III) Draw *AD*, *BE*, and *CF* in these planes.

Proof

1. *ABED* and *BCFE* are parallelograms.   1. Sec 7–12
2. *AD* = *BE*, *BE* = *CF*   2. Sec. 7–4
3. *AD* ∥ *BE*, *BE* ∥ *CF*   3. Sec. 7–2
4. *ACFD* is a parallelogram.   4. Sec. 7–12
5. *AC* = *DF*   5. Sec. 7–4
6. △*ABC* ≅ △*DEF*   6. s s s
7. ∠*ABC* = ∠*DEF*   7. c p c t e

What is the relation of two angles not in the same plane that have their sides parallel, initial to terminal, and terminal to initial?

10–15 Skew Lines Skew lines are straight lines that cannot lie in the same plane. From Sec. 10–8 it follows that skew lines cannot be parallel or intersect. However, a line in one plane M is not necessarily skew to another line in a second plane N. There may be a third plane which contains both lines.

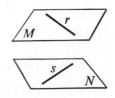

Use two pieces of heavy paper or cardboard as models for planes M and N. Draw or cut a line segment r in M and a line segment s in N. Move the models around to show the relative positions of r and s so that they are parts of (a) parallel lines, (b) intersecting lines, and (c) skew lines. Describe the position of the third plane containing r and s in cases (a) and (b).

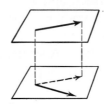

While skew rays do not form an angle, we frequently speak of the angle between skew rays. To find this angle, at the origin of either ray draw a line parallel to the other ray. In either case, the angles are equal by the theorem of Sec. 10–14.

EXERCISES

1. If each of two lines is parallel to a third line in space, then they are parallel to each other.
2. If two lines are parallel, any line that intersects them lies in the plane determined by them.
3. Show that no two lines that intersect two skew lines can be parallel to each other.
4. Through a given point there can be not more than one line that intersects both of two skew lines. Illustrate by drawing a figure. When is there no such line?
5. Draw figures or make models of portions of three planes to show the following relations: (a) the three planes are parallel, (b) two are parallel and a third intersects them, (c) they intersect but the three have no point in common, (d) they intersect in a common line, (e) they intersect in a common point.
6. How many planes are determined by four points not all in the same plane?
7. How many planes are determined by four lines any one of which intersects two others?

8. How many planes are determined by six lines, any three of which intersect in a common point?

9. A skew quadrilateral is one whose sides are not all in the same plane. Prove that the line segments joining the mid-points of the sides of a skew quadrilateral are in one plane and form the sides and diagonals of a parallelogram.

10. Given two skew lines and a point P on neither. Tell how to draw a line through P that meets both skew lines. *Hint.* Pass a plane through P and one skew line. If this plane is parallel to the other skew line, the problem is impossible. Suppose it intersects the line.

11. If no two of three planes are parallel, prove that the three lines of intersection are either parallel, or pass through one point, or coincide.

12. DeSargue's Theorem. If triangle ABC and triangle $A'B'C'$ are in different but not parallel planes, if AB and $A'B'$ intersect, AC and $A'C'$ intersect, and BC and $B'C'$ intersect, then AA', BB', and CC' meet in a common point.

10–16 *Definition.* A straight line and a plane are perpendicular to each other if the line is perpendicular to every line in the plane that passes through its foot.

For example, l is perpendicular to plane M because l is perpendicular to x, y, z, w, and so on, which lie in M and pass through A, the foot of l. Also, l is perpendicular to any other line in M that passes through A.

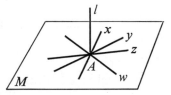

A line perpendicular to a plane is called a <u>normal</u> to the plane.

10–17 THEOREM If a line is perpendicular to each of two intersecting lines at their point of intersection, it is perpendicular to the plane that is determined by the intersecting lines.

Hypothesis CP and DP lie in plane M and intersect at P.
$AP \perp CP$, $AP \perp DP$

Conclusion $AP \perp M$

The plan is to prove $\angle APC$, $\angle APE$, $\angle APD$ are right angles.

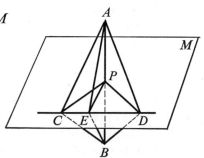

Construction. Let E be any point in M not on CP or DP. Draw a line through E and lying in M, this line intersecting CP at C and DP at D. Draw EP. Since E is a general point in M, EP represents any line in M through P. By proving $AP \perp EP$ we can prove $AP \perp M$. Now, AP and CP determine a plane, AP and EP determine a plane, and AC and AD determine a plane. In these planes draw AC, AD, and AE. Extend AP by its own length to B and draw CB, DB, and EB.

Proof

1. $AC = CB$, $AD = DB$	1. Sec. 8–11
2. $CD = CD$	2. Why?
3. $\triangle ACD \cong \triangle BCD$	3. Why?
4. $\angle ACE = \angle BCE$	4. Why?
5. $\triangle ACE \cong \triangle BCE$	5. Why?
6. $AE = BE$	6. Why?
7. $EP \perp AB$	7. Sec. 8–12
8. $AP \perp M$	8. Sec. 10–16

10–18   THEOREM   There is one and only one plane that passes through a given point and is perpendicular to a given line.

Let AB be the given line and P be the given point which may be on AB or not on AB. If P is not on AB, then a plane M is determined by P and AD. In this plane draw $PX \perp AB$. At X, in any other plane through AB draw $XQ \perp AB$. The plane N determined by XP and XQ is

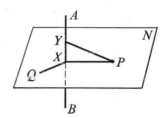

$\perp AB$. If there were another plane perpendicular to AB and passing through P, then there would be another line PY perpendicular to AB from P and lying in the plane M. Let the pupil draw the detailed figure and complete the proof, including the case when P is on AB.

10–19   THEOREM   There is one and only one line that passes through a given point and is perpendicular to a given plane.

Let the pupil draw the figure and give the proof. Compare Sec. 10–17. Consider the case when the given point is on the plane and the case when it is not on the plane.

10–20 Half-Plane. Dihedral Angles. Perpendicular Planes A line in a plane divides the plane into two regions that have no points in common. These regions are called half-planes. (Compare with half-lines.) The line belongs to neither region and is said to be the boundary of the half-planes.

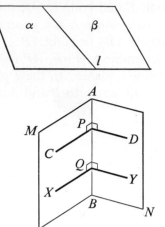

If two planes intersect, the line of intersection is the boundary of the four half-planes. Any two of these half-planes and the boundary line form a dihedral angle. If the two half-planes belong to the same plane, the figure is a straight dihedral angle. The boundary line is called the edge and the half-planes are called the faces of the dihedral angle. To name a dihedral angle, we place the name of the two half-planes in parentheses, as (D,C), or we can in order give a letter on one face only, the edge, and a letter on the other face only, as M–AB–N.

At any point P on the edge, erect lines, one in each face, perpendicular to the edge. Is there a plane which contains these two lines? Why? The angle CPD is called a plane angle of the dihedral angle. If at any other point Q on the edge we construct an angle in the same manner, such as $\angle XQY$, it would be equal to $\angle CPD$ (Sec. 10–14). Hence we use the measure of the plane angle as a measure of the dihedral angle and say:

A dihedral angle is measured by its plane angle. A right dihedral angle is one in which the plane angle is a right angle.

Definition. If two planes intersect and one of the dihedral angles thus formed is a right angle, the planes are perpendicular.

10–21 THEOREM If a line is perpendicular to a plane, then any plane that contains the line is perpendicular to the given plane.

Hypothesis AB is perpendicular to W; V contains AB and intersects W in DE.

Conclusion $V \perp W$

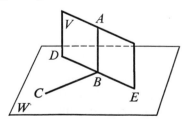

Construction. Draw $CB \perp DE$, and prove $\angle ABC$ is a right angle.

10–22   Angle between a Line and a Plane.   Projection   Let M be a plane and AB be a line that intersects M at B.   By Sec. 10–19 we know that there is a line that passes through A and is perpendicular to M. Let AC be this perpendicular.   Draw BC.   Then BC is defined to be the projection of segment AB on M and $\angle ABC$ is called the angle that line AB makes with plane M.

In general if a line intersects a plane, the foot of the line is the vertex of two rays, one on one side of the plane and one on the other.   If the line is not perpendicular to the plane, the angle (always acute) which is made by either ray and its projection on the plane is the angle the line makes with the plane.

Let D and E be two points neither of which is on M.   Let DH and EK be perpendicular to M.   Draw DE and HK.   Then HK is the projection of DE on M.   What is the projection of A on M?   What is the projection of any point on a plane?

EXERCISES

1. Three lines are perpendicular, each to the other two.   Prove (a) any line is perpendicular to the plane determined by the other two lines, (b) any plane determined by two lines is perpendicular to the other two planes.

2. Prove that a perpendicular segment from a point to a plane is the shortest distance from the point to the plane.

3. PA and PB are lines drawn from a point P to a plane M.   Tell how to determine which is the greater line, using the normal PQ to the plane.

4. Prove: If two planes are perpendicular, a line perpendicular to one plane at a point on the intersection lies on the other plane.
   Hint.   Use a plane angle of the dihedral angle.

5. Prove that two lines perpendicular to the same plane are parallel.
   Hint.   Connect their feet; pass a plane through this segment and one of the perpendiculars.

6. Prove: If two parallel planes are cut by a third plane, the alternate interior dihedral angles are equal.

7. State the converse of Exercise 6.   Prove.

8. State at least four other theorems about parallel planes and their dihedral angles.

9. Prove: Two planes perpendicular to the same line are parallel.
   Hint.   Pass any two planes through the line, intersecting the two given planes.

OUTLINE OF CHAPTER 10

This chapter presents meanings of the terms:

> concurrent lines   incenter   circumcenter
> orthocenter   centroid of a triangle
> relations of lines and planes in space

This chapter also presents information concerning relations of lines and planes in space:

1. The angle bisectors of a triangle. Page 228
2. The perpendicular bisectors of a triangle. Page 229
3. The altitudes of a triangle. Page 230
4. The medians of a triangle. Page 231
5. Introduction to solid geometry. Page 235
6. Conditions determining a plane. Pages 235, 236
7. Parallel planes. Page 237
8. Perpendicular line and plane. Pages 240–242

REVIEW

1. What is meant by concurrent lines? Illustrate.
2. Name three sets of concurrent lines relating to the triangle.
3. At what point are the altitudes of a right triangle concurrent?
4. In what kind of triangle are the angle bisectors, the medians, and the perpendicular bisectors of the sides the same lines?
5. In what kind of triangle does the circumcenter lie outside the triangle?
6. In what kind of triangle is the circumcenter on one of the sides?
7. One median of a triangle is 6 cm. long. At what point does it meet another median of the triangle?
8. What name is given to the point in which the medians of a triangle intersect?
9. What name is given to the point in which the perpendicular bisectors of the sides of a triangle meet?
10. What name is given to the point of concurrency of the bisectors of the angles of a triangle?
11. Prove: The bisectors of the angles of a triangle are concurrent.

YES–NO TEST

Approximately 10 minutes

Copy on your paper the numbers of the following questions. If the answer to a question is *yes* under all conditions, place a plus sign (+) after its number. If the answer is *not yes* under all conditions, place a zero (0) after its number.

1. If two lines intersect, are they concurrent?
2. Are the altitudes of a triangle concurrent?
3. Are the medians of a triangle concurrent?
4. Are the angle bisectors of a triangle concurrent?
5. Are the perpendicular bisectors of the sides of a triangle concurrent?
6. Are the sides of a triangle concurrent?
7. Are the diameters of a circle concurrent?
8. Does one median of a triangle bisect another?
9. If extended, would *AX*, *BY*, and *CZ* be concurrent? (You are not to extend these lines.)

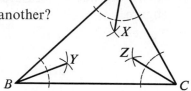

10. If drawn, would *DK*, *EH*, and *FG* meet at a point? (You are not to draw these lines.)

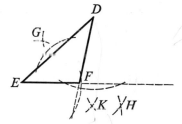

11. If drawn, would *AL*, *BM*, and *CN* be concurrent? (You are not to draw these lines.)

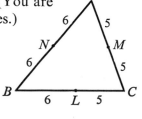

12. If extended, would *DG*, *EH*, and *FK* be concurrent? (Do not extend these lines.)

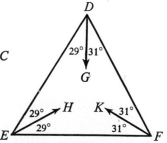

13. Is this figure accurately drawn? (You are not to measure the figure.)

14. Is the figure below accurately drawn? (You are not to measure the figure.)

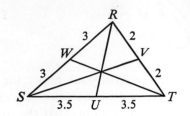

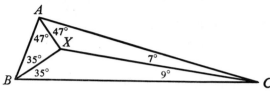

15. Is this figure accurately drawn? (You are not to measure the figure.)

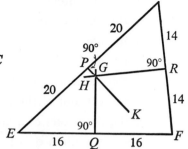

SUPPLEMENTARY EXERCISES

C.

1. $\angle x = $ _____° Why?

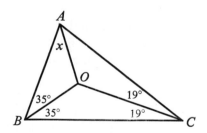

2. Hyp. *DP* bisects $\angle EDF$;
EP bisects $\angle DEF$.
$\angle EFD = $ _____° Why?

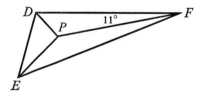

3. $MQ = $ _____ Why?

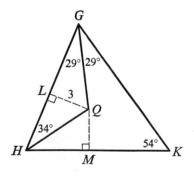

4. Hyp. $AR = CR$
$\angle y =$ _____° Why?

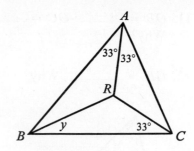

5. $\angle Z =$ _____° Why?
6. $\angle W =$ _____° Why?

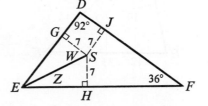

7. $RT =$ _____ Why?

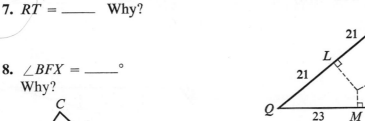

8. $\angle BFX =$ _____°
Why?

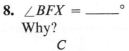
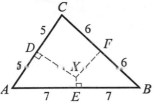

9. $GK = 39$
$GO =$ _____ Why?

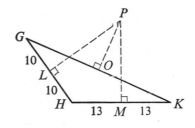

10. Hyp. $RX = XS$; $RY = YT$;
$TZ = ZS$
$QS =$ _____ $QT =$ _____
Why?

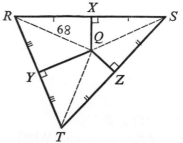

11. $OB = $ _____ $OC = $ _____
Why?

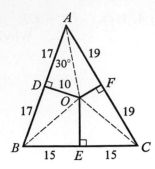

12. $GH = $ _____ Why?

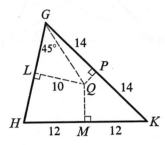

13. $RZ = $ _____ Why?

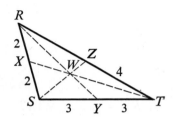

14. $AB = 29$
$AD = $ _____ Why?

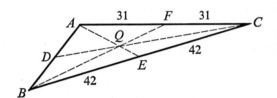

15. $GO = $ _____ Why?

16. $AC \perp BC$
$PF = $ _____ Why?

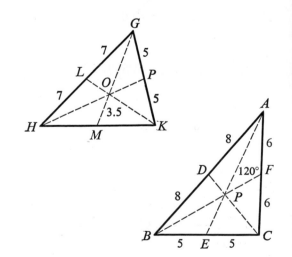

17. $\angle x =$ ____° Why?

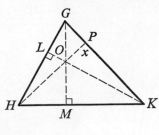

18. $\angle RYT =$ ____° Why?

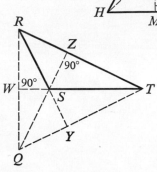

19. Draw a triangle the sides of which are $1\frac{1}{2}$ inches, 2 inches, and $2\frac{3}{4}$ inches and construct the angle bisectors.

20. Draw a triangle the sides of which are 2 inches, 3 inches, and $3\frac{1}{4}$ inches and construct the altitudes.

21. Draw a scalene triangle and construct the medians.

22. Draw an obtuse triangle and construct the perpendicular bisectors of the sides.

23. Draw an isosceles triangle and construct the medians.

24. Draw an equilateral triangle and construct the altitudes.

25. Construct the bisectors of two angles of a triangle and draw the bisector of the third angle using the straightedge only.

26. Construct the perpendicular bisectors of two sides of a triangle as in Sec. 1–2. Then construct the third perpendicular bisector in some other way.

27. Construct two medians of a triangle and draw the third median using the straightedge only.

28. Construct two altitudes of a triangle and draw the third using the straightedge only.

29. Draw a scalene triangle and construct the centroid.

30. Draw an obtuse triangle and construct the orthocenter.

31. Draw an acute triangle and construct the incenter.

32. Draw a scalene triangle and construct the circumcenter.

*Top: Japanese umbrel-
la makers examining
finished products
Left: The steel
superstructure of
a great dome*

CHAPTER | 11

ANGLES AT THE CENTER
OF A CIRCLE

WHEN a surveyor or an astronomer uses a transit or a telescope to measure an angle, the sides of the angle are the lines of sight from his position to each of two objects he is observing. Now, when the instrument is adjusted to observe first one object, then the other, the end of the transit or telescope moves over an arc. It is apparent that there is a very close relation between the angle and the arc. In this chapter we shall study the relation between such angles and arcs. We shall also study the relation between the angles and certain straight lines associated with the arcs.

DISCOVERY EXERCISE

Draw a triangle *RST* and construct its circumcenter. (See page 229.) Can you draw a circle that passes through each vertex of the triangle? What is the radius of the circle? Is there a situation where the radius is less than any side of the triangle? Is there a situation where the radius is greater than any side? Illustrate.

11–1 Problem To construct a circle which passes through three points not on a line.

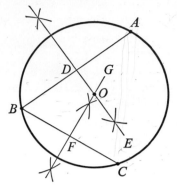

Given Three points A, B, and C, not on a line

Required To construct a ⊙ through A, B, and C

The plan is to locate the circumcenter of the triangle of which A, B, and C are vertices.

Construction. (1) Draw AB and BC. (2) Construct DE, the perpendicular bisector of AB, and FG, the perpendicular bisector of BC. Let DE and FG intersect at O. (3) With O as center and OA as radius, draw a ⊙. This passes through A, B, and C.

Proof

1. $OA = OB = OC$	1. Sec. 8–11
2. ∴ A ⊙ with O as center and OA as radius passes through A, B, and C.	2. Def. of a ⊙

11–2 Circumscribed Circle. Inscribed Polygon

A circle is circumscribed about a polygon if it passes through each vertex of the polygon. The polygon is inscribed in the circle.

⊙O is circumscribed about $ABCD$, and $ABCD$ is inscribed in ⊙O.

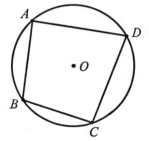

WRITTEN EXERCISES

C.

1. Prove there is only one circle that passes through three points not on a line.
2. Circumscribe a circle about an obtuse triangle.
3. Circumscribe a circle about a right triangle. Can you locate the center with one construction?

4. Can you construct a circle through three points on a line? Give reasons for your answer.
5. Can you construct a circle that passes through four points placed at random? Try.
6. Place a coin on your paper and draw a circle by marking around it. Remove the coin and construct the center of the circle.
7. Three villages, *A*, *B*, and *C*, agree to build a school to serve the three communities, the building to be equally distant from the villages. Make a drawing showing how to locate the school.
8. Draw an arc. Find its center.

11–3   Equal Circles.   Interior and Exterior of a Circle   A circle is said to be determined when its center and the length of its radius are given. Two circles having radii of the same length, but different centers, are congruent. However, it is customary to speak of such circles as equal circles. If two circles have unequal radii, they are called unequal circles.

The circle divides the plane into two separate regions. In the one region, if any two points such as *X* and *Y* are formed by a line segment, the segment does not intersect the circle. This region is called the interior of the circle.

The other region has some points, such as *X′* and *Y′*, for which the line segment *X′Y′* does intersect the circle. This region is called the exterior of the circle. The circle itself is the set of points that bounds these regions. It is a boundary line.

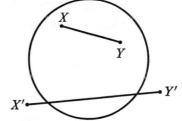

If a line is drawn in a plane, its distance from the center of the circle (how is this distance measured?) may be more than the length of the radius, equal to it, or less than it. We shall use the following postulate.

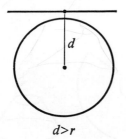

d>r

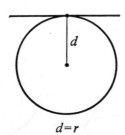

d=r

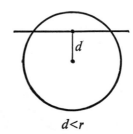

d<r

POSTULATE 32 **A straight line intersects a circle in precisely no points, one point, or two points according as its distance from the center is respectively greater than, equal to, or less than the length of the radius.**

NOTE: Frequently one says "radius," which is a line segment, and means by this the length of the radius, which is a number. No confusion will arise if hereafter we say the radius is 5 inches and mean its length. (See Sec. 1–6.)

11–4 Central Angle. Chord A central angle is an angle whose vertex is at the center of a circle. $\angle AOC$ is a central angle. This angle intersects the circle in two points A and C. The line segment connecting any two points on the circle is called a chord of the circle. Thus AC is the chord related to the central angle AOC. In this case we speak of the chord AC and its central angle AOC.

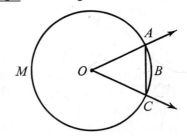

Every chord divides the circle into two regions. The arc on the same side of the chord as the center of the circle is called the major arc. In the figure this arc is AMC, which we write $\overset{\frown}{AMC}$. The other arc is the minor arc, $\overset{\frown}{ABC}$. When there is no confusion as to which arc is meant, we may use just two letters, as $\overset{\frown}{AC}$.

EXERCISES

1. Cut out a central angle of a circle as shown. Roll and fasten to form the cone illustrated in the second figure.
2. Draw two concentric circles with a central angle. Cut out the central angle and the smaller circle. Roll and fasten to form the frustum of a cone illustrated here.

DISCOVERY EXERCISE

Draw two equal circles O and O'. Draw an acute central $\angle AOB$, and construct central $\angle CO'D = \angle AOB$. Draw AB and CD. Does $AB = CD$? State your conclusion as a theorem. Compare Sec. 11–5.

11–5 THEOREM In the same circle or in equal circles, if two central angles are equal, they intercept equal chords.

Hypothesis $\odot O = \odot O'$;
$\qquad\qquad\quad \angle AOB = \angle CO'D$

Conclusion $AB = CD$

The plan is to prove
$\triangle AOB \cong \triangle CO'D$.

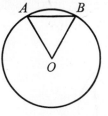 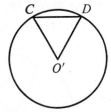

Proof

1. $AO = CO'$, $BO = DO'$
2. $\angle AOB = \angle CO'D$
3. $\triangle AOB \cong \triangle CO'D$
4. $AB = CD$

1. Radii of equal $\odot$s
2. Why?
3. Why?
4. Why?

11–6 THEOREM In the same circle or in equal circles, if two central angles are unequal, they intercept unequal chords, and the greater central angle intercepts the greater chord.

Hypothesis $\odot O = \odot O'$;
$\qquad\qquad\quad \angle O > \angle O'$

Conclusion $AB > CD$

Give the proof.
Use Sec. 9–8.

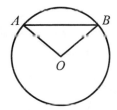 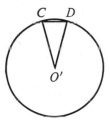

11–7 THEOREM In the same circle or in equal circles, if two chords are equal, they have equal central angles.

Give the complete proof.

11–8 THEOREM In the same circle or in equal circles, if two chords are unequal, they have unequal central angles, and the greater chord has the greater central angle.

Suggestion. Use Sec. 9–13.

EXERCISES

C.

1. Of what theorem is the theorem of Sec. 11–7 a converse?
2. Of what theorem is the theorem of Sec. 11–8 a converse?
3. Is a diameter of a circle a chord?
4. (*a*) Name the equal chords in ⊙*Q*. (*b*) Name the unequal chords in the order of length, naming the largest first.
5. (*a*) Name the equal central angles of ⊙*O*. (*b*) Name the unequal central angles, largest first.

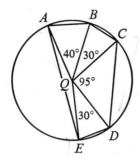 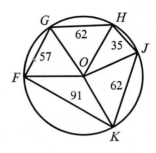

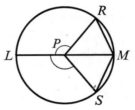

6. Hyp. $\angle LPR = \angle LPS$
   Con. $RM = MS$

7. Hyp. $XY \perp TV$;
   $\angle XUZ = \angle YUW$
   Con. $VZ = VW$

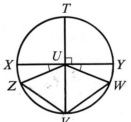

8. Hyp. $\angle 1 = \angle 2$
   Con. $AE = DE$

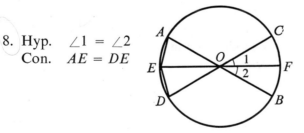

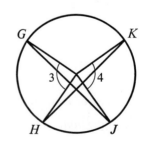

9. Hyp. $\angle 3 = \angle 4$
   Con. $GJ = HK$

10. Hyp. $\angle 5 = \angle 6$
    Con. $LX = TS$

11. Hyp. $\angle 5 = \angle 6$
    Con. $LX > XS$

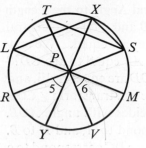

12. $\angle MOP$ is an acute $\angle$. Why?

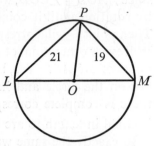

11–9 Length of a Circle To measure a line segment we first select a line segment of given length as a unit and apply this to the segment to be measured. However, we cannot do this to measure a circle, since no straight-line unit, no matter how small, will coincide with or be identical to a part of a circle. To measure the length of a circle we must resort to another procedure. One way, which we will study later, is to take points on the arc of the circle and measure the broken-line segment $ABCD$. The length of the broken-line segment $ABCD$ is larger than the segment AD. Why? It is also apparent that the length of $ABCD$ is approximately the length of arc $\overparen{AD}$. If each arc, $\overparen{AB}$, $\overparen{BC}$, and $\overparen{CD}$, were in turn approximated by taking points X, Y, and Z on the arcs and measuring the length of the broken line $AXBYCZD$, we could get a better approximation of the length of the arc.

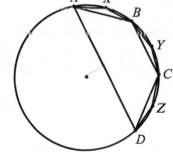

In your study in earlier years you learned that the length of a circle is given by the formula:

$$C = 2\pi R$$

Here π is a number with the approximate value 3.1416. Thus the length of a circle can be found if we know the radius. The larger the radius, the greater is the length of the circle. The length of a circle is called the circumference.

11–10   Relation of Central Angle to the Length of the Intercepted Arc

In the figure, angles *AOB* and *COD* are central angles of the circle and they are equal. We now ask the question, "Is arc *AB* equal to arc *CD*?" Since *OA*, *OB*, *OC*, and *OD* are equal radii, and since $\angle AOB = \angle COD$, we can transform $\angle COD$ by rotation until it coincides with angle *AOB*. Then point *C* will correspond to *A*, and *D* to *B*. Will every other point of arc *DC* correspond to a point of arc *AB*? Yes, because all these points are on the circle and hence the same distance from the center. Since there is complete correspondence of points, we shall agree that arc *AB* is equal in length to arc *CD* and we write $\overset{\frown}{AB} = \overset{\frown}{CD}$.

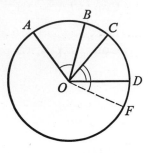

In exactly the same way we could compare angle *AOB* and *COF* with their arcs *AB* and *CF* when $\angle COF > \angle AOB$. In making the rotation it is evident that only a part of arc *CF*, namely *CD*, would correspond to arc *AB*. Hence

$$\overset{\frown}{AB} < \overset{\frown}{CF}$$

The above discussion leads us to adopt the following postulates:

11–11   POSTULATE 33   In the same circle or in equal circles equal central angles have equal arcs, and equal arcs have equal central angles.

POSTULATE 34   In the same circle or in equal circles if two central angles are unequal, they have unequal arcs, and the greater central angle has the greater arc; if two arcs are unequal, they have unequal central angles, and the greater arc has the greater central angle.

11–12   Semicircle   A semicircle is half of a circle.

11–13   Corollary   A diameter of a circle bisects it, and conversely, if a line segment bisects a circle, it is a diameter.

11–14   Arc Length and Degree of Arc   Since there are 360 angles each of one degree around the center of a circle, each of these angles intercepts an arc that is $\frac{1}{360}$ of the length of the circle. (Postulate 33)   We shall call the length of this arc an arc degree.

A degree of arc is one three-hundred-sixtieth of the length of a given circle.

Thus in the figure if angle *AOB* is 55°, then the length of arc *AB* is 55 arc degrees and the length of *XY* is also 55 arc degrees. Yet *XY* is longer in linear units than *AB*. Why? Thus an arc degree must be considered as a part of a given circle and not as a standard linear unit. An analogy in arithmetic is the idea of percent. One percent is $\frac{1}{100}$ of a whole. One percent of 250 lb. is not the same number as one percent of 400 lb., yet each is the same *part* of the quantities.

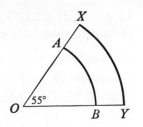

In the same circle or equal circles, if arcs are equal in degrees they are equal in linear units. In unequal circles, if arcs are equal in degrees, they are unequal in linear units.

EXERCISES

C. Oral

1. What arcs in figure (*a*) are equal? What arc is largest? Smallest? Why?
2. What central angles in figure (*b*) are equal? Which is largest? Why?

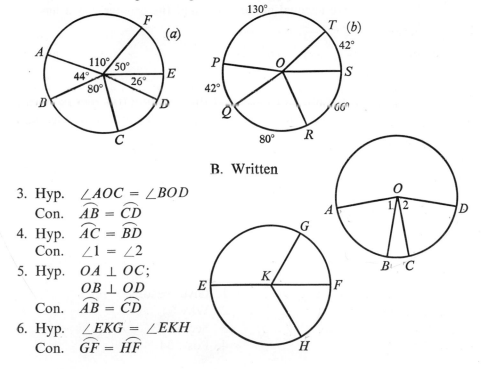

B. Written

3. Hyp. $\angle AOC = \angle BOD$
   Con. $\overset{\frown}{AB} = \overset{\frown}{CD}$
4. Hyp. $\overset{\frown}{AC} = \overset{\frown}{BD}$
   Con. $\angle 1 = \angle 2$
5. Hyp. $OA \perp OC;$
         $OB \perp OD$
   Con. $\overset{\frown}{AB} = \overset{\frown}{CD}$
6. Hyp. $\angle EKG = \angle EKH$
   Con. $\overset{\frown}{GF} = \overset{\frown}{HF}$

11–15 THEOREM In the same circle or in equal circles, if two chords are equal, they have equal minor arcs.

Hypothesis $\odot O = \odot O'$; $AB = CD$
Conclusion $\overset{\frown}{AB} = \overset{\frown}{CD}$

What plan can be used?

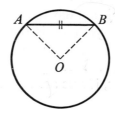 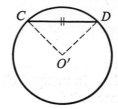

Construction. Draw AO, BO, CO', and DO'.
Complete the proof.
Suggestion. Prove $\angle O = \angle O'$ and use Post. 33.

11–16 THEOREM In the same circle or in equal circles, if two chords are unequal, they have unequal minor arcs, and the greater chord has the greater minor arc.

Hypothesis $\odot O = \odot O'$; $AB > CD$
Conclusion $\overset{\frown}{AB} > \overset{\frown}{CD}$

The plan is to draw radii and show that the resulting triangles have two sides of one equal to two sides of the other, but the third sides unequal.

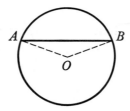 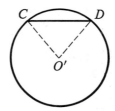

Proof

1. Draw AO, BO, CO', and DO'.	1. Give reasons.
2. $AB > CD$	2. Why?
3. $\angle O > \angle O'$	3. Sec. 9–13
4. $\therefore \overset{\frown}{AB} > \overset{\frown}{CD}$	4. Post. 34

11–17 THEOREM In the same circle or in equal circles, if two arcs are equal, they have equal chords.

Hypothesis $\odot O = \odot O'$; $\overset{\frown}{AB} = \overset{\frown}{CD}$

Conclusion $AB = CD$

Suggestion. Draw AO, BO, CO', and DO', and use Post. 33 and Sec. 11–5.

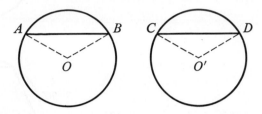

11–18 THEOREM In the same circle or in equal circles, if two minor arcs are unequal, they have unequal chords, and the greater minor arc has the greater chord.

Hypothesis $\odot O = \odot O'$; $\overset{\frown}{AB} > \overset{\frown}{CD}$

Conclusion $AB > CD$

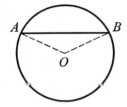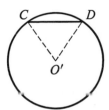

The plan is to draw radii and show that the resulting triangles have two sides of one equal to two sides of the other but the included angles unequal.

Proof

1. Draw AO, BO, CO', and DO'.   1. Give reasons.
2. $\overset{\frown}{AB} > \overset{\frown}{CD}$ 2. Why?
3. $\angle AOB > \angle CO'D$ 3. Post. 34
4. $\therefore AB > CD$ 4. Sec. 9–12

Can the theorem of Sec. 11–18 be proved if the word *minor* is omitted? Can you draw a figure to illustrate the fact that omission of this word gives a statement that is not true? Discuss substitution of the word *major* for *minor*.

C. Oral

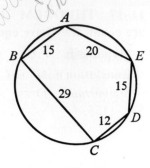

1. What arcs of this circle are equal?
   Which is largest? Smallest? Why?

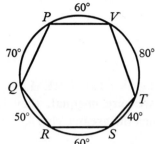

2. What chords of this circle are equal?
   Which is largest? Smallest? Why?

B. Written

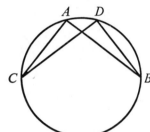

3. Hyp. $AB = CD$
   Con. $AC = BD$

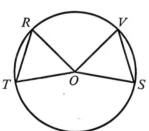

4. Hyp. $\overarc{RS} = \overarc{TV}$
   Con. $RT = SV$

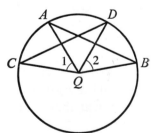

5. Hyp. $\angle 1 = \angle 2$
   Con. $\overarc{AB} = \overarc{CD}$

DISCOVERY EXERCISE

Draw a circle O. Draw a chord AB. Construct a line from $O \perp AB$ at E and extend it to intersect the circle at C and D. Draw AO and BO. Does $AE = EB$? Does $\angle AOE = \angle BOE$? Does $\overarc{AD} = \overarc{BD}$? State your conclusions as a theorem. Compare Sec. 11–19.

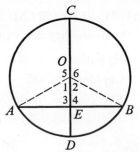

11–19 THEOREM If a diameter is perpendicular to a chord, it bisects the chord and its arcs.

Hypothesis $\odot O$; diameter $CD \perp AB$ at E

Conclusion $AE = EB$; $\overarc{AD} = \overarc{DB}$; $\overarc{AC} = \overarc{CB}$

The plan is to draw radii to the ends of the chord and prove the resulting triangles congruent.

Proof

1. Draw AO and BO.
2. _____ = _____
3. $OE = $ _____
4. $\angle 3 = \angle 4 =$ a rt. $\angle$
5. $\triangle AEO \cong \triangle BEO$
6. $AE = BE$
7. $\angle 1 = \angle 2$
8. $\angle 5 = \angle 6$
9. $\overarc{AD} = \overarc{DB}$; $\overarc{AC} = \overarc{CB}$

1. Give reasons.
2. Radii of same $\odot$
3. By identity
4. Explain.
5. Why?
6. Why?
7. Why?
8. Sec. 11–13; Post. 6
9. Post. 33

11–20 Corollary The perpendicular bisector of a chord passes through the center of the circle.

Suggestion. Use Sec. 8–12.

DISCOVERY EXERCISES

In this figure $RS = TV$, $QX \perp RS$, $QY \perp TV$. Prove $QX = QY$. If you need help, follow the steps suggested by these exercises.

1. Does $RX = TY$? Why?
2. Does $RQ = TQ$? Why?
3. Is $\triangle RQX \cong \triangle TQY$? Why?
4. Does $QX = QY$? Why?

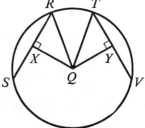

11–21 THEOREM In the same circle or in equal circles, if two chords are equal, they are equally distant from the center.

Hypothesis $\odot O = \odot Q$; $AB = CD$; $OE \perp AB$; $QF \perp CD$
Conclusion $OE = QF$

The plan is to draw a radius to an end of each chord and prove the resulting triangles congruent.

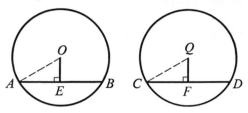

Proof

1. Draw AO and CQ	1. Give reasons.
2. $AB = CD$	2. Why?
3. $AE = CF$	3. Explain.
4. $AO = QC$	4. Why?
5. $\triangle AOE \cong \triangle CQF$	5. Why?
6. $OE = QF$	6. Why?

11–22 POSTULATE 35 If unequal quantities are divided by the same positive number, the results are unequal in the same order.

For example, if $p > q$, then $\dfrac{p}{2} > \dfrac{q}{2}$; and if $r = \dfrac{1}{2}p$ and $s = \dfrac{1}{2}q$, then $r > s$.

DISCOVERY EXERCISES

$LP > LM$; $RS \perp LM$; $RT \perp LP$. Prove that $RS > RT$. Do the following exercises if you need suggestions.

1. $LT = \frac{1}{2}$_____ Why?
2. $LS = \frac{1}{2}$_____ Why?
3. How do LT and LS compare in length? Why?
4. How do $\angle a$ and $\angle c$ compare in size? Why?
5. How do $\angle d$ and $\angle b$ compare in size? Why?
6. How do RS and RT compare in length? Why?

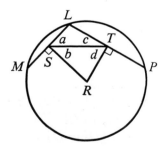

11–23 THEOREM In the same circle or in equal circles, if two chords are unequal, the shorter chord is at the greater distance from the center.

Hypothesis $\odot O$; $AB < CD$; $OE \perp AB$;
$\quad\quad\quad\quad\quad OF \perp CD$

Conclusion $OE > OF$

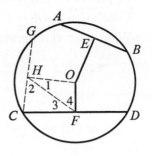

The plan is to draw a chord equal to the shorter given chord and having one end at C. Then show that the constructed chord is farther from the center than CD.

Proof

1. Draw chord $CG = AB$ so that O lies within $\angle GCD$. (If CD is a diameter, O is on CD.) Draw $OH \perp CG$. Draw HF.
2. $CD > AB$
3. $CG = AB$
4. $CD > CG$
5. $CF > CH$
6. $\angle 2 > \angle 3$
7. $\angle 4 > \angle 1$
8. $OH > OF$
9. $OH = OE$
10. $OE > OF$

1. Give reasons.

2. Given.
3. By construction
4. Why?
5. Post. 35
6. Why?
7. Post. 19
8. Why?
9. Why?
10. Why?

Question. How will this proof be changed if CD is a diameter?

DISCOVERY EXERCISES

In this figure $MX \perp HK$; $MY \perp LT$; $MX = MY$. Prove $HK = LT$. If you need suggestions, consider the following exercises.

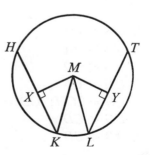

1. Does $MK = ML$? Why?
2. Is $\triangle MKX \cong \triangle MLY$? Why?
3. Does $KX = LY$? Why?
4. How do KX and KH compare in length? LY and LT? Why?
5. Does $HK = LT$? Why?

11–24 THEOREM In the same circle or in equal circles, if two chords are equally distant from the center, they are equal.

Hypothesis $\odot O = \odot Q$; $OE \perp AB$, $QF \perp CD$; $OE = QF$

Conclusion $AB = CD$

What plan can be used?

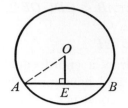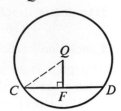

Proof

1. Draw OA and QC	1. Give reasons.
2. $OE = QF$	2. Why?
3. $OA = QC$	3. Why?
4. $OE \perp AB$; $QF \perp CD$	4. Def. of distance
5. $\angle OEA = \angle QFC = $ a rt. $\angle$	5. Explain.
6. $\triangle OEA \cong \triangle QFC$	6. Sec. 3–25
7. $AE = CF$	7. Why?
8. $2AE = 2CF$	8. Why?
9. $AB = 2AE$; $CD = 2CF$	9. Sec. 11–19
10. $AB = CD$	10. Why?

11–25 THEOREM In the same circle or in equal circles, if two chords are unequally distant from the center, the more remote is the shorter.

Hypothesis $\odot O$; $OE > OF$; $OE \perp AB$; $OF \perp CD$

Conclusion $AB < CD$

Proof

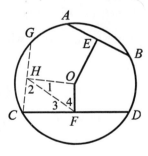

1. Construct chord $CG = AB$ so that O lies within $\angle GCD$. (If $OF = 0$, O will be on CD.) Construct $OH \perp CG$. Draw HF.   1. Give reasons.

2. $OH = OE$	2. Why?
3. $OH > OF$	3. Why?
4. $\angle 4 > \angle 1$	4. Why?
5. $\angle 3 < \angle 2$	5. Post. 19
6. $CH < CF$	6. Why?
7. $CG = 2CH$; $CD = 2CF$	7. Why?
8. $CG < CD$	8. Explain
9. $AB < CD$	9. Why?

C. Oral

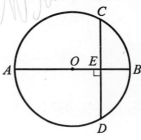

1. Of what theorem is the theorem of Sec. 11–25 a converse?

2. Hyp. Diameter $AB \perp CD$; $\overset{\frown}{CD} = 112°$; chord $CD = 88$.

   Con. $\overset{\frown}{BC} =$ _____° $CE =$ _____

   Why?

3. $RS = 21$; $ST = 7$
   Compare the lengths of QV and QW.

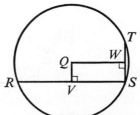

B. Written

4. $QF =$ _____ Why?

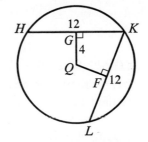

5. Hyp. $MN \perp PS$; $PS \parallel TV$;
   $\overset{\frown}{TV} - 148°$; $TV - 90$

   Con. $TY =$ _____ $\overset{\frown}{TN} =$ _____

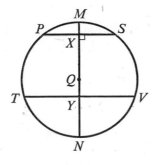

6. Hyp. $AB = 70$; $CD = 70$
   Con. $OF =$ _____

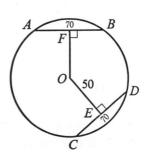

7. Hyp. $\angle RQS = \angle TQS$
   Con. $QV = QW$

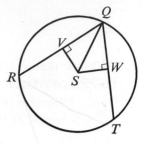

8. Prove: $AD > CE$

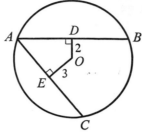

9. Prove: If a diameter of a circle bisects a chord that is not a diameter, it is perpendicular to the chord.

EXERCISES

Applying geometric methods of thinking to nongeometric problems.

1. A man was accused of having set fire to a building. Three people testified in court that they saw him do this. The defendant brought in four witnesses who did not see him start the fire. (*a*) Is there sufficient evidence for judging the man not guilty? (*b*) Is there sufficient evidence for judging him guilty? (*c*) Is there evidence that any of the witnesses gave false testimony?

2. Mr. A said, "All mechanics are drunkards." Mr. B said, "Why do you say that?" Mr. A said, "I once had a neighbor who was a mechanic and he was a drunkard." Mr. B said, "All mechanics are temperate, for I knew a mechanic when I was a boy and he did not drink." (*a*) Is there sufficient evidence for believing all mechanics are drunkards? (*b*) Is there sufficient evidence for believing all mechanics are temperate? (*c*) Is there any reason for believing either Mr. A or Mr. B is making a false statement about his neighbor?

3. Mr. X never works on Wednesday. (*a*) If today is Wednesday, is Mr. X working? (*b*) If today is Thursday, is Mr. X working? (*c*) If Mr. X is not working today, is today Wednesday? (*d*) If Mr. X is working today, is it Wednesday?

4. Mary said, "Mother was not a good student in geometry when she was in high school. Therefore I could not expect to succeed in the study of geometry." What is wrong with Mary's reasoning?

5. Mr. K said, "Two years ago Mr. M was governor and I was employed. Now Mr. R is governor and I am not employed. Therefore, if Mr. M becomes governor again I shall again find employment." Is Mr. K's reasoning correct?

6. Animals that have broad, flat teeth are vegetable eaters. Flesh-eating animals have sharp, pointed teeth. (*a*) The skeleton of a prehistoric animal was found at X. It had broad, flat teeth. Was it a vegetable eater? (*b*) The skeleton of a prehistoric animal was found at Y. It had pointed teeth. Was it a vegetable eater?

7. Mr. K asserts that Russia is better governed under the communists than it was under the Czar. Assuming this assertion is true, does it follow that the United States would be better governed if we should adopt the communist form of government? Does it follow that the United States would not be so well governed if we should adopt the communist form?

8. The presence of many smooth boulders of various sizes mixed in with the soil of a field indicates that the region was glaciated. In certain fields near Indianapolis there are smooth boulders of various sizes mixed in with the soil. Was this region glaciated? In the soil around another city no boulders are found. Was this region glaciated?

9. Robert Louis Stevenson was an invalid. He was a gifted writer. (*a*) Are all invalids gifted writers? (*b*) Are all gifted writers invalids? (*c*) If a person is an invalid, does it follow that he is a gifted writer?

10. H is a good polo player. He smokes the Smokering brand of cigarettes. (*a*) If you smoke Smokering cigarettes, will this make you a good polo player? (*b*) If you do not smoke this brand of cigarettes, does this mean that you cannot be a good polo player?

11. On the same day Mr. R and Mr. S bought fire insurance for one year on their homes from Company C. During the year Mr. R's house burned and the company paid his claim. Mr. S had no fire. A year and a day after the men bought insurance the organizer of Company C disappeared and it was proved that the company had been operating fraudulently. Mr. S brought suit to recover the premium he had paid. Should he be awarded the money?

12. The Mississippi River flows from north to south and it is in the Northern Hemisphere. Can any conclusions be drawn about the direction of other rivers in either the Northern or Southern Hemisphere? Explain your answer.

OUTLINE OF CHAPTER 11

This chapter introduces the following terms:

circumscribed circle	central angle
inscribed polygon	chord
equal circles	minor arc
circumference	major arc

arc degree

This chapter presents information concerning:

1. The method of constructing a circle through three given points. Page 252
2. The meaning of interior and exterior of a circle.   Page 253
3. The relation between the number of points at which a straight line intersects a circle and the distance of that straight line from the center of the circle.   Page 253
4. The relation between the chords of equal central angles.   Page 255
5. The relation between the chords of unequal central angles.   Page 255
6. The relation between the central angles of equal chords.   Page 255
7. The relation between the central angles of unequal chords.   Page 255
8. The relation between the arcs of equal central angles.   Page 258
9. The relation between the arcs of unequal central angles.   Page 258
10. The relation between the central angles of equal arcs.   Page 258
11. The relation between the central angles of unequal arcs.   Page 258
12. The relation between the minor arcs of equal chords.   Page 260
13. The relation between the minor arcs of unequal chords.   Page 260
14. The relation between the chords of equal arcs.   Page 261
15. The relation between the chords of unequal minor arcs.   Page 261
16. The relation of parts when a diameter is perpendicular to a chord. Page 263
17. The relation between the distances of equal chords from the center. Page 264
18. The relation between the distances of unequal chords from the center.   Page 265
19. The relation between chords equally distant from the center. Page 266
20. The relation between chords unequally distant from the center. Page 266

1. Draw an obtuse triangle and circumscribe a circle about it.
2. Draw an acute scalene triangle and inscribe a circle in it.
3. Draw a circle and inscribe a polygon in it.
4. A central angle in a circle has 29°. How many degrees are in the arc of the angle?
5. An arc has 34°. How many degrees are in its central angle?
6. *AB* and *CD* are chords of the circle whose center is *O*. Radii *AO*, *BO*, *CO*, and *DO* are drawn. $\angle AOB = 110°$, $\angle OCD = 35°$. What is the length of *CD* if *AB* = 3 cm.? Give reasons for the steps by which you arrive at your answer.
7. What is the angle formed by a diameter of a circle and a chord that it bisects?
8. Theorem. In the same circle if two chords are equal, they are equally distant from the center. Give a complete demonstration.
9. Chord *AB* and chord *CD* are in the same circle. *AB* is 3 inches long, and *CD* is 2 inches long. One chord is 1 inch from the center of the circle, and the other is 2 inches from the center. How far is *AB* from the center?
10. Place three points at random on your paper and construct a circle that passes through each of them.

YES–NO TEST

Approximately 15 minutes

Copy on your paper the numbers of the following questions. If the answer to a question is *yes* under all conditions, place a plus sign (+) after its number. If the answer is *not yes* under all conditions, place a zero (0) after its number.

1. Do two points determine a circle?
2. Do three points determine a circle?
3. Do four points determine a circle?
4. If two circles are equal, does every radius of one equal every radius of the other?
5. Can a circle be circumscribed about an obtuse triangle?

6. Is the center of a circle that is circumscribed about a right triangle on the hypotenuse?

7. Do two central angles in the same circle have equal arcs?

8. Do two equal chords in a circle have equal central angles?

9. If two central angles in the same circle are not equal, do they have equal arcs?

10. If two central angles in equal circles are not equal, does the greater central angle have the greater chord?

11. If two chords of the same circle are unequal, is the greater chord at the greater distance from the center?

COMPLETION TEST

Approximately 20 minutes

Copy on your paper the numbers of the following statements. After each number write a word, or letters, or number, or an expression which, if written in the blank, would complete the statement and make it true. If two blanks occur, give expressions to fill both.

1. An angle formed by two radii of a circle is called a _____ angle of the circle.

2. A line segment that connects two points on a circle is called a _____ of the circle.

3. If a chord passes through the center of a circle, it is called a _____ of the circle.

4. $\overarc{CD}$ = _____

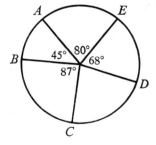

5. $\angle 1 = \angle$ _____

6. The largest angle in circle O is $\angle$ _____.

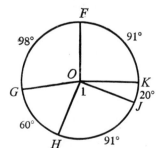

7. $\overarc{AE} = \overarc{BC}$

$AE =$ _____

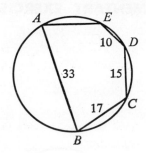

8. $\angle GOH =$ _____

9. In circle O, the longest chord
is _____.

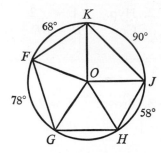

10. $x =$ _____

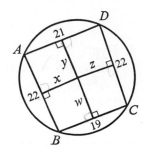

11. $PS =$ _____

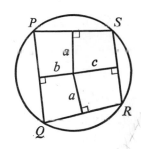

12. $\overarc{AD} = \overarc{BC}$

$x =$ _____

13. $\overarc{AB} =$ _____ °

14. $\overarc{CD} =$ _____ °

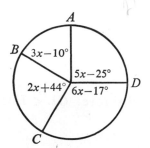

C.

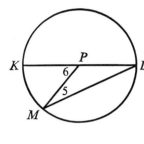

1. Hyp. $BC = BD$
   Con. $\angle 1 = \angle 2$
2. Hyp. $\angle 1 = \angle 2$
   Con. $CB = BD$

3. Prove: $\angle 6 = 2\angle 5$

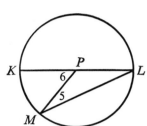

4. Hyp. $SX \perp RT$
   Con. $VS = 2SX$

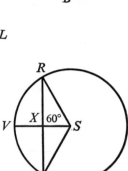

5. Hyp. AB is a diameter.
        $AB \parallel CD$
   Con. $\angle 1 = \angle 2$

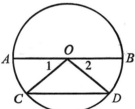

6. $PT = $ _____ Why?
7. Hyp. $PZ = 7$
   Con. $XY = $ _____ Why?

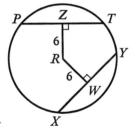

8. Prove: $GL < HM$

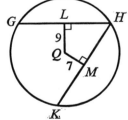

B.

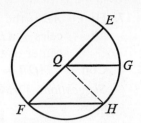

9. Hyp. $\overset{\frown}{EG} = \overset{\frown}{GH}$
   Con. $QG \parallel FH$

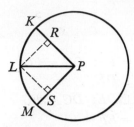

10. Hyp. $\overset{\frown}{LK} = \overset{\frown}{LM}$; $LR \perp KP$;
    $LS \perp PM$
    Con. $LR = LS$

11. Hyp. $PR = PS$; $LR \perp KP$;
    $LS \perp PM$
    Con. $\overset{\frown}{LK} = \overset{\frown}{LM}$

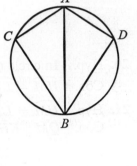

12. Hyp. $AC = AD$; $BC = BD$
    Con. AB is a diameter.

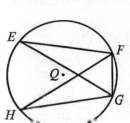

13. Hyp. $EF = GH$
    Con. $\triangle EFG \cong \triangle FGH$

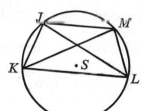

14. Hyp. $KM = JL$
    Con. $JK = LM$

15. Hyp. $XY = WZ$; $XW = YZ$
    Con. $XYZW$ is a rectangle.

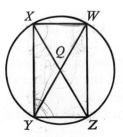

16. Hyp. XZ and YW are diameters.
    Con. $XYZW$ is a rectangle.

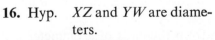

17. Hyp. *AB* is the base of isos-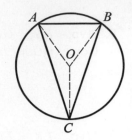
celes △*ABC*. *O* is the
center of the ⊙.
Con. ∠*AOB* = 4∠*OCB*
Suggestion. Draw any needed
lines.

18. Hyp. $\overset{\frown}{DF}$ = $\overset{\frown}{EF}$; *DG* = *EG*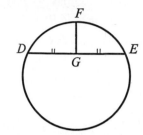
Con. *FG* ⊥ *DE*
19. Hyp. *FG* ⊥ *DE*; *DG* = *EG*
Con. $\overset{\frown}{DF}$ = $\overset{\frown}{EF}$

20. Hyp. In circle *Q*, *QM* ∥ *KH*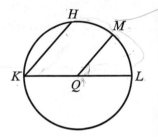
Con. $\overset{\frown}{HM}$ = $\overset{\frown}{LM}$
21. Hyp. $\overset{\frown}{HM}$ = $\overset{\frown}{LM}$
Con. *QM* ∥ *KH*

22. Show how to mark off two equal arcs on a circle, and prove they are equal.
23. Prove: An inscribed equilateral triangle divides the circle into three equal arcs.
24. Prove: Two equilateral triangles inscribed in the same or equal circles are congruent.
25. Prove: The diagonals of an inscribed parallelogram are equal.
26. In a circle draw adjacent central angles of 70°, 140°, and 150° respectively. Connect the end points of the radii and find the number of degrees in each angle of the triangle.
27. In a circle draw adjacent central angles of 88° and 136°. Connect the end points of the radii and find the number of degrees in each angle of the triangle.
28. Prove: Two parallel chords drawn from the ends of a diameter are equal.

29. Through a point in a circle draw the longest possible chord.

30. Prove: Any triangle that has two vertices on a circle and the third vertex at the center is isosceles.

31. Prove: Vertical central angles have equal chords and equal arcs.

32. A and B are points on $\odot O$ and P is any point inside or outside the circle except the center, equally distant from A and B. Prove PO bisects $\angle AOB$.

33. In a given circle construct a chord equal and parallel to a given chord.

34. In a given circle draw adjacent central angles of 120° each, connect the ends of the radii, and prove an equilateral triangle is formed.

A.

35. Prove: If two equal chords intersect, the parts of one are equal respectively to the parts of the other.

36. Prove: If two chords bisect each other, they are diameters.

37. Prove: An inscribed parallelogram is a rectangle.

38. Prove: Two chords perpendicular to the same chord at its ends are equal.

39. Prove: If two intersecting chords make equal angles with the radius through the point of intersection, they are equal.

40. Prove: If chords equally distant from the centers of two circles are equal, the circles are equal.

41. Prove: If a straight line is drawn through two equal circles parallel to the line which passes through their centers, the chords intercepted by the circles are equal.

42. Prove: If two equal chords are drawn from the same point on a circle, the center of the circle lies on the bisector of the angle formed by the chords.

43. In a given circle, construct a chord equal to one given chord and parallel to another.

44. Through a point inside a circle construct the shortest possible chord. Construct the longest chord.

45. Unequal circles O and Q intersect at A and B. OA is drawn and extended to intersect $\odot Q$ at C. OB is drawn and extended to intersect $\odot Q$ at D. Prove that $AC = BD$.

Approximately 30 minutes

Copy on your paper the numbers of the following questions. If the answer to a question is *yes* under all conditions, place a plus sign (+) after its number. If the answer is *not yes* under all conditions, place a zero (0) after its number.

1. Is this ∠*ABC*?

2. Is ∠*x* = ∠*y*?

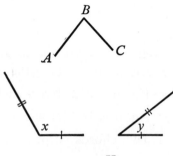

3. Is ∠*GEH* acute?

4. Is ∠*GEF* acute?

5. Are ∠*DEG* and ∠*GEH* adjacent?

6. Does a right angle contain 90°?

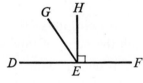

7. Does *LM* bisect *JK*?

8. Does *TV* bisect *RS*?

9. Is *TV* ⊥ *RS*?

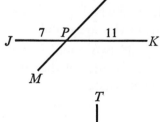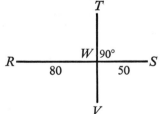

10. Do congruent figures have the same shape and the same size?

11. Are ∠DBE and ∠EBC complementary angles?
12. Are ∠ABD and ∠DBC supplementary angles?
13. Are ∠ABE and ∠FBC vertical angles?

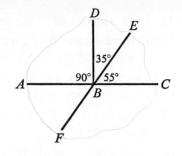

14. Is a 70° angle the complement of a 20° angle?
15. Is a 90° angle the supplement of a 100° angle?
16. Are vertical angles supplementary?
17. Is an isosceles triangle equilateral?
18. Are two angles of an equilateral triangle equal?
19. Can a scalene triangle be congruent to an equilateral triangle?
20. If two triangles are congruent, are the three sides of one equal respectively to the three sides of the other?
21. Are two triangles congruent if two sides and any angle of one are equal respectively to two sides and the corresponding angle of the other?
22. Are two triangles congruent if two angles and any side of one are equal respectively to two angles and the corresponding side of the other?
23. Are two right triangles congruent if an arm and either acute angle of one are equal respectively to the corresponding arm and acute angle of the other?

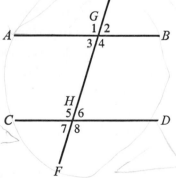

24. Are ∠1 and ∠5 corresponding angles?
25. Are ∠3 and ∠6 alternate interior angles?
26. Are ∠1 and ∠7 alternate exterior angles?
27. If ∠2 = ∠6, is AB ∥ CD?
28. If AB ∥ CD, does ∠3 = ∠6?
29. Is AB a transversal?

30. If two angles have their sides parallel, initial side to terminal side and terminal side to initial side, are they equal?

31. If two angles of a triangle are 60° and 20°, is the third angle 80°?
32. If three angles of a quadrilateral are 65°, 75°, and 110°, is the fourth angle 110°?
33. Does the sum of the exterior angles of a quadrilateral equal the sum of the interior angles?
34. Does the sum of the exterior angles of a triangle equal the sum of the interior angles?
35. If an exterior angle of a triangle is 120° and one nonadjacent interior angle is 40°, is the other nonadjacent interior angle 80°?
36. Are the opposite sides of a parallelogram equal?
37. Are the opposite angles of a parallelogram equal?
38. Do the diagonals of a parallelogram bisect each other?
39. Are the diagonals of a parallelogram equal?
40. Are the sides of a rhombus equal?
41. Are the angles of a rhombus equal?
42. If the diagonals of a parallelogram are equal, is it a rectangle?
43. Does a trapezoid have one pair of sides that are both parallel and equal?
44. Is the median of a trapezoid parallel to the bases?
45. If a line bisects two sides of a triangle, does it intersect the third side?
46. Is every point on the bisector of an angle equally distant from the sides of the angle?
47. Is every point on a line that bisects a given line segment equally distant from the end points of the segment?
48. If the hypotenuse of a right triangle is 10 inches, is the vertex of the right angle 10 inches from the mid-point of the hypotenuse?
49. If the bases of a trapezoid are 12 and 26, is the median 18?
50. Can a triangle have sides the lengths of which are 17, 23, and 41?
51. If the sides of a triangle are 5, 6, and 7, does the largest angle lie opposite the side the length of which is 6?
52. If two angles of a triangle are 50° and 60°, does the longest side of the triangle lie opposite the 60° angle?
53. Are the altitudes of a triangle concurrent?
54. Are the sides of a triangle concurrent?
55. Can a circle be circumscribed about a scalene triangle?
56. If two chords of equal circles are equal, do they have equal arcs?

57. Without measuring, state whether the left figure below is a true representation of the given measurements.

58. Without measuring, state whether the right figure is a true representation of the given measurements.

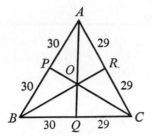
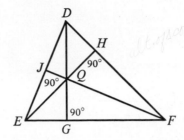

59. If two arcs of equal circles are equal, are their chords equally distant from the centers of their respective circles?

60. If two minor arcs of the same circle are unequal, is the chord of the greater arc farther from the center than the chord of the smaller arc?

COMPLETION TEST

Approximately 30 minutes

Copy on your paper the numbers of the following statements. After each number write a word, or number, or expression, which, if written in the blank, would complete the statement and make it true. If more than one blank occurs, give an expression to fill each.

1. $\angle B =$ _____ °

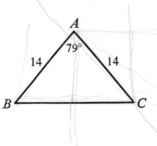

2. $GE =$ _____

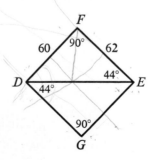

3. $\angle x =$ _____°

4. $\angle y =$ _____°

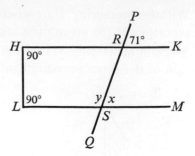

5. $\angle A =$ _____°

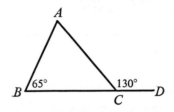

6. $\angle EFK =$ _____°

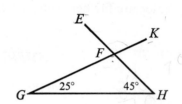

7. $PQRS$ is a parallelogram.

$OS =$ _____

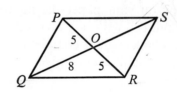

8. $XYZW$ is a parallelogram.

$\angle Y =$ _____°

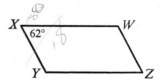

9. $ABCD$ is a parallelogram.

$AB =$ _____

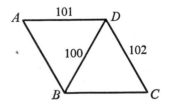

10. $x =$ _____

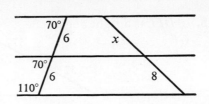

11. $AC = 48$
    $EC =$ _____

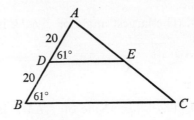

12. $\angle H =$ _____°
13. $JK =$ _____

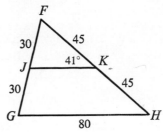

14. $RS =$ _____
15. $\angle P =$ _____°

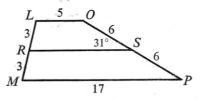

16. $x =$ _____

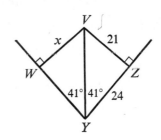

17. $AC =$ _____

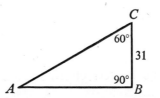

18. ∠DFE is a right angle.

GF = _____

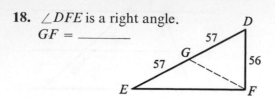

19. The largest angle of △HJK is

∠_____.

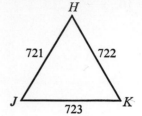

20. The longest side of △LMP is

_____.

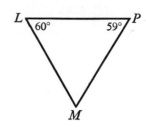

21. The greatest arc of ⊙O is

_____.

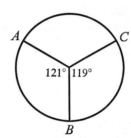

22. The largest central angle of ⊙Q is ∠_____.

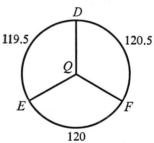

23. The shortest chord in ⊙P is

_____.

24. The longest chord in ⊙P is

_____.

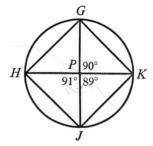

25. $AE =$ _____

26. $AD =$ _____

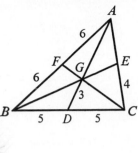

27. $\angle LJK =$ _____ °

28. $\angle HLJ =$ _____ °

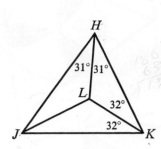

To construct a perpendicular to a line AB from a point C not on line AB.

29. With C as center and any radius greater than the distance from C to _____ draw an arc.

30. This arc intersects AB at _____ and _____.

31. With centers _____ and _____ and equal radii greater than half DE, draw arcs that intersect at F.

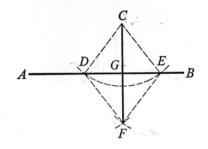

32. Draw _____.

33. Then _____ $\perp AB$.

Proof. Draw CD, CE, DF, and EF.

34. $CD =$ _____   By construction

35. $DF =$ _____   By construction

36. _____ = _____   By identity

37. $\triangle CDF \cong \triangle CEF$ _____

38. $\angle DCG = \angle$_____   c p c t e

39. $CG =$ _____   By identity

40. $\triangle DCG \cong \triangle$_____   s a s

41. $\angle DGC = \angle$_____   c p c t e

42. _____ $\perp AB$ By def. of $\perp$

CHAPTER 12

LINES THAT INTERSECT A CIRCLE

We have seen that a line may intersect a given circle in no points, one point, or two points depending upon how the distance from the center of the circle to the line compares with the radius of the circle. In this chapter, we shall study the relationships of intersecting circles, of angles formed by lines intersecting the circle, and of angles and the corresponding arcs of the circle.

12–1 Tangent A line is tangent to a circle if it intersects the circle at one and only one point. (Recall that a line is unlimited in length.) The circle is also tangent to the line. XY is tangent to $\odot O$ at Z; $\odot O$ is tangent to XY at Z.

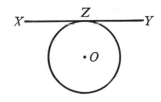

12–2 Recall that *any point less than a radius distance from the center of a circle is inside the circle, and any point more than a radius distance from the center is outside the circle.* The converse of this statement is true also. State the converse. Draw a figure to illustrate the various conditions that are mentioned here.

T is a point on $\odot C$. $XY \perp CT$ at T. V is any
point on XY other than T.

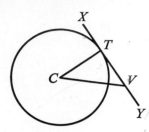

1. What kind of triangle is $\triangle CTV$? *right*
2. What is side CV of $\triangle CTV$ called?
3. Compare the length of CV with that of CT.
4. Is V inside, on, or outside $\odot C$?
   Give a reason.
5. Is XY tangent to $\odot C$? Why?

12–3 THEOREM **If a line is perpendicular to a radius at its end on the
circle, it is tangent to the circle.**

Hypothesis $\odot O$; radius OC; $AB \perp OC$ at C.

Conclusion AB is tangent to O.

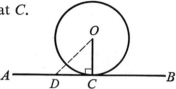

The plan is to draw from O to AB any
segment other than OC and show that it is
greater than OC.

Proof

1. Let D be any point on AB other
   than C. Draw OD.
2. $OD > OC$
3. D is outside $\odot O$.
4. $\therefore$ AB is tangent to $\odot O$ since
   any point on AB other than C is
   outside $\odot O$.

1. Give reasons.

2. Sec. 9–9
3. Sec. 12–2
4. Def. of tangent

12–4 Corollary If a line passes through a point inside a circle, it intersects the circle in two points. See Postulate 32.

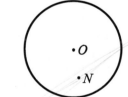

For example, the point N is inside
circle O. Then any line through N intersects the circle in two points. Illustrate this by means of a drawing.

EXERCISES

1. If a line passes through a point on a circle, can it intersect the circle
   in two points? Illustrate.
2. If a line passes through a point outside a circle, can it intersect the
   circle in two points? In one point? In no point? Illustrate.

12–5 THEOREM If a line is tangent to a circle, it is perpendicular to the radius drawn to the point of contact.

Hypothesis $\odot O$; AB is tangent to $\odot O$ at C.

Conclusion $AB \perp OC$

The plan is to draw from the center to the tangent any line segment other than the radius and prove that it is greater than the radius.

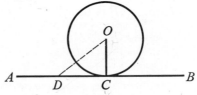

Proof

1. Let D be any point on AB other than C. Draw OD.
2. D is not on $\odot O$.
3. D is not inside $\odot O$.
4. D is outside $\odot O$.
5. $\therefore OD > OC$
6. Since any point on AB other than C is at a greater distance from O than C, $OC \perp AB$, or $AB \perp OC$.

1. Give reason.

2. Def. of a tangent
3. Sec. 12–4
4. Why?
5. Sec. 12–2
6. Sec. 9–9

12–6 Corollary If a line is perpendicular to a tangent at the point of contact, it passes through the center of the circle.

Suggestion. Draw the radius to the point of contact and show that the radius and the perpendicular coincide.

12–7 Corollary If a perpendicular is drawn from the center of a circle to a tangent, it passes through the point of contact.

EXERCISES

C. Oral

1. Is XY tangent to $\odot Z$? Why?

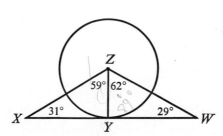

2. Is WY tangent to $\odot Z$? Why?

3. Hyp. $AB \parallel OC$;
          $\angle COD$ = a rt. $\angle$
   Con. AB is tangent to $\odot O$.

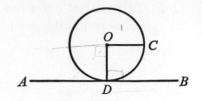

4. Hyp. MN is tangent to $\odot Q$;
          $QS \parallel MN$
   Con. $\angle Q$ = a rt. $\angle$

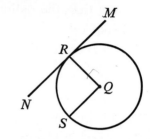

5. Hyp. AB is tangent to $\odot O$;
          $EF \parallel AB$
   Con. $\overset{\frown}{DE} = \overset{\frown}{DF}$

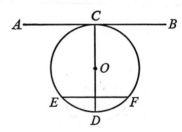

12–8 Length of a Tangent   If a line is drawn from a point outside a circle tangent to the circle, the length of the segment from the point to the point of tangency is called the <u>length of the tangent.</u>

DISCOVERY EXERCISE

Draw a circle O and from a point A outside the circle draw tangents AB and AC meeting the circle at B and C.   Does $AB = AC$?

Suggestions.   Draw AO, BO, and CO.

State your conclusions as a theorem. Compare the following theorem.

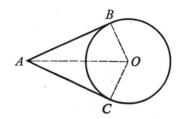

THEOREM Lengths of tangents to a circle from a common point are equal.

Hypothesis *AB* and *AC* are tangent to ⊙*O*.
Conclusion *AB* = *AC*
Give the complete proof.

12–9 Points on a line. Half-Plane. Line of Centers A point *P* is between two points *A* and *B* if it is on the segment *AB* and *AP* < *AB*. *B* is between *A* and *Q* if *AB* < *AQ*.

$$A \qquad P \quad B \quad Q$$

Recall that a line divides a plane into two half-planes having no points in common.   The line itself belongs to neither half-plane.   In the figure *α* and *β* are the half-planes. (*α*, alpha, and *β*, beta, are Greek letters.) If a point *P* in *α* is joined to a point *Q* in *β* by a line segment, the segment *PQ* meets *l* in a point *O* which is between *P* and *Q*.   However, a segment joining points *P'* and *Q'*, both in the same half-plane, never intersects the boundary line *l*.

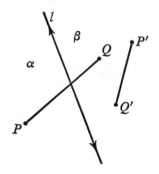

If two circles not having the same center are given in a plane, the line determined by their centers is called the line of centers.   Frequently we are concerned with the length of the segment *OO'* joining the centers of these circles. The length of this segment is also referred to as the length of the line of centers.   In the following discussions, no confusion will arise as to whether we are talking of the line or of the length of the segment joining the centers.

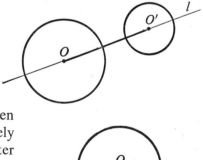

If a circle is tangent to a line *t* at *A* then the circle except for the point *A* lies entirely in that half-plane which contains the center of the circle.   In the figure, no point of the circle can lie in the half-plane *β*.   Prove this by showing that any point in *β* is more than a radius distance from *O*.

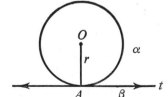

12–10   Intersecting and Tangent Circles   Using the above relations we can now determine when circles intersect and when they are tangent. In the following we assume that the circles are unequal and that radius OA of circle O is less than radius OB of circle O'. We shall also designate the radius of circle O by r and that of O' by R.

CASE 1.   The line of centers is greater than the sum of the radii. $OO' > R + r$.

$$O'A = O'B + AB$$
$$\underline{\;0 < \qquad\quad AB\;} \text{ (subtract)}$$
$$O'A > O'B$$

Let the line of centers meet circle O at A and circle O' at B. Draw t tangent to circle O at A. The computation shows that $O'A > O'B$. Hence B is between A and O' and B is in half-plane β. Every point except A of circle O is in α and every point of circle O' is in β. Hence the circles can have no points in common. They are externally nonintersecting circles.

CASE 2.   The line of centers equals the sum of the radii. $OO' = R + r$.
Subtracting r from each side of the equality we obtain $O'A = R$. Since $O'B$ is also equal to R, A and B are the same point. This is the only point the circles have in common, since all other points of O are in α, and those of O' in β. Thus:

$$OO' = R + r$$
$$\underline{\;r = \qquad\quad r\;} \text{ (subtract)}$$
$$O'A = R$$

Two circles are tangent externally when they are tangent to the same line at the same point and their centers are on opposite sides of the tangent line. The line of centers is equal to the sum of the radii.

CASE 3. The line of centers is less than the sum of the radii but greater than the difference of the radii. $R + r > OO' > R - r$. This relation will hold when OO' is greater than R, equal to R, or less than R.

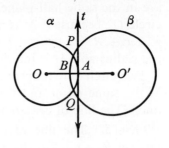

We consider first the situation in which $OO' > R$. $R = O'B$; hence B is between O and O'. Also, the computation

$$OO' < R + r$$
$$O'B = R \qquad \text{(subtract)}$$
$$\overline{OB <} \qquad r$$

shows that $OB < OA$. Then on segment OA, B is between O and A. Thus part of the circle O' is in α, and at least one part, B, is in the interior of circle O. Hence the circles intersect in two points, P and Q.

The figures for $OO' = R$ and $OO' < R$ are shown below.

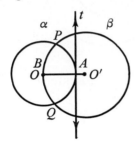 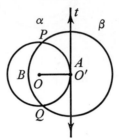

CASE 4. The line of centers is equal to the difference of the radii. $OO' = R - r$.

Let the line of centers meet circle O at A and A'. Draw the tangent t to circle O at A'. Computation shows that $O'B = O'A'$ and hence B and A' are the same point.

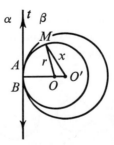

$$OO' = R - r$$
$$r = r \qquad \text{(add)}$$
$$\overline{OO' + r = R}$$

Hence both circles are tangent to t at the same point. Since the centers are in the same half-plane, every point of O except point A' is interior to circle O', because if M is any other point on circle O in $\triangle OMO'$ we have $x < r + R - r$ or $x < R$. Hence the distance of M from O' is less than the radius and M is interior to O'.

Two circles are tangent internally when they are tangent to the same line at the same point and their centers are on the same side of the tangent line. The line of centers is equal to the difference of their radii.

CASE 5. The line of centers is less than the difference of the radii. $OO' < R - r$. The figures illustrate this case and the student should prove that the circles are internally nonintersecting. If $OO' = $ zero, the circles are called concentric.

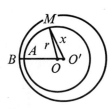
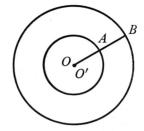

In summary:
If $OO' > R + r$ or $OO' < R - r$, the circles are nonintersecting.
If $OO' = R + r$ or $OO' = R - r$, the circles are tangent.
If $R - r < OO' < R + r$, the circles intersect in 2 points.

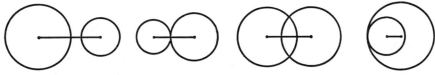

Lines of centers

12–11 Common Tangents A common internal tangent of two circles is a line that is tangent to both circles and intersects their line of centers.

A common external tangent of two circles is a line that is tangent to both circles and does not intersect their line of centers.

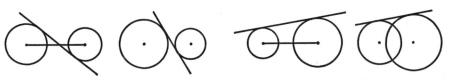

Common internal tangents   Common external tangents

EXERCISES

C. Oral

1. What is the length of the line of centers of concentric circles?
2. Can concentric circles have a common tangent?
3. Hyp. $AB \perp OB$; $AC \perp OC$
   $AC =$ _____ Why?

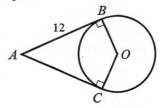

B. Written

4. Prove: If two circles are tangent externally, their line of centers passes through the point of contact.

5. Hyp. $\odot O$ and $\odot Q$ are externally tangent at T. PR is tangent to $\odot Q$, and PS is tangent to $\odot O$. PT is tangent to $\odot O$ and to $\odot Q$.

   Con. $PR = PS$

NOTE: The line PT is the radical axis of $\odot O$ and $\odot Q$. See Ex. 13 and 14 on pages 401, 402.

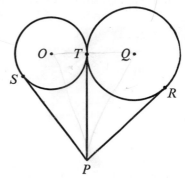

6. $\odot$s A, B, and C are externally tangent. $AB = 12$, $BC = 11$, $AC = 10$. Find the radius of each circle.

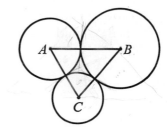

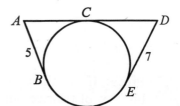

7. AB, AD, and DE are tangents. Find AD.

8. In the figure the sides of the quadrilateral are tangent to the circle. Prove: The sum of one pair of opposite sides equals the sum of the other pair.

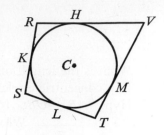

9. Prove: If two circles are externally tangent, their common internal tangent bisects their common external tangent.

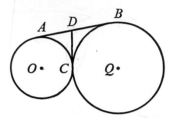

10. Hyp.   *H* and *K* are externally tangent at *E*.   *FG* is a common external tangent.   *EF* and *EG* are drawn.

   Con. $\angle FEG$ = a rt. $\angle$.

   Hint: Consider the common internal tangent.

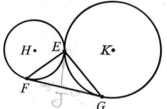

11. Prove: If two circles are externally tangent, their common internal tangent intercepted by a common external tangent equals one half the common external tangent.

12. Prove: The common internal tangents of two circles are equal; and their common external tangents are equal.

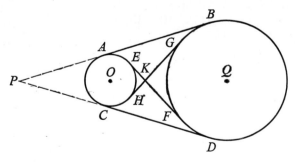

13. Prove: If two circles intersect, their line of centers is the perpendicular bisector of their common chord.

14. Prove: If two circles are externally tangent and a line segment is drawn through their point of contact and terminated by the circles, the diameters drawn through the ends of the segment are parallel.

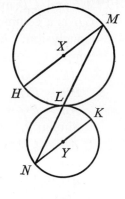

15. Hyp. △ABC is circumscribed about ⊙O.
    $AB = 7$; $AC = 8$;
    $BC = 9$
    Find AD, BD, CE.

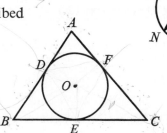

16. Hyp. $FG \parallel HJ$. FG, FH, and HJ are tangent to circle Q.
    Con. ∠FQH is a rt. ∠.

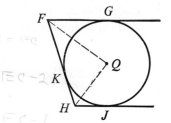

17. Hyp. PX and PY are tangent to ⊙Q. QX and XY are drawn.
    Con. $\angle P = 2\angle QXY$

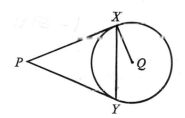

18. Prove: The common external tangents of two unequal circles with the chords that connect the points of tangency form an isosceles trapezoid.

Suggestions.
    $\angle OAB = \angle OCD$
    $\angle OAC = \angle OCA$
    $\angle CAB = \angle ACD$

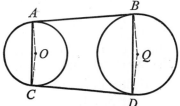

19. *AB* and *CD* are common external tangents of $\odot O$ and $\odot Q$, and *GH* is a common internal tangent.

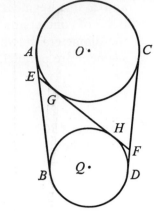

Conclusion. $EG = FH$

Supply reasons for the proof given below.

$AE = EG$

$EB = EH$

$AB = EG + EH$

Similarly, $CD = FH + FG$

$AB = CD$ (See Ex. 12.)

$EG + EH = FH + FG$

$EG + EG + GH = FH + FH + GH$

$2EG = 2FH$

$EG = FH$

20. Prove: The extensions of the common external tangents of two unequal circles and their line of centers are concurrent.

Suggestions. Is O equally distant from *PB* and *PD*? Is Q equally distant from *PB* and *PD*? On what line do O and Q lie?

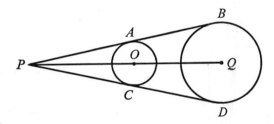

21. Prove: The line of centers of two unequal circles extended is the perpendicular bisector of the bases of the isosceles trapezoid formed by the common external tangents and the chords that connect the points of tangency.

Proof. Extend *AB*, *CD*, and *OQ* to intersect at *P*. (See Ex. 20.) Draw *AO*, *CO*, *BQ*, *DQ*. Then *OP* is the $\perp$ bisector of *BD* (Sec. 8–13). Complete the proof.

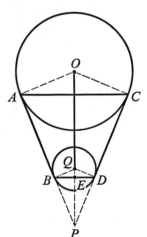

298   **GEOMETRY**

22. Prove: The common internal tangents of two unequal circles and their line of centers are concurrent.

23. Construct a line tangent to a given circle and parallel to a given line.
24. Construct a line tangent to a given circle and perpendicular to a given line.

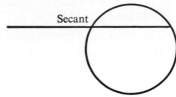
Secant

12–12 Secant A secant is a line that intersects a circle in two points.

DISCOVERY EXERCISES

ZW is tangent to $\odot P$ at V. XY is a secant that is parallel to ZW. Does $\overset{\frown}{VN} = \overset{\frown}{VT}$? Prove your answer. If you need help in doing this, do the following exercises.

1. What is the relation of PV to ZW? Why?
2. What is the relation of PR to XY? Why?
3. What is the relation of $\overset{\frown}{VN}$ to $\overset{\frown}{VT}$? Why?

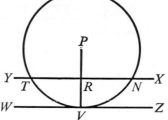

12–13 THEOREM If two parallel lines intersect a circle or are tangent to it, they intercept equal arcs.

CASE 1. One line is a tangent and one is a secant.

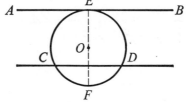

Hypothesis $\odot O$; AB is tangent at E; CD is a secant; $AB \parallel CD$

Conclusion $\overset{\frown}{CE} = \overset{\frown}{DE}$

The plan is to draw a diameter through the point of tangency and show that an arc intercepted by the secant is bisected.

Proof

1. Draw diameter EF.
2. $EF \perp AB$
3. $EF \perp CD$
4. $\therefore \overset{\frown}{CE} = \overset{\frown}{DE}$

1. Give reason.
2. Sec. 12–5
3. Why?
4. Sec. 11–19

CASE 2. Both lines are tangents.

Hypothesis $\odot Q$; *GH* and *KL* are tangent to $\odot Q$ at *M* and *N* respectively; *GH* ∥ *KL*

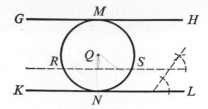

Conclusion $\overset{\frown}{MRN} = \overset{\frown}{MSN}$

The plan is to construct a secant parallel to *KL* and use Case 1.

Proof

1. Construct *RS* ∥ *KL*.
2. *RS* ∥ *GH*
3. $\overset{\frown}{RM} = \overset{\frown}{SM}$; $\overset{\frown}{RN} = \overset{\frown}{SN}$
4. ∴ $\overset{\frown}{MRN} = \overset{\frown}{MSN}$

1. Give reason.
2. Why?
3. Case 1
4. Why?

CASE 3. Both lines are secants.

Hypothesis $\odot P$; *TZ* and *VW* are secants; *TZ* ∥ *VW*

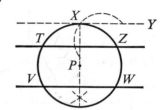

Conclusion $\overset{\frown}{TV} = \overset{\frown}{ZW}$

The plan is to construct a diameter perpendicular to one of the secants, and construct a line perpendicular to the diameter at one end, then use Case 1.

Proof

1. Construct *PX* ⊥ *TZ*.
   Construct *XY* ⊥ *PX* at *X*.
2. *XY* is tangent to *P*.
3. $\overset{\frown}{VX} = \overset{\frown}{WX}$; $\overset{\frown}{TX} = \overset{\frown}{ZX}$
4. ∴ $\overset{\frown}{TV} = \overset{\frown}{ZW}$

1. Give reasons.

2. Sec. 12–3
3. Why?
4. Why?

EXERCISES

C. Oral

1. Hyp. *AB* ∥ *CD* ∥ *EF* ∥ *GH*
   $\overset{\frown}{IJ} = \underline{\hspace{1cm}}$ $\overset{\frown}{KM} = \underline{\hspace{1cm}}$
   $\overset{\frown}{IKMN} = \underline{\hspace{1cm}}$ Why?

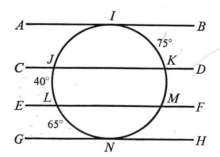

B. Written

2. Prove: An inscribed trapezoid is isosceles.
3. Prove: The diagonals of an inscribed trapezoid are equal.
4. Hyp. *PQRS* is a trapezoid.
    Con. $\angle POR = \angle QOS$
5. Hyp. $AB \parallel CD$; *AB* is tangent to the circle at *E*; *CE* and *DE* are drawn.
    Con. $\triangle CDE$ is isosceles.

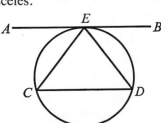

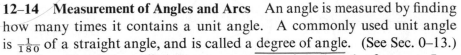

12–14 Measurement of Angles and Arcs An angle is measured by finding how many times it contains a unit angle. A commonly used unit angle is $\frac{1}{180}$ of a straight angle, and is called a <u>degree of angle</u>. (See Sec. 0–13.)

In Sec. 11–14 we studied the measurement of the length of an arc. In a given circle, we also measured an arc by using a <u>degree of arc</u>, which is $\frac{1}{360}$ of the circumference of the circle.

Since equal central angles have equal arcs, a central angle of 1° intercepts an arc of 1°, and a central angle of 5° 42′ 12″ intercepts an arc of 5° 42′ 12″, etc. The axioms of addition, subtraction, multiplication, division, and substitution apply to arcs and angles.

12–15 The number of degrees in a central angle is equal to the number of degrees in its intercepted arc, or, briefly, a central angle is measured by its intercepted arc. This follows from consideration of Sec. 12–14.

The symbol used for "arc *AB* is equal in degrees to angle *AOB*" is $\overset{\frown}{AB} \overset{\circ}{=} \angle AOB$.

12–16 Consider an arc of a circle. An angle with vertex on the arc and whose sides contain the end points of the arc is said to be <u>inscribed</u> in the arc. The other arc of the circle is said to be <u>intercepted</u> by the angle.

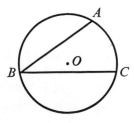

In the figure, $\angle ABC$ is inscribed in arc *ABC* and intercepts arc *AC*.

Draw a circle O and draw a diameter BC. Draw a chord AB. Draw AO. Compare $\angle A$ and $\angle B$. Compare $\angle AOC$ and the sum of $\angle A$ and $\angle B$. Compare $\angle B$ and $\angle AOC$. Compare $\angle AOC$ and $\overset{\frown}{AC}$. Compare $\angle B$ and $\overset{\frown}{AC}$. Can you state a theorem regarding the relation of $\angle B$ and $\overset{\frown}{AC}$? Compare your theorem with that of Sec. 12–17.

12–17 THEOREM An inscribed angle is one half of a central angle having the same intercepted arc.

Hypothesis $\odot O$; $\angle CBA$ inscribed; $\angle AOC$ a central angle; intercepted arc AC.

Conclusion $\angle CBA = \frac{1}{2} \angle COA$

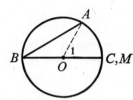 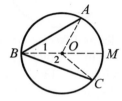 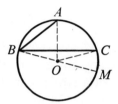

Proof

1. Draw the diameter BM.	1. Give reason.
2. $AO = BO$; $\angle OBA = \angle OAB$	2. Why?
3. $\angle MOA = \angle OBA + \angle OAB$	3. Why?
4. $2\angle OBA = \angle MOA$	4. Subst.
5. $\angle OBA = \frac{1}{2}\angle MOA$	5. $=$s $\div$ $=$s
6. $\angle OBC = \frac{1}{2}\angle MOC$	6. Steps 1 to 5
7. $\angle CBA = \frac{1}{2}\angle COA$	7. Post. 5 or 6

NOTE: In the first figure $\angle OBC$ and $\angle MOC$ are zero.

12–18 Corollary An inscribed angle is measured by one half of its intercepted arc.

12–19 Corollary An angle inscribed in a semicircle is a right angle.

12–20 Corollary If inscribed angles intercept the same or equal arcs, they are equal.

If an angle is inscribed in an arc that is less than a semicircle, what kind of angle is it? Prove your answer.

EXERCISES

C. Oral

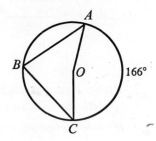

1. ∠O = _____° Why?
   ∠B = _____° Why?

2. $\overset{\frown}{PR}$ = _____° Why?

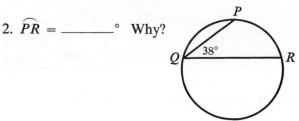

3. ∠D = _____° Why?

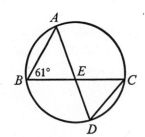

B. Written

4. $\overset{\frown}{MN}$ = _____° Why?

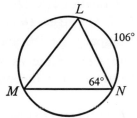

5. $\overset{\frown}{EH}$ = _____° Prove.

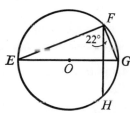

6. Hyp. PR ∥ ST
   ∠PQR = _____° Prove.

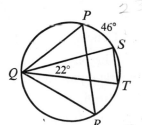

7. Hyp. AB ∥ CD
   ∠E = _____° Prove.

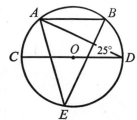

8. *ABCD* is a trapezoid.
   ∠*ABD* = _____° Prove.

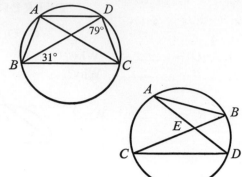

9. Prove that for each angle of
   △*ABE* there is an equal angle
   in △*CDE*.

10. Prove: The opposite angles of an inscribed
    quadrilateral are supplementary.
11. Prove the second construction in Sec. 1–5.

DISCOVERY EXERCISE

Draw a circle *O*. Draw *AB* tangent to the circle at *C*. Draw chord
CD. Construct *DE*, a chord parallel to *AB*. Compare ∠*ACD* and ∠*CDE*.
Compare ∠*CDE* and $\overset{\frown}{CE}$. Compare ∠*ACD* and $\overset{\frown}{CD}$. Compare $\overset{\frown}{CE}$
and $\overset{\frown}{CD}$. State as a theorem the relation between ∠*ACD* and $\overset{\frown}{CD}$.
Compare your theorem with that of Sec. 12–21.

**12–21   THEOREM   The angle formed by a tangent and a chord drawn
to the point of contact is measured by one half its intercepted arc.**

> **Hypothesis**   ⊙*O*; *AB* is tangent to ⊙*O* at *C*;
>   chord *CD*
>
> **Conclusion** $\angle ACD \overset{\circ}{=} \frac{1}{2}\overset{\frown}{CD}$

The plan is to construct an inscribed
angle equal to the given angle.

Proof

1. Construct ∠*CDE* = ∠*ACD*.
2. ∠*ACD* = ∠*CDE*
3. *AB* ∥ *DE*
4. $\overset{\frown}{CD} = \overset{\frown}{CE}$
5. $\angle CDE \overset{\circ}{=} \frac{1}{2}\overset{\frown}{CE}$
6. ∴ $\angle ACD \overset{\circ}{=} \frac{1}{2}\overset{\frown}{CD}$

1. Give reason.
2. Why?
3. Why?
4. Sec. 12–13
5. Sec. 12–18
6. Post 2

12–22 THEOREM An angle formed by two chords that intersect inside a circle is measured by one half the sum of the arcs intercepted by it and by its vertical angle.

Hypothesis $\odot O$; AB and CD are intersecting chords.

Conclusion $\angle 1 \stackrel{\circ}{=} \frac{1}{2}(\widehat{AD} + \widehat{BC})$

Proof

1. Draw DB.   1. Give reason.
2. $\angle 1 = \angle B + \angle D$ 2. Why?
3. $\angle D \stackrel{\circ}{=} \frac{1}{2}\widehat{BC}$; $\angle B \stackrel{\circ}{=} \frac{1}{2}\widehat{AD}$ 3. Why?
4. $\angle 1 \stackrel{\circ}{=} \frac{1}{2}(\widehat{AD} + \widehat{BC})$ 4. Why?

12–23 THEOREM An angle formed by two lines that intersect a circle and intersect each other in the exterior of the circle is measured by half the difference of the intercepted arcs.

Hypothesis $\angle P$ with sides either tangent or secant to circle O, intersecting $\odot O$ and intercepting $\widehat{AXC}$ and $\widehat{DYB}$

Conclusion $\angle P \stackrel{\circ}{=} \frac{1}{2}(\widehat{AXC} - \widehat{DYB})$

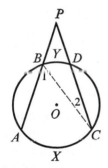 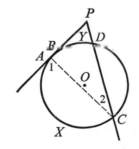 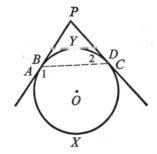

Proof

1. Draw chord BC.   1. Give reason.
2. $\angle 1 = \angle P + \angle 2$ 2. Ext. $\angle$ of a $\triangle$
3. $\angle P = \angle 1 - \angle 2$ 3. Subtraction
4. $\angle 1 \stackrel{\circ}{=} \frac{1}{2}\widehat{AXC}$; $\angle 2 \stackrel{\circ}{=} \frac{1}{2}\widehat{DYB}$ 4. Why?
5. $\angle P \stackrel{\circ}{=} \frac{1}{2}(\widehat{AXC} - \widehat{DYB})$ 5. Why?

12–24 Positive and Negative Arcs

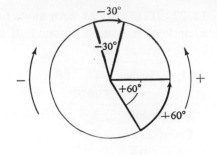

On a straight line we have a number scale by taking one point as zero and measuring the distances to the right as positive and those to the left as negative. In a similar way we can agree that on a circle arcs measured counterclockwise are positive, and those measured clockwise are negative.

In the figures below, a pair of intersecting lines meet a circle. The lines may be either both secants, or a tangent and a secant, or both tangents to the circle.

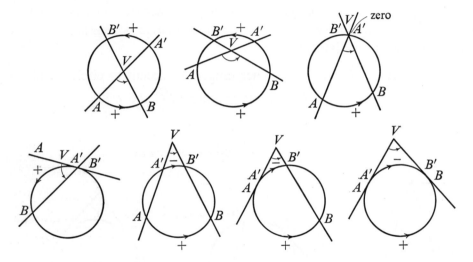

In each figure the intersection points of the two lines with the circle are lettered A and A', and B and B', and the point of intersection of the two lines is V. We consider the angle AVB and the arcs intercepted on the circle by the lines containing the rays of angle AVB. The positive and negative directions of the arcs are indicated. When V is on the circle, one of the intercepted arcs is zero. The positive direction of the angle is also indicated. Show that in every figure the following formula holds.

$$\angle AVB \overset{\circ}{=} \tfrac{1}{2}(\overset{\frown}{AB} + \overset{\frown}{A'B'})$$

Modern mathematics is concerned with the search for patterns. This section shows one such pattern.

WRITTEN EXERCISES

B.

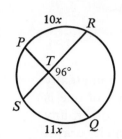

1. $DE \parallel AB$
$\overparen{DE} = $ _____°
Prove.

2. $\overparen{RP} = $ _____°
$\overparen{SQ} = $ _____°
Prove.

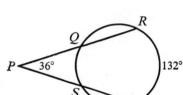

3. $\angle A = $ _____°
Prove.

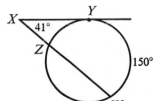

4. $\overparen{QS} = $ _____°
Why?

5. $\overparen{BD} = $ _____°
$\overparen{EC} = $ _____°
Why?

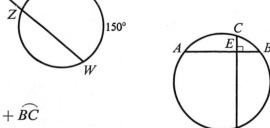

6. $\overparen{YZ} = $ _____°
Why?

7. Prove: $\overparen{CA} + \overparen{DB} = \overparen{AD} + \overparen{BC}$

8. Prove: The chords that join the ends of two intersecting diameters form a rectangle.

9. Equal circles intersect at *P* and *Q*.
   RS is any segment through *P* terminated by the circles. *QR* and *QS*
   are drawn.
   Con. *QR = QS*

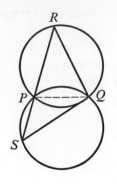

10. Prove: If two circles are internally
    tangent and the diameter of one is
    half the diameter of the other, any
    chord of the larger circle drawn
    through the point of tangency is bi-
    sected by the smaller circle. Use
    Sec. 8–3.

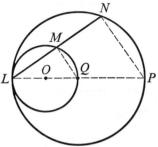

11. Hyp. *AE = CF*
    Con. $\angle A = \frac{1}{3} \angle DCF$

    NOTE: *Trisection of an angle.*

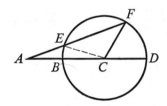

One of the three famous problems of ancient times was the attempt to
divide an angle into three equal parts using only a pair of compasses and
an unmarked straightedge. The problem seems so simple that many
people still try it, hopefully expecting to find a solution. Nearly every
year the newspapers print stories about people who claim to have solved
the problem. It has now been absolutely proved impossible to trisect
an angle by use of compasses and straightedge only. This proof is
given in college books on theory of equations. Of course, if other tools
are permitted, the construction is easily accomplished.

In this exercise you will note that no suggestion is made as to how angle
A is obtained. You can readily figure out how to get it, but notice that
you have to mark the straightedge, which is not permitted in our geometry.
This method was suggested by Archimedes more than two thousand years
ago, but he knew that the method was not admissible in our geometry.

12. *The Tomahawk Trisector.* This figure shows an instrument which can be used to trisect any angle. Note that it is neither compasses nor straightedge, and so cannot be admitted as a tool in our geometry. *BD* is a diameter of the semicircle of which *C* is the center, *AB* is equal to a radius, and *EF* is the perpendicular bisector of *AC*. Suppose angle *XYZ* is to be trisected. The tomahawk is placed so 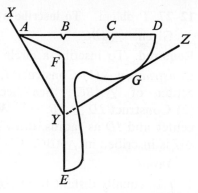 that the point *A* is on one side of the angle, *FE* passes through the vertex, and the semicircle is tangent to the other side of the angle. Mark the points *B* and *C*, lift the tomahawk, and connect these points with the vertex. These lines trisect the angle. Prove this.

13. Prove: If a circle is drawn with one of the equal sides of an isosceles triangle as diameter, it bisects the base.

14. Prove: Circles drawn with any two sides of a triangle as diameters intersect on the third side.

12–25   Problem   To bisect an arc.

Given $\overset{\frown}{AB}$ with center *O*.

Required   To bisect $\overset{\frown}{AB}$.

Construction.   (1) With *A* and *B* as centers and any radius longer than half the chord *AB*, draw arcs intersecting at *C*   (2) Draw *OC* intersecting $\overset{\frown}{AB}$ at *D*. Then $\overset{\frown}{AD} = \overset{\frown}{DB}$.

Proof

1. $\angle 1 = \angle 2$	1. Why?
2. $\therefore \overset{\frown}{AD} = \overset{\frown}{DB}$	2. Post. 33

12–26   Inscribed Circle.   Circumscribed Polygon   A circle is inscribed in a polygon if it is tangent to each side of the polygon. The polygon is circumscribed about the circle.

DISCOVERY EXERCISE

Draw any triangle and construct its incenter. Draw a circle that is tangent to each side of the triangle. What is its radius? (See page 228.)

12–27 Problem   To inscribe a circle in a triangle.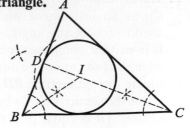

Given   △ABC

Required   To inscribe a circle in △ABC

Construction.   (1) Construct *I*, the incenter of △ABC.   See Sec. 10–2. (2) Construct *ID* ⊥ *AB*. (3) With *I* as center and *ID* as radius, draw a circle. ⊙*I* is inscribed in △ABC.

Proof

1. *I* is equally distant from *AB*, *AC*, and *BC*.   1. Sec. 10–2
2. *AB*, *AC*, and *BC* are tangent to ⊙*I*.   2. Sec. 12–3
3. Hence ⊙*I* is inscribed in △ABC.   3. Sec. 12–26

WRITTEN EXERCISES

1. Inscribe a circle in an obtuse triangle.
2. Inscribe a circle in a right triangle.
3. Prove: If a circle is inscribed in a right triangle, the vertex of the right angle, the center of the circle, and the points at which the sides of the right angle are tangent to the circle are vertices of a square.
4. Construct a circle that is tangent to one side of a triangle and to the other two sides extended.   (This circle is called an escribed circle of the triangle.   How many escribed circles does a triangle have?   Are they equal?)

DISCOVERY EXERCISE

Read again Sec. 12–3.   Use the fact proved there to construct a tangent to a circle at a point on the circle.

12–28 Problem   To construct the tangent to a circle at a point on the circle.

Given   ⊙*O*; *A* is a point on ⊙*O*.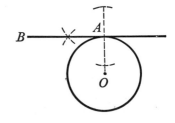

Required   To construct a tangent to ⊙*O* at *A*.

Construction.   (1) Draw *AO*.   (2) At *A* construct *AB* ⊥ *AO*.   *AB* is tangent to ⊙*O*.   Why?

12–29 Problem   To construct tangents to a circle from a point outside the circle.

> **Given** $\odot O$; A is a point outside $\odot O$.
>
> **Required**   To construct tangents to $\odot O$ from A.

Construction. (1) Draw AO. (2) On AO as diameter, construct a circle that intersects $\odot O$ at B and C. (3) Draw AB and AC. These lines are tangent to $\odot O$. Draw BO and CO.

Proof

1. $\angle ABO$ = a rt. $\angle$, and $\angle ACO$ = a rt. $\angle$	1. Sec. 12–19
2. $\therefore$ AB and AC are tangent to $\odot O$.	2. Sec. 12–3

MISCELLANEOUS WRITTEN EXERCISES

A.

1. Two circles are externally tangent at E. Through E the line segments AB and CD are drawn terminated by the circles. Prove $AC \parallel BD$.

2. Two circles intersect at F and K. The line GH is a common external tangent. Prove $\angle GFH \parallel \angle GKH$ = a st. $\angle$.

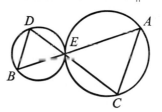

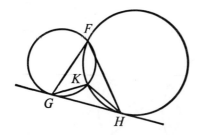

3. MN and PQ are line segments drawn through the points of intersection of two circles and terminated by the circles. Prove $MP \parallel NQ$.

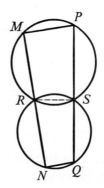

4. Prove: If perpendiculars are drawn to a tangent from the ends of a diameter, the sum of the perpendiculars equals the diameter.

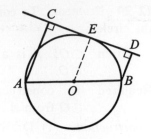

5. Hyp. GH ∥ JK
   Con. FG = FH

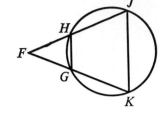

6. Prove: If a chord and a tangent are drawn from a point on a circle, the perpendiculars to them from the mid-point of their intercepted arc are equal.

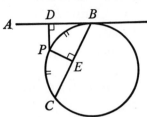

7. Prove: If one arm of a right triangle is the diameter of a circle, the other arm is bisected by the tangent drawn at the point where the circle intersects the hypotenuse.

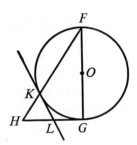

8. Through one of the points of intersection of two circles, a diameter of each circle is drawn. Prove the line connecting the ends of the diameters passes through the other point of intersection of the circles.

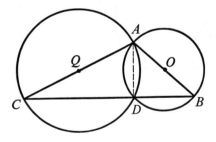

9. Construct a line tangent to a given circle and making a given angle with a given line.

10. The bisectors of the angles formed by the opposite sides (extended) of an inscribed quadilateral intersect at right angles.

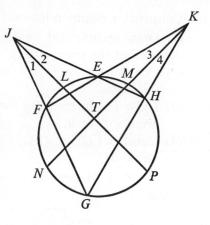

Suggestions. $\angle 1 \overset{\circ}{=} \tfrac{1}{2}(\overset{\frown}{GP} - \overset{\frown}{LF})$. $\angle 2 \overset{\circ}{=} \tfrac{1}{2}(\overset{\frown}{PH} - \overset{\frown}{EL})$. $\overset{\frown}{GP} - \overset{\frown}{LF} = \overset{\frown}{PH} - \overset{\frown}{EL}$. Likewise, $\overset{\frown}{NG} - \overset{\frown}{HM} = \overset{\frown}{FN} - \overset{\frown}{ME}$. Adding: $\overset{\frown}{GP} + \overset{\frown}{NG} - \overset{\frown}{HM} - \overset{\frown}{LF} = \overset{\frown}{PH} + \overset{\frown}{FN} - \overset{\frown}{EL} - \overset{\frown}{ME}$, or $\overset{\frown}{GP} + \overset{\frown}{NG} + \overset{\frown}{EL} + \overset{\frown}{ME} = \overset{\frown}{PH} + \overset{\frown}{HM} + \overset{\frown}{FN} + \overset{\frown}{LF}$. This gives $\overset{\frown}{PN} + \overset{\frown}{LM} = \overset{\frown}{PM} + \overset{\frown}{LN}$. But $\angle PTN \overset{\circ}{=} \tfrac{1}{2}(\overset{\frown}{PN} + \overset{\frown}{LM})$, and $\angle LTN \overset{\circ}{=} \tfrac{1}{2}(\overset{\frown}{PM} + \overset{\frown}{LN})$. Etc.

11. Construct a circle concentric to a given circle and tangent to a given chord of the given circle.

12. Construct a circle having a given radius and tangent to the sides of a given angle.

13. Using some round object draw a circle; then construct a tangent to the circle at a given point on it without locating the center of the circle.

14. Construct a circle tangent to a given arc of a circle and to the sides of the central angle of the arc.

15. Construct a circle tangent to a given line at a given point and passing through a given point not on the line.

16. Construct a circle with a given radius tangent to a given circle and to a given line.

17. Construct a circle with a given radius tangent to two given circles.

18. Construct a common external tangent of two unequal circles.

(1) Draw a circle with center Q and radius equal to the difference of the radii of the given circles.

(2) Construct OA tangent to this circle.

(3) Draw QA intersecting the given $\odot Q$ at B.

(4) Construct $OC \perp OA$.

(5) Draw CB.

Prove CB is tangent to each circle.

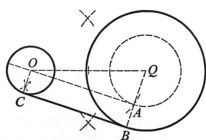

19. Construct a common internal tangent of two circles.

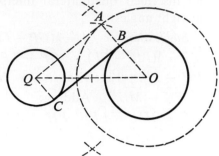

(1) Draw a circle with center O and radius equal to the sum of the radii of the given circles.
(2) Construct QA tangent to this circle.
(3) Draw OA intersecting the given $\odot O$ at B.
(4) Construct $QC \perp QA$.
(5) Draw BC.

Prove BC is tangent to each circle.

OUTLINE OF CHAPTER 12

This chapter introduces the following terms:

tangent line	secant
tangent circles	degree of angle
internally tangent	degree of arc
externally tangent	inscribed angle
line of centers	inscribed circle
common tangent	circumscribed polygon
common internal tangent	escribed circle
common external tangent	

This chapter presents information concerning:

1. The relation between a circle and a line perpendicular to a radius at its end on the circle.   Page 288
2. The relation between a tangent and the radius drawn to the point of contact.   Page 289
3. The relation between the tangents to a circle from an outside point. Page 291
4. The relation between arcs intercepted by parallel lines.   Page 299
5. The relation between an inscribed angle and its arc.   Page 302
6. The relation between the angle formed by a tangent and chord and the intercepted arc.   Page 304
7. The relation between the angle formed by two chords intersecting inside a circle and the intercepted arcs.   Page 305

8. The relation between the angle formed by two secants and the intercepted arcs. Page 305

9. The relation between the angle formed by a secant and a tangent and the intercepted arcs. Page 305

10. Positive and negative arcs. Page 306

11. The method of bisecting an arc. Page 309

12. The method of inscribing a circle in a triangle. Page 310

13. The method of constructing a tangent to a circle at a point on the circle. Page 310

14. The method of constructing tangents to a circle from a point outside the circle. Page 311

REVIEW

1. What is a tangent? Illustrate.

2. Draw a circle and construct a tangent to it at a certain point on the circle. Describe the steps in the construction. Prove that the constructed line is tangent to the circle.

3. *P* is a point on circle *O*. *S* is a point outside the circle. *PO*, *PS*, and *OS* are drawn. $\angle S = 59°$, $\angle O = 31°$. Is *PS* tangent to the circle? Why?

4. *AB* and *AC* are each tangent to circle *Q*. $AB = 1.5$ inches. How long is *AC*? Why?

5. *HL* and *JK* are parallel chords of a circle. $\overset{\frown}{TH} - 36°$. How many degrees are in $\overset{\frown}{LK}$?

6. *AB* is tangent to circle *M* at *C*. *DE* is a chord that is parallel to *AB*. $\overset{\frown}{CD} = 48°$. How many degrees arc in $\overset{\frown}{EC}$?

7. $\angle ABC$ is inscribed in a circle. $\overset{\frown}{AC} = 64°$. How many degrees are in $\angle ABC$? Why?

8. $\angle RST$ is inscribed in a circle. It has 28°. How many degrees are in $\overset{\frown}{RT}$? Give a reason for your answer.

9. *TM* is a straight line tangent to a circle at *Q*, and *QV* is a chord. Minor arc *QV* has 138°. How many degrees are in $\angle TQV$? Give a reason for your answer.

10. *P* is a point outside circle *O*. *PQR* and *PST* are secants. $\overset{\frown}{QS} = 38°$, and $\overset{\frown}{RT} = 104°$. How many degrees has $\angle RPT$?

11. *M* is a point outside circle *C*. *MX* and *MY* are tangents. Minor arc *XY* has 100°. How many degrees has ∠*XMY*? Why?

12. Draw a scalene triangle and construct its inscribed circle. Explain the steps.

13. Bisect an arc of a circle, describe the process, and prove that the arc is bisected.

14. Construct tangents to a given circle from a point outside the circle, describe the steps, and prove that the lines are tangent to the circle.

15. △*ABC* is inscribed in a circle. ∠*A* has 41°, ∠*B* has 69°. Find the number of degrees in each arc of the circle.

YES–NO TEST

Approximately 10 minutes

Copy on your paper the numbers of the following questions. If the answer to a question is *yes* under all conditions, place a plus sign (+) after its number. If the answer is *not yes* under all conditions, place a zero (0) after its number.

1. If a line is tangent to a circle, is the circle tangent to the line?

2. If a line is perpendicular to a radius, is it tangent to the circle?

3. Are the tangents to a circle from the same point equal?

4. If the distance between the centers of two circles equals the sum of their radii, are the circles tangent to each other?

5. If two circles are tangent to the same line, are they tangent to each other?

6. If two parallel secants intercept one arc of 89°, is the other intercepted arc 91°?

7. Is a central angle equal in degrees to its arc?

8. Is an inscribed angle equal in degrees to its arc?

9. Is an angle that is formed by two chords that intersect inside the circle measured by the sum of its intercepted arc and that of its vertical angle?

10. If an inscribed angle is 20°, is its intercepted arc 10°?

11. If the arc intercepted by a tangent and the chord drawn to the point of contact is 68°, is the angle 34°?

12. If the arcs intercepted by two intersecting secants are 72° and 28° respectively, is the angle 100°?

COMPLETION TEST

Approximately 25 minutes

Copy on your paper the numbers of the following statements. After each number write a word, or letters, or a number, or an expression which, if written in the blank, would complete the statement and make it true. If more than one blank occurs, give expressions to fill both.

1. A line that touches a circle at only one point, however far the line may be extended, is a ———.

2. A line of unlimited length which intersects a circle in two points is a ———.

3. An angle the vertex of which is on the circumference of a circle and the sides of which are chords is an ——— angle.

4. ——— is tangent to circle O.

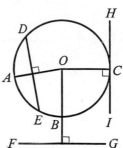

5. MN is tangent to circle Q.
   $\angle QMN$ is a ——— angle.

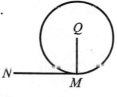

6. AB and AC are tangent to circle O. The length of AC is ———.

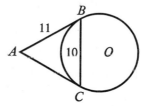

7. The sides of $\triangle LMN$ are tangent to circle Q.
   $LM + MN + LN =$ ———.

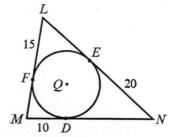

8. *PQRS* is a parallelogram.

$\widehat{ZW}$ = _____°

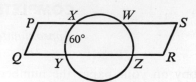

9. $\widehat{BD}$ = _____°
10. $\angle ABC$ = _____°

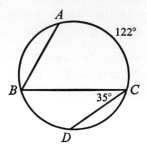

11. $\widehat{QR}$ = _____°

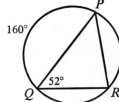

12. *AC* is tangent to $\odot O$ at *B*.

$\angle DBC$ = _____°

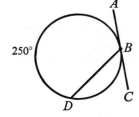

13. $\angle R$ = _____°

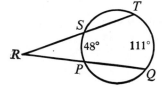

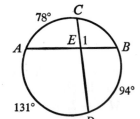

14. $\angle 1$ = _____°

To bisect a given arc *GH*, the center of which is *K*.

15. With centers _____ and _____ and any radius longer than one half *GH*, draw arcs intersecting at *L*.

16. Draw _____.

17. ⌒ = ⌒

Proof. Draw *GL, HL, GK,* and *HK*.

18. *GL* = _____ By construction

19. *HK* = _____ Radii of same ⊙

20. _____ = _____ By identity

21. △_____ ≅ △_____ s s s

22. ∠*x* = ∠_____ c p c t e

23. ⌒ = ⌒ Equal central angles of the same circle have equal arcs.

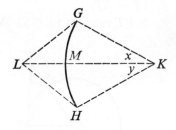

SUPPLEMENTARY EXERCISES

C.

1. Is *AB* tangent to ⊙*C*? Why?

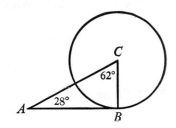

2. Is *DE* tangent to ⊙*F*? Why?

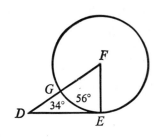

B.

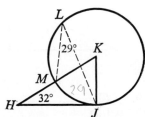

3. Is *HJ* tangent to ⊙*K*? Why?

4. Major arc $PR = 308°$. Is PQ tangent to $\odot O$? Why?

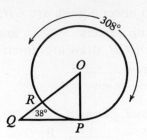

5. $XT = ST$
Is VT tangent to $\odot S$? Why?

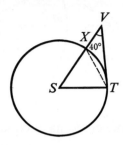

6. AB is tangent to C. $\angle DBA = 28°$
$\angle C =$ _____°
$\angle A =$ _____° Why?

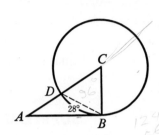

7. Is EF tangent to $\odot G$?
Why?

8. PQ is tangent to $\odot O$.
$\angle S =$ _____°
Why?

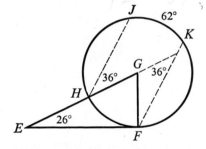

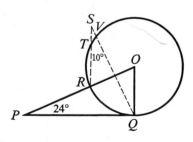

9. $\angle C =$ _____°
Why?

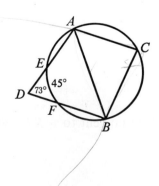

10. ∠P = _____°
Why?

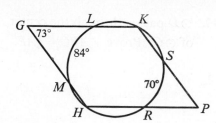

11. ∠1 = _____°
Why?

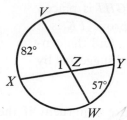

12. $\overarc{BC}$ = _____°
Why?

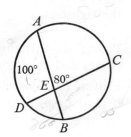

13. Hyp. FG ∥ HK
Con. $\overarc{FH}$ = $\overarc{GK}$

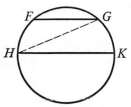

14. T is any point on $\overarc{RM}$.
Prove: ∠1 = ∠2

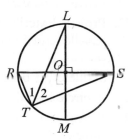

15. Hyp. XW = WZ
Con. XY = YZ

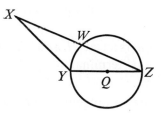

16. Hyp. FJ and JH are tangents.
Con. ∠GFJ + ∠GKJ = 3 rt. ∠s.

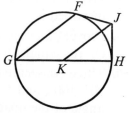

17. $\odot D$ passes through the center of $\odot C$. Prove $\angle ABC \overset{\circ}{=} \frac{1}{4}\widehat{AE}$.

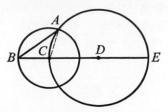

18. If a rectangular card $EGHJ$ is placed on a circle as shown, prove FK is a diameter. Show how to find the center of a circle by a method suggested by this figure.

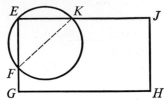

19. Prove: Two triangles are congruent if they are inscribed in equal circles and have corresponding angles equal.

20. Prove: Two isosceles triangles inscribed in equal circles are congruent if their bases are equal and if the center of each circle is inside the triangle.

21. Prove: Two isosceles triangles inscribed in equal circles are congruent if their bases are equal and if the center of each circle is outside the triangle.

22. Prove: Isosceles right triangles inscribed in equal circles are congruent.

23. Prove: Exterior segments of secants formed by extending two non-parallel equal chords of a circle until they meet are equal.

24. Prove: If a circle is drawn on one side of an equilateral triangle as diameter, it bisects each of the other sides.

25. A circle inscribed in an equilateral triangle trisects the altitudes.

26. Prove: An exterior angle of an inscribed quadrilateral equals the opposite interior angle.

27. Two equal circles intersect at H and K. Prove that the end points of any line through K terminated by the circles are equally distant from H.

28. Prove: If a line is drawn tangent to a circle through the vertex of an inscribed isosceles triangle, it is parallel to the base.

29. Prove: The sum of one pair of arcs intercepted by perpendicular chords equals the sum of the other two.

30. Three consecutive sides of an inscribed quadrilateral intercept arcs of 70°, 100°, and 110° respectively. Find the number of degrees in each angle of the quadrilateral.

31. Prove: If tangents to a circle are drawn at the vertices of an inscribed equilateral triangle, another equilateral triangle is formed.

32. 2100 years ago, Eratosthenes found the circumference of the earth as follows: At Syene (*S*) in southern Egypt, he noticed that the sun's rays came down vertically at noon on a certain date. At the same time, at Alexandria (*A*), 500 miles north of Syene, the sun's rays

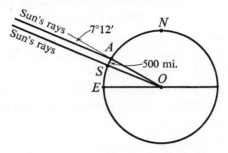

came down at an angle of 7° 12′. He came to the conclusion that *AS* = .02 of the circumference of the earth. Prove that the principle he used was correct.

33. Inscribe and circumscribe a circle on the same triangle.

34. Draw a circle having a radius of 1.25 inches and construct a tangent at a point on the circle.

35. Draw a circle having a radius of $1\frac{1}{2}$ inches and construct tangents to it from a point 2 inches from the center.

36. A tangent is drawn to a circle of 1-inch radius from a point 2 inches from the center. What is the size of the angle between the tangent and the line from the outside point to the center?

37. A tangent makes an angle of 45° with the line drawn to the center of a circle. If the radius is 3 inches, how long is the tangent?

38. Prove: The bisector of an inscribed angle bisects the arc intercepted by the sides of the angle.

39. Prove: If a central angle is doubled, its arc is doubled.

40. Prove: If an inscribed angle is increased by $\frac{1}{7}$ its given size, its arc is increased by $\frac{1}{7}$ its given size.

41. Prove: A parallelogram circumscribed about a circle is equilateral.

42. Prove: The sum of the arms of a right triangle equals the sum of the hypotenuse and the diameter of the inscribed circle.

43. Prove: A rectangle circumscribed about a circle is a square.

44. Two circles, *A* and *B*, are tangent externally at *C*. A line through *C* is terminated by circle *A* at *D*, and by circle *B* at *E*. Prove *AD* ∥ *BE*.

45. Circles *O* and *Q* are tangent externally at *P*. A line is drawn through *P* and is terminated by the circles at *S* and *T*. Tangents are drawn at *S* and *T*. Prove the tangents are parallel.

46. Two circles H and K are tangent externally at L. A line through L is terminated by circle H at P and by circle K at Q. Another line through L is terminated by circle H at R and by circle K at S. PR and QS are drawn. Prove $PR \parallel QS$.

47. A polygon inscribed in a circle has 5 equal sides. Prove that the two diagonals drawn from any vertex trisect the angle. (See note to Ex. 11, Sec. 12–24.)

48. Prove that if the sides of a triangle are bisected at the points of contact of the inscribed circle, the triangle is equilateral.

49. Prove that if the sum of two opposite angles of a quadrilateral is a straight angle, a circle can be circumscribed about the quadrilateral.

50. Two triangles, ABC and DBC, have the same base BC, and the vertices A and D are on the same side of BC. $\angle BAC = \angle BDC$. Prove that the circle circumscribed about $\triangle ABC$ passes through D.

51. A line is drawn which is a secant of each of two equal circles through the mid-point of their line of centers. Prove that the chords intercepted on this secant line by the circles are equal.

52. $x = $ _____° Why?

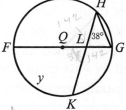

53. $\angle LHG = 38°$
$\overset{\frown}{y} = $ _____° Why?

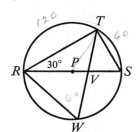

54. $\angle W = $ _____° Why?

55. Construct a circle which passes through a given point, is tangent to a given circle, and has a given radius.

56. Two circles are tangent internally at *E*. A chord *FG* of the larger circle is tangent to the smaller circle at *H*. *EH* is drawn. Prove that *EH* bisects ∠*FEG*.

57. Construct a line that passes through a given point and intersects a given circle in such a way that the chord cut off on the line by the given circle has a given length.

58. Construct a chord of a given circle which has a given length and is parallel to a given line outside the circle.

59. Through a given point on a chord of a given circle construct a chord equal to the given chord.

60. This figure illustrates the method of drawing the four-center arch often seen in bridges and doors. *AB* is bisected at *C*, and *CD* is constructed perpendicular to *AB*. *AB* and *CD* give the width and height of the arch and can be made any desired length. Next *AD* is drawn. Mark off *DE* = *AC* − *DC*. Construct *FG*, the perpendicular bisector of 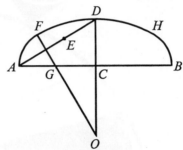 *AE*, and extend *FG* and *DC* to intersect at *O*. With *G* as center and radius equal to *GA* draw arc *AF*. With *O* as center and *OF* as radius draw arc *FD*. Prove the arcs are tangent to each other at *F*. How can arcs *HB* and *DH* be drawn?

61. Draw three circles of different sizes. For each pair of circles draw the 2 common external tangents and extend these lines to meet at a point, (See Ex. 20, page 298). It may take more than one trial to get the entire diagram small enough for your sheet of paper. The six lines will intersect at three points. What properties do you notice about these three points? Essentially this idea has been illustrated by the cover design of this book.

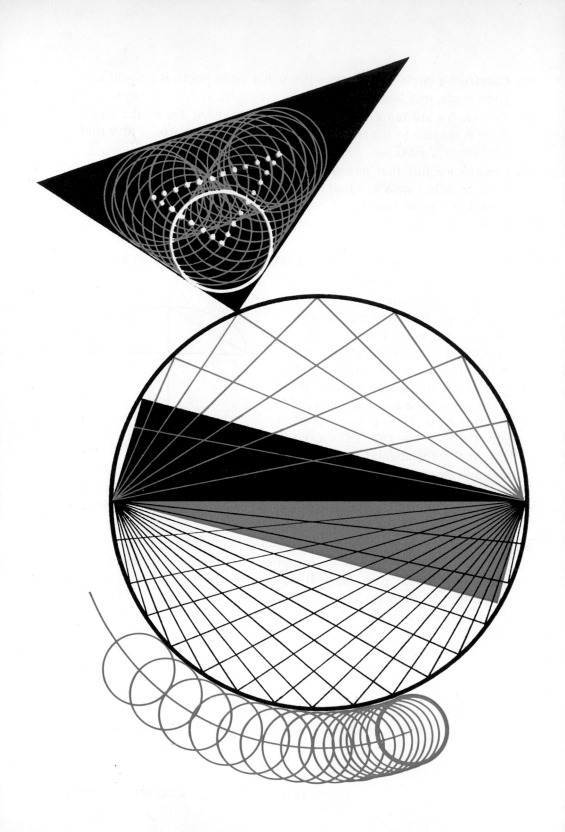

CHAPTER 13

LOCUS

13–1 If you look at the tip of a propeller of an airplane motor as it starts to spin, you notice that it occupies a series of points. If we combine all these points together as the propeller makes a complete turn, we get a circle. Thus, the set of all possible points occupied by the tip of the propeller as it turns is a circle. We can also think of this circle as being formed or traced by the tip of the propeller.

In geometry we call the set of all points satisfying given conditions a <u>locus</u>. The word *locus* means *place*.

An Experiment:

Cut an equilateral triangle *ABC* out of cardboard. On a board place two thumbtacks at points *P* and *Q* a distance apart slightly less than the length of a side of the triangle. Now move the triangle to various possible points so that two sides *AB* and *AC* are always in contact with the thumbtacks. As the triangle occupies these positions, place small thumbtacks in the several positions occupied by the vertex *A*. Now remove the triangle and describe the locus of

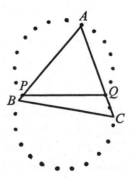

vertex *A*. Note that the triangle can be inserted between the tacks so that *A* falls above or below the line *PQ* joining the tacks.

The locus should appear similar to that in the figure on page 327. Later in this chapter we shall prove that these curves are major arcs of circles with *PQ* as a chord.

13–2   Describing Loci   When we find the locus of points satisfying a given condition, we must meet two specific requirements.

> NOTE: *locus* is pronounced "lō-kus"; the plural is *loci,* pronounced "lō-sigh."

1. Every point on the locus must satisfy the condition.
2. Every point that satisfies the condition must be on the locus.

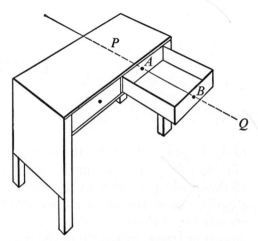

Consider a point on the end of a knob on a desk drawer. What is the locus of this point as the drawer is pulled wide open? The only points that satisfy the condition are on the line segment *AB*, where *A* is the point when the drawer is closed and *B* is the point when the drawer is wide open. We cannot say it is the line *PQ*. Neither point *Q* on the ray *BQ* nor *P* on the ray *AP* meets the conditions.

Consider the various positions of the point of a pencil that is tied to the end of a string, the other end of which is fastened to a box that has a square base, the length of the string being equal to the perimeter of the box, and the string being kept taut as the pencil moves. Make a drawing to show the positions of the pencil. Can you describe the figure made by the pencil?

In describing or finding a locus, it is convenient to think of a material point as *moving* through all possible positions that satisfy a stated condition. While strictly speaking a point has a position and cannot move, yet the motion idea often helps to give us a cue to the nature of the locus. After the motion has been completed, we can think of the locus as all the points traced by the material point.

The set of all points whose positions are determined by a given condition is called the locus of points subject to the condition.

EXERCISES

C.

In Exercises 1–12 describe in words and sketch a figure to show the locus.

1. A point on the rim of a moving ferris wheel
2. The tip of a plumb bob as the line is carefully lowered
3. The tip of a swinging pendulum
4. A point on the knob of a door that opens to an angle of 120°
5. The top of your head as you ride on a swing
6. The top of your head as you stand on an ascending escalator
7. The center of a bicycle wheel as it rolls on a level plane
8. The center of a wheel of a toy locomotive as it runs on a circular track
9. A mark on a casement window as the window is opened 90°
10. The vertices of triangles which have the same base, altitudes to this base being the same length
11. The center of a ball that rolls over every point on a billiard table
12. The prow of a ship as it heads directly east

B.

In the following exercises draw several positions of the point satisfying the given condition; then estimate and describe the entire locus.

13. The points equally distant from the two arms of a right triangle
14. The points equally distant from two particular vertices of a triangle
15. The vertex of the right angle of a right triangle having a given line segment as hypotenuse
16. The points midway between two concentric circles
17. The points that are always 1 inch from a given line
18. The points that are always 1 inch from a given line segment
19. The points that are less than 1 inch from a given line
20. The points that are more than 1 inch from a given line
21. The points less than a radius' distance from the center of a given circle
22. The points more than or equal to a radius' distance from the center of the circle
23. The center of a circle as it rolls around the outside of a given circle
24. The center of a circle as it rolls around the inside of a given circle
25. The center of a circle that rolls around a triangle on the inside of the triangle

26. The center of a circle that rolls around a triangle on the outside
27. The centroids of triangles inscribed in a given circle and having a fixed chord *AB* as a base (See definition of centroid on page 231.)
28. The intersections of the diagonals of parallelograms having a fixed base *AB* = 2 inches, the side *BC* being always 1 inch in length
29. The mid-point of the side of a ladder as the bottom slides outward and the top slides down a vertical wall from its highest possible position to the level ground

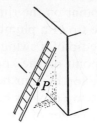

30. A point on a wheel as it rolls along a level and straight track

13–3 Proving Theorems on Locus In every locus theorem there is a rule or condition which determines the position of all the points on the locus. Thus, in these theorems the locus is one of the hypotheses. We must then prove two facts about this locus, namely:

1. If a point is on the locus, it satisfies the condition.
2. If a point satisfies the condition, it is on the locus.

Note that 1 and 2 are a theorem and its converse.

In some exercises the name of the locus itself is not mentioned, but only the rule is stated. In this case we must first use analysis or discovery to determine the locus, and then prove the two conditions of the previous paragraph. Once we have established a few theorems on locus, we can use these theorems to discover new loci. The following examples illustrate the proof of theorems on locus.

13–4 THEOREM The locus of the vertices of the right angles of right triangles having a given line segment as hypotenuse is a circle with the line segment as diameter. The ends of the segment are not included in the locus.

Hypothesis Line segment *AB*, mid-point *O*, circle with center *O* and radius *OA*

Conclusion Circle *O* minus points *A* and *B* is the locus.

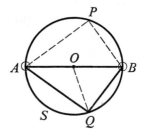

PART 1. Additional hypothesis: Let *P* be any point on circle *O* except *A* and *B*.

Conclusion $\angle APB$ is a right angle for any position of *P* on the circle (Sec. 12–19).

PART 2. Additional hypothesis: Let Q be a point such that $\angle AQB = 90°$.

Conclusion Q is on the circle.

Proof Draw OQ. By Sec. 8–16, $OQ = OA$. Hence Q is on the circle since it is a radius distance from the center.

Discussion. Note that in Part 1 of the proof we took a point on the locus and proved it is the vertex of a right angle. In Part 2 of the proof we took a point that is the vertex of a right angle of a triangle with hypotenuse AB and proved it is on the locus, that is, on the circle. The points A and B are excluded because if P occupies either of these positions we do not have a triangle.

A second example.

In the following example we must first discover the locus, then prove that our discovery is in fact the stated locus.

A quadrilateral $ABCD$ has four equal sides. One of its sides, AB, is fixed in position. Find the locus of the intersection of the diagonals and prove your conclusion.

We note that the quadrilateral is either a square or a rhombus and hence the diagonals bisect each other and are perpendicular to each other (Sec. 7–6, 7–15, 7–19). We draw three possible positions of the quadrilateral and locate the points P, Q, and R on the locus. We also note that for any one position of the quadrilateral there is a symmetrical position with respect to the line AB. We conclude that the locus is a circle with AB as a diameter, and with the points A and B excluded. (Why?)

Hypothesis Line segment AB, fixed base of an equilateral quadrilateral, circle M with AB as diameter.

Conclusion Circle M is the locus of points of the intersection of diagonals of all equilateral quadrilaterals having AB as one side.

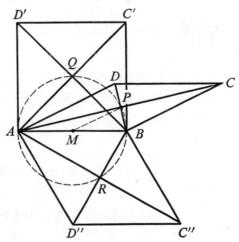

PART 1. Additional hypothesis: Let P be any point on the circle except A and B.

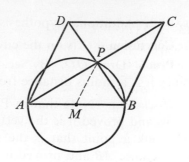

Conclusion P is the intersection of diagonals of an equilateral quadrilateral of which AB is a side.

Construction.   Draw AP, PB and extend each segment its own length to C and D. Draw $AD, DC, CB,$ and PM.

Proof

1. $PM \parallel CB$; $PM = \frac{1}{2}CB$	1. Sec. 8–6
2. $PM \parallel DA$; $PM = \frac{1}{2}DA$	2. Why?
3. $CB \parallel DA$; $CB = DA$	3. Sec. 5–15 and Post. 2
4. $PM = \frac{1}{2}AB$; $DA = AB$	4. Rad. $= \frac{1}{2}$ diam. and Post. 2
5. $ABCD$ is an equilateral quadrilateral.	5. $\square$ with 2 adj. sides $=$

PART 2. Additional hypothesis: Let P be the intersection of the diagonals of $ABCD$.

Conclusion P is on the circle.

Proof P is on the circle by Sec. 13–4.

Discussion.   In Part 2 we used the same figure as in Part 1. However, Part 2 is a converse of Part 1 and is proved independently of Part 1. We could have drawn a separate figure in which the equilateral quadrilateral and circle were given, the diagonals drawn, and their intersection labeled Q, but this would merely reproduce the figure used in Part 1.

We shall now state eight important locus theorems. The students should supply the detailed proof of each theorem (both parts) where it is not given.

13–5 THEOREM   The locus of points equidistant from two fixed points is the line which is the perpendicular bisector of the segment joining them.

This theorem is proved by using Sec. 8–11 for Part 1 and Sec. 8–12 for Part 2.

13–6 THEOREM   The locus of points equidistant from the sides of an angle is the ray bisecting the angle.

This theorem is proved by using Sec. 8–14 for Part 1 and Sec. 8–15 for Part 2.

13–7 THEOREM **The locus of points equidistant from two intersecting lines is the pair of lines bisecting the vertical angles formed by the intersecting lines.**

Hypothesis   Lines AB, CD intersecting at O; l_1 bisects $\angle DOB$; l_2 bisects $\angle AOD$.

Conclusion   Lines l_1 and l_2 are the locus.

PART 1. Additional hypothesis: Let P be a point on l_1 (or l_2).

Conclusion P is equidistant from AB and CD.

Proof   Draw $PF \perp AB$, $PE \perp CD$. Then the right triangles PFO and PEO are congruent (why?) and $PF = PE$.

PART 2.   Additional hypothesis: Let $P'F'$ be $\perp AB$, $P'E' \perp CD$; $P'F' = P'E'$.

Conclusion P' is on l_1 or l_2.

Proof   Draw $P'O$ and prove that it is an angle bisector and hence coincides with l_1 or l_2.

NOTE: Earlier in your study of geometry (see Ex. 11, page 52) we saw that $l_1 \perp l_2$.

13–8 THEOREM The locus of points equidistant from two parallel lines is a line perpendicular to their common perpendicular segment at its midpoint.

The pupil should supply the proof, using the figure shown, where $l \perp EF$ at its mid-point M. In Part 2, P is the mid-point of QS. Show then that $PM \parallel AB$ and thus coincides with l.

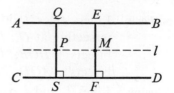

13–9 THEOREM The locus of points at a given distance from a given point is a circle with the given point as center and the given distance as radius.

The proof follows from the definition of a circle. (See Sec. 0–7.)

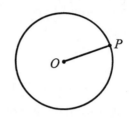

13–10 THEOREM The locus of points at a given distance from a given line is a pair of parallel lines, one on either side of the given line and at the given distance from it.

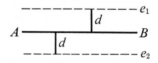

The proof is based on the Parallel Postulate (Post. 18) and Sec. 7–16.

13–11 THEOREM The locus of points at a given distance from a given circle is a pair of circles concentric to the given circle with radii equal to the sum and (if $r > d$) to the difference of the radius and the given distance.

To prove this theorem we must first define distance from a circle. If we draw a ray from the center of the circle O through a given point P, this ray meets the circle in only one point R. Why? The length of the segment PR is the distance of the point P from the circle O.

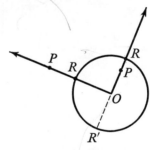

NOTE: If we should draw a line instead of a ray it would meet the circle in two points. In this case there would be two distances between the point and the circle. To avoid uncertainty we use the definition above, which gives the shorter distance as the defined distance between the point and the circle.

Supply the proof, which again depends on the definition of a circle. Note that if $d = r$, the inner circle of the locus degenerates to the center point. If $d > r$, then $r - d$ is negative and the locus consists of only one circle with radius $r + d$. Draw figures to illustrate this.

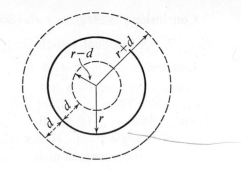

13–12 THEOREM The locus of vertices of angles of the same size intercepting a given line segment consists of two arcs having the given segment as chord and inscribing the given angle. The ends of the segment are not points of the locus.

NOTE: This is the locus discovered in the experiment of Sec. 13–1. Before studying the theorem, review Sec. 12–17 to Sec. 12–20. To inscribe an angle T on a given chord, we construct (1) $\angle BAY = \angle T$; (2) $MO \perp$ bisector of AB; (3) $OA \perp AY$. Then O is the center, OA the radius of the arc, and $\angle T' = \angle T$. Prove this, using Sec. 12–18 and 12–20.

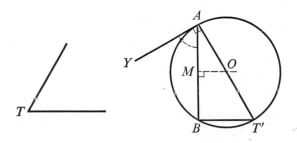

Hypothesis $\angle R$; segment AB; $\overset{\frown}{APB}$ and $\overset{\frown}{AQB}$ inscribing $\angle R$ on AB as chord.

Conclusion $\overset{\frown}{APB}$–$\overset{\frown}{BQA}$ is the locus of vertices of $\angle R$ intercepting AB.

PART 1. Additional hypothesis: P is any point on $\overset{\frown}{APB}$–$\overset{\frown}{BQA}$ except A and B.

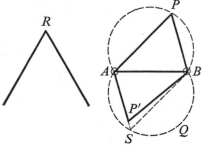

Conclusion $\angle APB = \angle R$ (Sec. 12–18, 12–20)

PART 2. Additional hypothesis: $\angle AP'B = \angle R$

Conclusion P' is on $\overset{\frown}{APB}$–$\overset{\frown}{BQA}$.

Proof Suppose P' is not on the arc. Then AP' meets the arc at S. Draw BS. Then $\angle ASB = \angle R$ since it is inscribed in the arc AQB. Then $\angle ASB = \angle AP'B$. But $\angle AP'B > \angle P'SB$ since it is an exterior angle of triangle $P'SB$. Hence the statement P' is not on the arc is false, and its contradictory, namely P' is on the arc, is true.

EXERCISES

A.

Write the complete proof of these theorems.

1. Sec. 13–5
2. Sec. 13–6
3. Sec. 13–8
4. Sec. 13–9
5. Sec. 13–10
6. Sec. 13–11
7. Show that theorem 13–4 is a special case of 13–12.
8. A is the center of a circle of radius r. B is a point outside the circle. From B perpendiculars are drawn to diameters of circle A. Find and prove the locus of the feet of these perpendiculars.
9. AB is a fixed line segment. $ABXZ$ is a parallelogram. Find and prove the locus of intersection of the diagonals.
10. Find and prove the locus of the centers of all circles tangent to a given line at a given point.
11. Find and prove the locus of the centers of all circles tangent to both sides of an angle.
12. A circle O of radius r is fixed in position. Another circle M of radius d, with $d < r$, is tangent to circle O in all possible positions. Find and prove the locus of the center of circle M.

13. In $\triangle ABC$, E_1 bisects AB, E_2 bisects AE_1, E_3 bisects AE_2, etc. Through E_1, E_2, E_3, and so on, lines E_1F_1, E_2F_2, E_3F_3, etc. are drawn $\parallel BC$. Find and describe the locus of the mid-points of these segments. Is the locus a line or a set of separate points? What is the locus of points one third as far from E_i as from F_i?

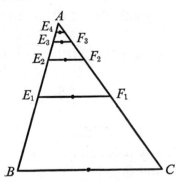

13–13 Intersection of Loci Sometimes more than one condition is imposed on a point. Then the locus consists of those points and only those points that are common to the loci for the separate conditions. The following examples illustrate how we find the common set of points.

I. Find the locus of points equidistant from two given points A and B, and also at a given distance r from a fixed point C. Let A, B, and C be the given points and r the given distance. We now apply the separate conditions.

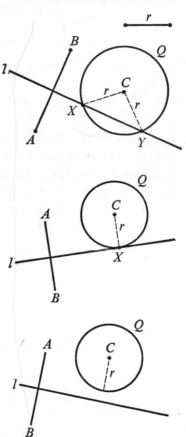

1. By Sec. 13–5, the locus of points equidistant from A and B is the line l which is the perpendicular bisector of AB.

2. By Sec. 13–9, the locus of points a distance r from C is the circle Q with center C and radius r.

3. The line l intersects the circle Q in points X and Y. These are the only two points that satisfy both conditions. The required locus is the set of two points X and Y.

4. *Discussion.* If point C is a distance r from line l, then the circle is tangent to line l and the locus is a *set of one point X*. If C is greater than a radius distance from l, there is no intersection and the locus has no points. We also say the locus is an *empty set* of points.

Can you think of any special situations that are not covered by (3) and (4) above? Consider the case when C is at the midpoint of AB. Consider the case when C is at A and $r < \frac{1}{2}AB$. Does the discussion provide for these cases? If C is at the midpoint of AB, can the locus be the empty set? If C coincides with A and $r = \frac{1}{2}AB$, how many points are in the locus? Has this case been provided for in (4) above?

II. A point P is a distance d from a given line and also a distance d outside a given circle of radius r. Find the locus of all possible points P.

1. l_1 and l_2 satisfy the first condition. Explain.
2. Circle Q satisfies the second condition. Explain.
3. l_1, l_2, and Q intersect in points X, Y, Z, W. The required locus is the set of these four points.

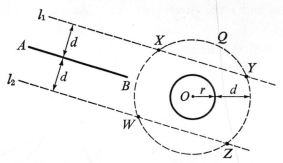

4. *Discussion.* The lines l_1 and l_2 may also take any of the positions shown here. Hence the locus may be a set of 4 points, 3 points, 2 points, 1 point, or the empty set.

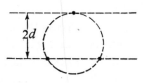

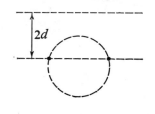

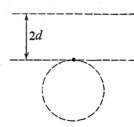

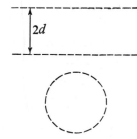

EXERCISES

B.

In the following, find and describe the required locus. In the discussion, draw sketches to illustrate all possible cases.

1. The locus of points at a given distance d from a point P and equidistant from the sides of a given angle.
2. The locus of points equidistant from two parallel lines and also equidistant from two other intersecting lines.

3. The locus of points a distance $\frac{1}{2}''$ from a circle of radius $1''$ and also equidistant from two parallel lines.

4. The locus of points equidistant from two intersecting lines and also $\frac{1}{2}''$ from either of the two lines.

5. The locus of points at a distance $1''$ from a circle of radius $1''$ and also $1''$ from a given line.

6. The locus of points equidistant from points A and B and also equidistant from points C and D.

7. The locus of points equidistant from the sides of an angle and also equidistant from two points, one on each side of the angle.

8. The locus of points at the distance $1''$ from each of two points A and B.

9. The locus of points at a distance d from a circle of radius r and also equidistant from two intersecting lines. Consider the three cases (a) $d = r$, (b) $d < r$, (c) $d > r$.

10. The locus of points 1 inch from the vertex of an angle and 1 inch from the bisector of the angle. When will the locus be the empty set?

13–14 Locus and the Construction of Triangles

Suppose you know the base AB of a triangle and its altitude h. Since only two parts of the triangle are given, you cannot construct the triangle. But you can tell the *locus* of the vertex C. It must be the line parallel to AB at a distance h from AB.

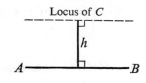

Suppose we know the base AB and angle B. Then we know the locus of the vertex C in this case is on the side BX of the given angle ABX. However, we cannot construct the triangle since we know only two parts.

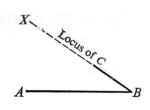

Now suppose we are given the base AB, the altitude h, and one base angle B. Using the base and altitude, we find the locus of the vertex C of all triangles having these parts; using AB and angle B, we find the locus of the vertex C. The intersection of the two loci satisfies the altitude and base angle conditions and hence locates the vertex C of the required triangle. Thus the triangle is determined.

The foregoing discussion illustrates how locus can be used to construct a triangle.

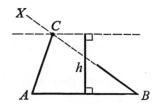

We illustrate further with the following problem:

Construct a right triangle, given the hypotenuse and the altitude on the hypotenuse.

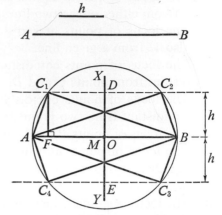

Analysis. Since the vertices A and B are known, we must locate the vertex C. Since C is the vertex of the right angle, one locus of C is the circle on AB as a diameter (Sec. 13–4). The vertex C is also a distance h from AB. Hence a second locus of C is a pair of lines parallel to AB and a distance h from AB.

Construction. Bisect AB at O; draw a circle with O as center and OA as radius. At any point M on AB draw a perpendicular XY and rays $MD = ME = h$. Through D and E draw parallels to AB, meeting the circle in points C_1, C_2, C_3, C_4. Any of these points is the vertex of the desired triangle.

Proof. AC_1B is a right angle and $C_1F = h$. Why? Also $\angle C_1BA = \angle C_2AB = \angle C_4BA = \angle C_3AB$ and hence all the triangles ABC_i are congruent.

13–15 In constructing triangles, we label the vertices A, B, C; the sides opposite these vertices a, b, c; the medians to these sides m_a, m_b, m_c; the altitudes to these sides h_a, h_b, h_c; and the bisectors of the angles at these vertices t_a, t_b, t_c, where the letters a, b, and c are in corresponding order to the letters A, B, and C.

In making a construction, follow the suggestions given on page 339.

Example:

Construct a triangle given m_a, h_a, a.
1. Make a sketch of a completed triangle indicating the parts that are given.
2. The median AE meets BC at its mid-point E. Then one locus of A is a circle with E as a center and m_a as a radius. Another locus of A is a line $\parallel BC$ at a distance h_a. These two loci determine the position of A.

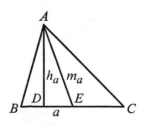

3. *Construction.* On a segment
$BC = a$ construct the $\perp$ bisector XY meeting BC at E.
Using E as center and m_a
as radius, draw a circle.
Mark off $EM = EM' = h_a$
and through M and M' draw
parallels to BC. These parallels meet the circle in the required vertex A.

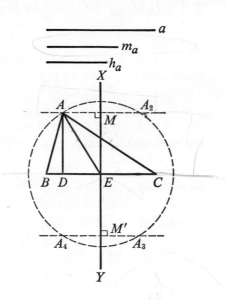

4. *Proof.* $AE = m_a$ (all radii are
equal). $AD = h_a$ (parallels
are everywhere equidistant).
5. *Discussion.* All four triangles formed are congruent,
so there is essentially only
one solution. For a solution
h_a must be $\not> m_a$.

EXERCISES

A.

Construct a triangle given:

1. a, $\angle B$, h_a
2. h_a, t_a, $\angle A$
3. h_a, c, b
4. $\angle A$, h_a, a
5. a, m_a, $\angle A$
6. a, m_b, m_c
7. a, m_b, m_a
8. a, b, m_a
9. Construct a parallelogram given the two diagonals and an altitude.
10. Construct a right triangle given the hypotenuse and the median to
one side.
11. Construct a parallelogram given the two sides and the longer diagonal.
12. Construct a triangle, given two sides and the median to the third side.
Hint. Construct a triangle whose sides are a, b, and $2m$, where a and
b are the given sides and m is the median. Complete a parallelogram
one of whose sides is $2m$, and so on.
13. Construct a triangle given the three medians. *Hint.* Construct a
triangle whose sides are $\frac{1}{3}m_1$, $\frac{1}{3}m_2$, $\frac{1}{3}m_3$, and so on.
14. Construct a right triangle given an acute angle and the median to
the hypotenuse.

SPACE LOCI

Optional

13–16 Locus in Three-Space If we permit points outside of the plane to enter into the locus we must accordingly modify the locus theorems in this chapter.

13–17 The locus of points in space equally distant from two fixed points is a plane which is a perpendicular bisector of the line segment joining the two points.

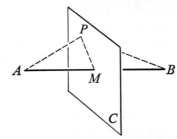

Hypothesis Plane $C \perp AB$ at M; $MA = MB$.

Conclusion C is the locus of points P such that $PA = PB$.

I. Let P be any point in the plane C. Join P to A, B, and M. Then right $\triangle PMA \cong$ right $\triangle PMB$ and $PA = PB$.

II. If $PA = PB$, join P to M. Then $\triangle PMA \cong \triangle PMB$ and thus $\angle AMP = \angle PMB = 90°$. Since $PM \perp AB$ at M, PM must be in the plane C and hence P is in C.

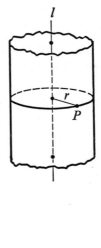

13–18 The locus of points in space at a given distance r from a given line l is a circular cylindrical surface with the line as axis and the radius equal to the given distance. The pupil should give an informal proof.

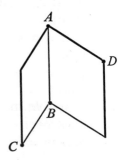

13–19 The dihedral angle shown is C–AB–D. The locus of points equidistant from the faces of a dihedral angle is a plane bisecting the angle. Illustrate this theorem using three leaves of a book.

EXERCISES

A.

1. Two searchlights, a units apart, send out straight-line light beams. Light L_1 rotates twice as fast as light L_2, both rotations being clockwise. At the start both lights point north. By means of a drawing find the locus of the intersection of their beams. The locus is a curve called a strophoid. Show that $\angle L_1PL_2 = \angle L_2PA = \theta$ (θ = theta).

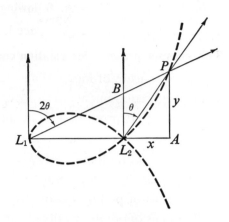

B.

In exercises 2–5, what is the locus of points in space:

2. At a given distance from a given plane. Illustrate with a drawing.
3. At a distance 2″ from a sphere of radius 4″
4. Equidistant from two given points A and B and also at a distance d from the line AB
5. Equidistant from the faces of a dihedral angle and also from two fixed points
6. A line segment AB subtends a right angle with vertex C. What is the locus in space of vertex C?
7. Find the locus of points not more than 2″ from a given line.
8. Find the locus of points not more than 3″ from a given point.
9. The loci of Ex. 7 and 8 are space-filling loci because they fill a part of space; the loci of Ex. 2 and 3 are space-separating loci because they are surfaces that separate one part of space from another. Give another example of each of these kinds of loci.
10. A variable line AB always makes an angle of 30° with a fixed line XY. Describe the locus of AB.

OUTLINE OF CHAPTER 13

This chapter introduces the following terms:

    locus   three-space loci   intersection of loci

This chapter presents information concerning:

  1. The nature of locus. Page 327
  2. Two requirements for a locus. Page 328
  3. Two-part proof of a locus theorem. Page 330
  4. How to discover a geometric locus. Page 331
  5. Intersecting loci. Page 337
  6. Use of knowledge of locus in making constructions. Page 339
  7. Locus of points equally distant from two given points. Page 332
  8. Locus of points equally distant from two intersecting lines. Page 333
  9. Other fundamental loci. Pages 334, 335
 10. Loci in three dimensions. Page 342

REVIEW

1. Define locus of points.

2. What is the locus of points at a distance 5″ from a given line?

3. What is the locus of points at a distance 5″ from a circle of (*a*) radius 10″? (*b*) radius 5″? (*c*) radius 3″?

4. What is the locus of points equidistant from two parallel lines 6″ apart?

5. What is the locus of points equidistant from two points 10″ apart?

6. What is the locus of points equidistant from (*a*) the vertices of a triangle? (*b*) the sides of a triangle?

7. What is the locus of the vertex of an angle of 60° that intercepts a line 2″ long?

8. What is the locus of a point on a doorknob of a hinged door when the door is opened?

9. In quadrilateral *ABCD* find a point *E* so that *EA* = *EB* and *EC* = *ED*.

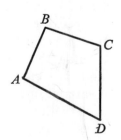

10. In quadrilateral *ABCD* find a point *X* which is equidistant from sides *AB*, *BC*, and *CD*.

11. In quadrilateral *ABCD* find a point *M* so that *MA* = *MB* and *M* is also equidistant from sides *DA* and *DC*.

12. In △*ABC* with ∠*B* > ∠*C* find a point *P* on *AC* equidistant from *B* and *C*.

13. Find the locus of points 2″ from a given fixed point and also 2″ from a given fixed line. Discuss the solution.

14. Find the locus of points 3″ from a circle of radius 5″ and also equidistant from the sides of a given angle.

15. Construct a triangle given ∠*B*, h_a, *b*.

16. Construct a right triangle with hypotenuse *AB* which is a line segment inside a given circle so that the vertex *C* is on the circumference of the given circle. Discuss the possible solutions.

17. In a circle a point other than the center is selected. Chords are drawn through this point. Find the locus of the mid-points of these chords. (*Hint.* Connect the mid-point of any chord and the given point to the center of the circle.)

18. What is the locus of points at least 2 inches from a given point?

TEST

1. Define locus of points and illustrate your definition by the locus of points equidistant from the sides of an angle.

2. Prove. The locus of points which are the vertices of right angles intercepting a given line segment *AB* is a circle on *AB* as a diameter with the end points of *AB* omitted.

3. An angle and a line are given. Find the locus of points equidistant from the sides of the angle and at a given distance *d* from the line. Discuss your solution.

4. Construct by the use of locus an isosceles triangle with a given base *BC* and a given vertex angle *A*.

5. *AX* and *AY* are sides of an angle. A variable line cuts these sides in *M* and *N* respectively. The bisectors of angles *XMN* and *YNM* meet in *P*. (Two positions of *MN* are shown in the figure.) Find and prove the locus of point *P*.

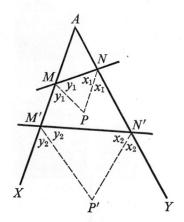

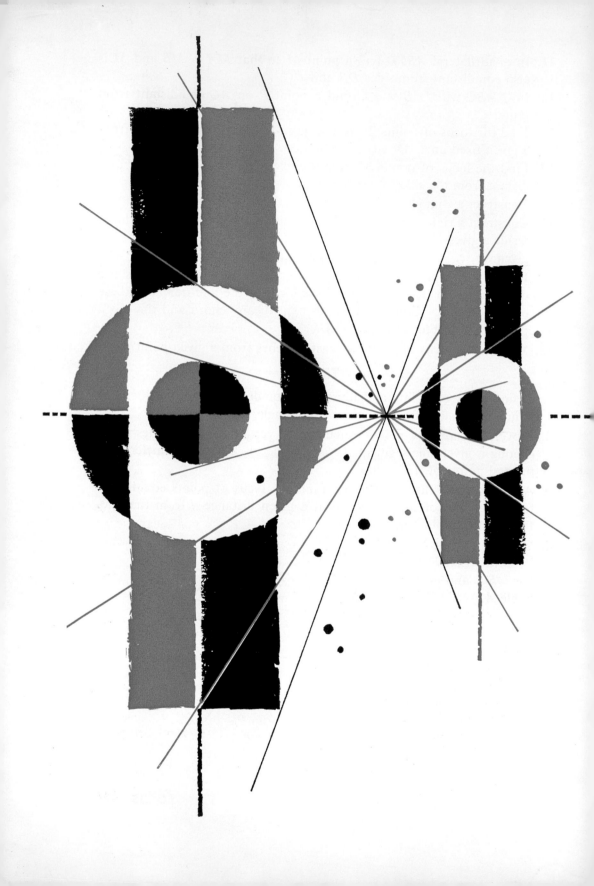

CHAPTER | 14

RATIO, PROPORTION, AND PROPORTIONAL SEGMENTS

Comparison of Quantities   When we measure a quantity of milk, cloth, electricity, light, time, or distance, we compare that quantity with a certain definite quantity called a unit.   For example, when we measure gasoline and say we have five gallons, we mean we have five times as much as the unit quantity which is one gallon.   Another way of saying the same thing is, "This quantity compares with the unit quantity as 5 to 1, or 5:1 or $\frac{5}{1}$."   Still another way of saying this is, "This quantity and the unit quantity are in the ratio of 5 to 1."

Whenever we compare any two quantities by division, we are using the ratio concept.   Another concept involving ratios is called a proportion.

So frequently must ratios and proportions be used in mathematics and science that we find it advantageous to develop certain principles for operating with them.   In geometry proportion, as applied to line segments, areas, and other measurable quantities, is a very powerful tool. It is a basis of indirect measurement.

You are familiar with various kinds of graphs, maps, building plans, blueprints, and sketches.   You know the meanings of such expressions as "1 inch = 1 mile."   Since 1 mile equals 63,360 inches, this expression

347

is equivalent to saying "1 inch represents 63,360 inches." What is meant is that the distance represented by 1 inch on the map is to the distance represented by 1 inch on the earth as 63,360 is to 1. If 1_E represents 1 inch on the earth and 1_M represents 1 inch on the map, then we have the proportion $\dfrac{1_M}{1_E} = \dfrac{63,360}{1}$. All graphs, maps, and plans make use of such proportional line segments.

14–1   Ratio   The ratio of two numbers is their indicated quotient. Thus, the ratio of 8 to 4 is $\frac{8}{4}$, or $8 \div 4$, or as frequently written, $8:4$. Notice that a ratio is a fraction and can be treated as such.

The *ratio of two measures of quantities* of the same kind is the indicated quotient of numbers that express their measures in terms of a common unit. For example, the *ratio* of 84 inches to 9 inches is $\frac{84}{9}$. Note the ratio has no unit of measure; it is a fraction.

The terms of a ratio are the dividend and divisor, or the numerator and denominator. Thus, in the ratio $\dfrac{a}{b}$, a and b are the terms.

14–2   Proportion   A proportion is the statement that two ratios are equal: $\dfrac{a}{b} = \dfrac{c}{d}$. This proportion is read "a is to b as c is to d," or "a divided by b equals c divided by d."

The terms of a proportion are the terms of the equal ratios. In the proportion $\dfrac{a}{b} = \dfrac{c}{d}$, a, b, c, and d are the first, second, third, and fourth terms, respectively.

The extremes of a proportion are the first and fourth terms. In the proportion $\dfrac{a}{b} = \dfrac{c}{d}$, a and d are the extremes.

The means of a proportion are the second and third terms. In the proportion $\dfrac{a}{b} = \dfrac{c}{d}$, b and c are the means.

A proportion is an equation and can be treated as such. In particular, the axioms concerning equal quantities (Postulates 3 to 6) are useful in dealing with proportions. For example, $\dfrac{5}{x} = \dfrac{60}{120}$ is a proportion if x is not zero. Then, $120x\left(\dfrac{5}{x}\right) = 120x\left(\dfrac{60}{120}\right)$ (Post. 4). Hence, $600 = 60x$. $\therefore x = 10$ (Post. 3).

NOTE: Proportions connected with geometric figures are proportions of the members which represent the measures of the geometric magnitudes.

14–3 Fourth Proportional. Mean Proportional The fourth proportional is the fourth term of a proportion. In the proportion $\dfrac{a}{b} = \dfrac{c}{d}$, d is the fourth proportional. The mean proportional is the mean in a proportion in which the means are the same. In the proportion $\dfrac{a}{x} = \dfrac{x}{b}$, x is the mean proportional.

EXERCISES

Each of the following exercises is based upon the proportion $\dfrac{x}{y} = \dfrac{z}{w}$.

1. Transform the equation so that it has no fractions.

2. Does $\dfrac{y}{x} = \dfrac{w}{z}$? Prove this.

3. Does $\dfrac{x}{z} = \dfrac{y}{w}$? Prove this.

4. Does $\dfrac{x + y}{y} = \dfrac{z + w}{w}$? Prove this.

5. Does $\dfrac{x - y}{y} = \dfrac{z - w}{w}$? Prove this.

6. Does $\dfrac{x + y}{x - y} = \dfrac{z + w}{z - w}$? Prove this.

   Suggestion: Use No. 4 and No. 5.

14–4 THEOREM If four quantities are in proportion, the product of the extremes equals the product of the means.

Hypothesis $\dfrac{a}{b} = \dfrac{c}{d}$

Conclusion $ad = bc$

Proof

1. $\dfrac{a}{b} = \dfrac{c}{d}$ 1. Given

2. $bd\left(\dfrac{a}{b}\right) = bd\left(\dfrac{c}{d}\right)$. That is, $ad = bc$.   2. Post. 4

14–5 THEOREM If four quantities are in proportion, the second term is to the first as the fourth is to the third.

Hypothesis $\dfrac{a}{b} = \dfrac{c}{d}$

Conclusion $\dfrac{b}{a} = \dfrac{d}{c}$

Proof

1. $\dfrac{a}{b} = \dfrac{c}{d}$ 1. Why?

2. $\underline{\hspace{2cm}} = bc$ 2. Sec. 14–4

3. $\dfrac{ad}{ac} = \dfrac{bc}{ac}$. That is, $\dfrac{d}{c} = \dfrac{b}{a}$, or $\dfrac{b}{a} = \dfrac{d}{c}$.   3. Post. 3

14–6 THEOREM If four quantities are in proportion, the first term is to the third as the second is to the fourth.

Hypothesis $\dfrac{a}{b} = \dfrac{c}{d}$

Conclusion $\dfrac{a}{c} = \dfrac{b}{d}$

Proof

1. $\dfrac{a}{b} = \dfrac{c}{d}$ 1. Why?

2. $ad = \underline{\hspace{2cm}}$ 2. Sec. 14–4

3. $\dfrac{ad}{cd} = \dfrac{bc}{cd}$. That is, $\dfrac{a}{c} = \dfrac{b}{d}$.   3. Why?

14–7 THEOREM If the product of two quantities equals the product of two other quantities, either pair can be made the extremes of a proportion of which the other pair are the means.

Hypothesis $ad = bc$

Conclusion $\dfrac{a}{b} = \dfrac{c}{d}$

Proof

1. $ad = bc$ 1. Why?

2. $\dfrac{ad}{bd} = \dfrac{bc}{bd}$. That is, $\dfrac{a}{b} = \dfrac{c}{d}$.   2. Why?

NOTE: Divide step 1 by ac to obtain another proportion.

14–8 THEOREM If three terms of one proportion are equal respectively to three terms of another proportion, the fourth terms are equal.

Hypothesis $\dfrac{a}{b} = \dfrac{c}{d}; \dfrac{x}{y} = \dfrac{z}{w}; \ a = x; \ b = y; \ c = z$

Conclusion $d = w$

Proof

1. $\dfrac{a}{b} = \dfrac{c}{d}; \dfrac{x}{y} = \dfrac{z}{w}$ 1. Why?
2. $ad = bc; \ xw = yz$ 2. Why?
3. $b = y; \ c = z$ 3. Why?
4. $bc = yz$ 4. Post. 4
5. $ad = xw$ 5. Post. 2
6. $a = x$ 6. Why?
7. $d = w$ 7. Post. 3

WRITTEN EXERCISES

C.

1. $4 \times 5 = 2 \times 10$. From these equal products, write two proportions each having 4 as its first term. Write two proportions each having 10 as its first term.

Solve the following equations for x.

2. $\dfrac{x}{3} = \dfrac{7}{11}$

3. $4 = \dfrac{3}{x}$

4. $9 = \dfrac{x}{12}$

5. $\dfrac{1}{x} = 2$

6. $\dfrac{x - 1}{5} = \dfrac{2 - x}{11}$

7. $\dfrac{x + 1}{x - 1} = 2$

8. $\dfrac{7}{x} = \dfrac{7}{y}$

9. $\dfrac{x}{11} = \dfrac{a}{11}$

10. $\dfrac{x}{20} = \dfrac{5}{x}$

11. $\dfrac{x + 2}{2} = \dfrac{\frac{1}{2}x + 1}{x - 2}$

12. Find the fourth proportional of 1, 5, and 3.
13. Find the fourth proportional of 7, 2, and 1.
14. Find the fourth proportional of 2, 4, and 16.
15. Find the fourth proportional of 12, 1, and 1.
16. Find the mean proportional of 3 and 27.
17. Find the mean proportional of 9 and 1.

18. Find the fourth proportional of a, b, and c.

   Suggestion. Let x be the fourth proportional.

   Then $\dfrac{a}{b} = \dfrac{c}{x}$. Now solve for x.

   Find the ratio of x to y if:

19. $5x = 7y$
20. $2x - 19y = 0$
21. $ax = b(x + y)$
22. $\dfrac{2\pi r}{x} = \dfrac{2\pi R}{y}$
23. What is the ratio of the length of a yardstick to the length of a foot ruler?
24. A segment 24 inches long is divided into two parts the ratio of which is 3 to 5. How long is each part?
25. Two supplementary angles have the ratio 4 to 5. How large is each angle?
26. The angles of a triangle have the ratio $1:2:3$. Find each angle.
27. The acute angles of a right triangle have the ratio $2:1$. The hypotenuse is 10 inches. What is the length of the shortest side of the triangle?

14–9   Segments Divided Proportionally   Two line segments are divided proportionally if the ratio of the parts of one equals the ratio of the parts of the other.

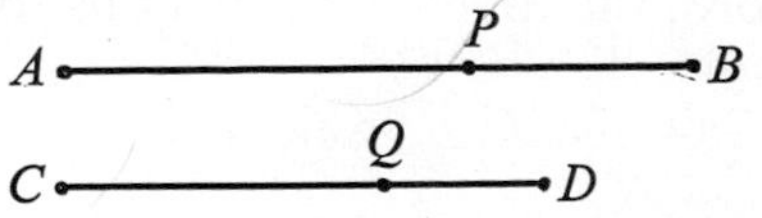

If AB is divided into two parts,

AP and PB, by a point P between A and B, and CD is divided into two parts, CQ and QD, by a point Q between C and D, and if $\dfrac{AP}{PB} = \dfrac{CQ}{QD}$, then AB and CD are divided proportionally.

Since the points of division are between A and B, C and D, the segments are divided internally.

We may extend the idea of dividing a line segment to the case where a point is not on the segment, but on the line containing the segment. Such points are P and P' as shown in the figure below.

Using the lengths of the segments AP and PB, we say AB is divided externally in the ratio $AP:PB$. Similarly a point P' on the opposite side of

A divides AB externally in the ratio $AP':P'B$. This must be taken merely as a definition.

If a point P divides AB internally in the ratio $AP:PB$, and a point P' divides AB externally in the ratio $AP':P'B$, then if the ratios are equal, i.e. $\dfrac{AP}{PB} = \dfrac{AP'}{P'B}$, the line segment AB is divided internally and externally in the same ratio.

If the points of division on two segments $A'B'$ and $C'D'$ are external, the segments are divided <u>externally</u> in the same ratio.

14-10 THEOREM If a line is parallel to one side of a triangle and intersects the other two sides, it divides proportionally the sides which it intersects.

Hypothesis $\triangle ABC$; $DE \parallel BC$; DE intersects AB and AC.

Conclusion $\dfrac{AD}{DB} = \dfrac{AE}{EC}$

The plan is to divide the segments of one side into equal parts, and draw parallels to the base intersecting the other side.

Construction. Suppose some unit of length to be contained m times in AD and n times in DB, m and n representing any two whole numbers.* Divide AD into m equal parts and DB into n equal parts. Through each point of division, construct lines $\parallel BC$.

Proof

1. AE is divided into m equal parts, each of size x, and EC is divided into n equal parts, each of size y. Why?

2. $\dfrac{AD}{DB} = \dfrac{m}{n}$; $\dfrac{AE}{EC} = \dfrac{m}{n}$

3. $\therefore \dfrac{AD}{DB} = \dfrac{AE}{EC}$ Why?

Using the theorems concerning proportions we can now also write:

$$\frac{AD}{AE} = \frac{DB}{EC}; \quad \frac{AB}{AD} = \frac{AC}{AE}; \quad \frac{AB}{DB} = \frac{AC}{EC}$$

* There are situations in which there is *no* unit which is contained a whole number of times in each segment AD and DB. These situations are discussed in advanced courses. We shall assume that the theorem holds in these situations also.

14–11 Corollary If three or more parallel lines intersect two transversals, the ratio of any two intercepted segments on one transversal equals the ratio of the corresponding segments on the other transversal.

1. $\dfrac{l}{r} = \dfrac{m}{s}$ 1. Why?

2. $\dfrac{m}{v} = \dfrac{n}{w}$ 2. Why?

3. $\therefore \dfrac{l}{o} = \dfrac{m}{p} = \dfrac{n}{q}$ 3. Give details.

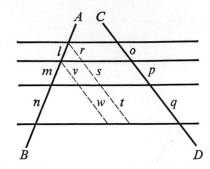

WRITTEN EXERCISES

C.

In exercises 1–7, use the figure of Sec. 14–10.

1. If $AD = 4$, $DB = 3$, and $AE = 5$, find EC.
2. If $AB = 12$, $AD = 5$, and $AE = 80$, find AC.
3. If $AB = 125$, $BD = 45$, and $AE = 80$, find AC.
4. If $AD = BD$ and $AC = 16$, find AE.
5. If $AD = 2.3$, $AB = 7.5$, and $EC = 3.4$, find AC.

B.

6. If $AD = \sqrt{3}$, $AB = 4$, and $AE = \sqrt{5}$, find AC.
7. If $AB = 7\sqrt{2}$, $AD = 1$, and $AC = 3\sqrt{7}$, find EC.
8. The nonparallel sides of a trapezoid are 9 and 14. A line parallel to the bases divides the altitude in the ratio $1:3$. Find the segments into which this line divides each of the nonparallel sides.

9. Hyp. $AD = 12$; $EH = 10$
   Find CD, EF, FG, and GH.

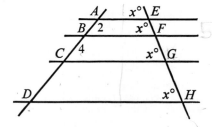

r, s, and t are lengths of line segments on HL and LX. Construct v so that $\dfrac{r}{s} = \dfrac{t}{v}$. How could Sec. 14–10 be used in making this construction?

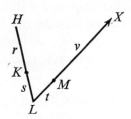

14–12 Problem **To construct the fourth proportional to three given segments.**

Given Segments a, b, and c.

Required To construct x so that $\dfrac{a}{b} = \dfrac{c}{x}$

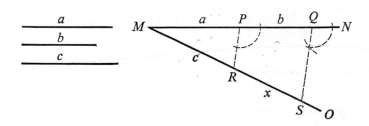

Proof

1. (*a*) Draw any angle *NMO*. (*b*) On *MN* mark off *MP* = a, and *PQ* = b. (*c*) On *MO* mark off *MR* = c. (*d*) Draw *PR*.

   (*e*) Construct *QS* ∥ *PR*. Then $RS = x$, and $\dfrac{a}{b} = \dfrac{c}{x}$.

  1. Give reasons.

2. *QS* ∥ *PR*

  2. Why?

3. $\dfrac{MP}{PQ} = \dfrac{MR}{RS}$

  3. Sec. 14–10

4. ∴ $\dfrac{a}{b} = \dfrac{c}{x}$

  4. Post. 2

A House Plan A draftsman makes constant use of proportional segments. It is usually not possible for him to make a drawing of a piece of machinery or a house of the same size as the object itself. Therefore, he makes a *scale drawing*. He adopts a fixed ratio of a unit of length on his drawing and a unit of length on the object and maintains this ratio in drawing all lines. In the accompanying illustration, the scale is 1 inch = 10 feet; that is, a length of one inch on the drawing represents a length of 10 feet in the house.

(*a*) What is the size of the kitchen? (Measure and compute.)
(*b*) What is the width of the living room? its length?
(*c*) What is the width of the fireplace in the living room?
(*d*) What is the size of the smaller bedroom?
(*e*) What is the size of the dining room?
(*f*) What is the size of the bathroom?
(*g*) What is the width of the stairway going up?
(*h*) What is the full length of the house? the width?
(*i*) Draw a rectangle to represent the lot on which this house stands, using the same scale as that used for the house, given its width as 80 feet and its length as 150 feet.
(*j*) If the ceilings in this house are 8 feet high, what should be the length of a line showing this height?

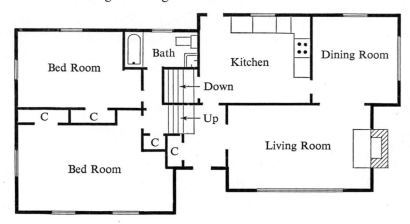

WRITTEN EXERCISE

Construct the fourth proportional to segments whose lengths are 1 in., 1.5 in., and 2.25 in. Check your construction by measurement and calculation.

14–13 Problem **To divide a segment into parts proportional to given segments.**

Given Segments MN, a, b, and c

Required To divide MN into parts x, y, and z such that $\dfrac{a}{x} = \dfrac{b}{y} = \dfrac{c}{z}$

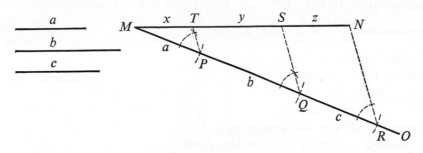

Proof

1. (a) Draw MO making any angle with MN. (b) On MO mark off $MP = a$, $PQ = b$, and $QR = c$. (c) Draw RN. (d) Construct $QS \parallel RN$, and $PT \parallel RN$ intersecting MN at S and T respectively and dividing MN into parts x, y, and z. Then $\dfrac{a}{x} = \dfrac{b}{y} = \dfrac{c}{z}$.

1. Give reasons.

2. $\dfrac{MP}{x} = \dfrac{PQ}{y}$

2. Sec. 14–10

3. $\dfrac{PQ}{y} = \dfrac{QR}{z}$

3. Sec. 14–11

4. $\dfrac{MP}{x} = \dfrac{PQ}{y} = \dfrac{QR}{z}$

4. Post. 2

5. $\therefore \dfrac{a}{x} = \dfrac{b}{y} = \dfrac{c}{z}$

5. Post. 2

WRITTEN EXERCISES

C.

1. Divide a 3-inch segment into parts proportional to 1, 2, and 5.

2. Given $\angle ABC$, and P a point inside the angle. Draw a line through P so that the segment intercepted on it by the sides of the angle is divided at P in the ratio $2:3$.

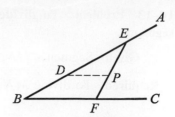

Suggestion. If $PD \parallel BC$, and E is so located that $\dfrac{BD}{DE} = \dfrac{2}{3}$, and if EPF is drawn, what is the ratio of FP to EP?

3. ABC is any $\triangle$. $DE \parallel BC$

Prove $\dfrac{AF}{FG} = \dfrac{AE}{EC}$

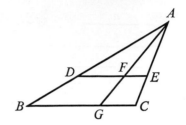

4. The point H can be seen from L but cannot be reached for direct measurement. A point Q is selected from which both H and L can be seen and a line is run from Q to L. Then a line PK is run parallel to QH. Show how to calculate the distance LH from measurements that can be made.

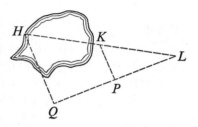

14–14 THEOREM If a line divides two sides of a triangle proportionally, it is parallel to the third side.

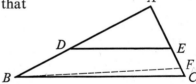

Hypothesis DE meets AB and AC so that
$$\frac{AD}{DB} = \frac{AE}{EC}.$$

Conclusion $DE \parallel BC$

Proof

1. Assume $DE \not\parallel BC$. Through B draw a line $\parallel DE$ meeting AC at F; extend if necessary.

2. F and C are distinct points.

3. $\dfrac{AD}{DB} = \dfrac{AE}{EC}$ and $\dfrac{AD}{DB} = \dfrac{AE}{EF}$

4. $EC = EF$

5. Then C and F coincide.

6. $\therefore DE \parallel BC$

1. Added hypothesis and Sec. 5–20

2. Explain.

3. Hyp. and Sec. 14–10

4. Sec. 14–8

5. Explain.

6. Since statements 1 and 2 have led to a contradiction

In this figure $\angle a = \angle b$, and $TY \parallel XS$. Prove $\dfrac{RX}{XT} = \dfrac{RS}{ST}$.

Follow the steps suggested by these exercises.

1. Does $\angle c = \angle b$? Why?
2. Does $\angle a = \angle d$? Why?
3. Does $\angle c = \angle d$? Why?
4. Does $SY = ST$? Why?

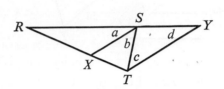

5. Does $\dfrac{RX}{XT} = \dfrac{RS}{SY}$? Why?

6. Does $\dfrac{RX}{XT} = \dfrac{RS}{ST}$? Why?

14–15 THEOREM If a line bisects an angle of a triangle, it divides the opposite side internally into parts whose ratio equals the ratio of the sides adjacent to the bisected angle.

Hypothesis $\triangle ABC$; $\angle 1 = \angle 2$

Conclusion $\dfrac{BD}{DC} = \dfrac{AB}{AC}$

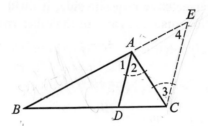

The plan is to construct lines forming a triangle whose base is parallel to the angle bisector, etc.

Proof

1. (a) Construct $CE \parallel AD$. (b) Extend AB through A to intersect CE at E.
2. $\angle 3 = \angle 2$
3. $\angle 2 = \angle 1$
4. $\angle 1 = \angle 4$
5. $\angle 3 = \angle 4$
6. $AC = AE$
7. $\dfrac{AB}{AE} = \dfrac{BD}{DC}$
8. $\therefore \dfrac{AB}{AC} = \dfrac{BD}{DC}$

1. Give reasons.

2. Why?
3. Why?
4. Corresponding $\angle$s
5. Post. 2
6. Why?
7. Sec. 14–10
8. Post. 2

Suppose $\angle B$ rather than $\angle A$ is bisected. Draw the figure and give the proof.

1. Is $DE \parallel BC$? 2. Is $VW \parallel ZY$? 3. Is $ST \parallel PQ$? Why?

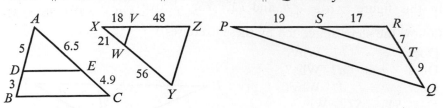

4. Divide a segment internally in a given ratio.

   Suggestion. Let AB be the given segment to be divided in the ratio of $x:y$, x and y being given lengths. Construct a triangle having AB, x, and y as sides. In case x and y are too short to make a triangle, use $2x$ and $2y$, or $3x$ and $3y$. Complete the construction. Compare this method with that given in Sec. 14–13.

14–16 THEOREM If a line bisects an exterior angle of a triangle and intersects the opposite side, it divides that side externally into parts whose ratio equals the ratio of the other two sides.

Hypothesis ABC; exterior angle CAX; AD bisects $\angle CAX$ meeting BC extended at D.

Conclusion $\dfrac{AB}{AC} = \dfrac{BD}{DC}$

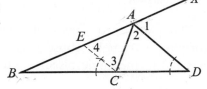

The plan is to construct a line which is parallel to the given angle bisector and which passes through a vertex of the given triangle and intersects the opposite side.

Proof

1. Construct $CE \parallel AD$.
2. $\angle 3 = \angle 2$
3. $\angle 2 = \angle 1$
4. $\angle 1 = \angle 4$
5. $\angle 3 = \angle 4$
6. $AC = AE$
7. $\dfrac{AB}{AE} = \dfrac{BD}{DC}$
8. $\therefore \dfrac{AB}{AC} = \dfrac{BD}{DC}$

1. Give reason.
2. Why?
3. Why?
4. Why?
5. Why?
6. Why?
7. Why?
8. Why?

14-17 Harmonic Division A line segment is <u>harmonically divided</u> if it is divided internally and externally in the same ratio.

The bisectors of the interior and exterior angles at a vertex of a triangle divide the opposite side harmonically if the bisector of the interior angle is not parallel to the opposite side. In the figure shown

$$\frac{2}{1} = \frac{BP}{PA} = \frac{BP'}{P'A} = \frac{1\frac{1}{2} + l}{l};$$
$$\therefore l = 1\frac{1}{2}$$

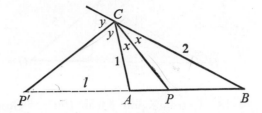

EXERCISES

C. Oral

1. Under what conditions will the bisector of an exterior angle of a triangle not intersect the opposite side?

B. Written

2. Divide a given segment externally in a given ratio. See the suggestion to Ex. 4, page 360.

3. $DC =$ _____ Why?

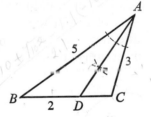

4. $EG = 12.$ $GH =$ _____
   Why?

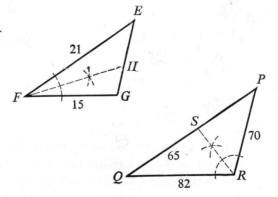

5. $PQ =$ _____ Why?

6. $BD = $ _____ Why?

7. $EF = $ _____

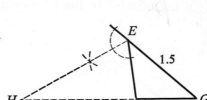

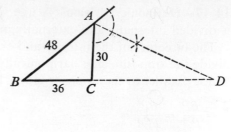

14–18 Extreme and Mean Ratio. Golden Section A line segment is divided in <u>extreme and mean ratio</u> if one of its parts is the mean proportional between the other part and the whole segment. AB is divided at C in extreme and mean ratio.

$$\frac{AB}{AC} = \frac{AC}{CB}$$

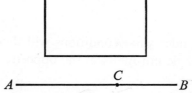

It is believed that a line divided in extreme and mean ratio gives a pleasing proportion, and particularly that rectangular objects such as pictures and building stones are most pleasing if the length and width are parts of a line that has been divided in extreme and mean ratio. This ratio has been used in famous paintings. The extreme and mean ratio division has been called the <u>Golden Section</u>.

WRITTEN EXERCISES

B.

1. If a line segment 10 inches long is divided in extreme and mean ratio, how long is each part?

   Suggestion. Let x represent one part. Then $\dfrac{10}{x} = \dfrac{x}{10 - x}.$ Explain.

2. If a line segment 1 inch long is divided in extreme and mean ratio, how long is each part?

3. A piece of picture moulding 60 inches long is to be cut into 4 parts to frame a mirror. Explain how to cut the moulding so that the frame will illustrate the Golden Section.

4. If a line segment r units long is divided in extreme and mean ratio, show that the parts are $\frac{r}{2}(\sqrt{5}-1)$ and $\frac{r}{2}(3-\sqrt{5})$.

MISCELLANEOUS WRITTEN EXERCISES

B.

1. State and prove the converse of Sec. 14–15. *Suggestion.* Use the indirect method.
2. The sum of the three sides of a triangle is 72 and they have the ratio 2:3:4. Find the length of each side.
3. The sum of the sides of a quadrilateral is 330 and they have the ratio 1:2:3:5. Find the length of each side.

In exercises 4, 5, and 6, a, b, and c are given line segments.

4. Construct a segment x so that $x = bc + a$.
5. Construct a segment x so that $x = ab$. Select some line segment to represent 1, the unit of length.
6. Construct a segment x so that $x = a \div b$.
7. A straight angle is divided into supplementary angles that have the ratio 3:7. How many degrees are there in each angle?
8. A 2-inch segment is divided in extreme and mean ratio. Find algebraically the size of each part.
9. The cover of a book is 5 inches wide. What is the length of the book if it is made on the principal of the Golden Section?
10. The sides of a triangle are 5 inches, 7 inches, and 9 inches. The smallest angle is bisected. Find the lengths of the segments of the side intersected by the angle bisector.
11. Find the lengths of the segments of the shortest side of the triangle described in Ex. 10 if the angle opposite it is bisected.
12. A man has a picture that measures 12 inches by 22 inches. He studies the subject and decides to reduce the size of the picture by cutting a strip off the end so that the dimensions are in extreme and mean ratio. How wide is the strip that is cut away? Give the result to the nearest eighth of an inch.
13. If a line segment has been divided in extreme and mean ratio and the smaller part is 10 inches how long is the entire segment?

14–19 THEOREM (Optional) If three parallel planes intersect two skew lines, the corresponding segments are proportional.

Hypothesis $R \parallel S \parallel T$; AB and BC are segments of line AC; DE and EF are segments of line DF intercepted by R, S, and T.

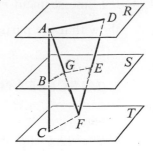

Conclusion $\dfrac{AB}{BC} = \dfrac{DE}{EF}$

Proof

1. Draw AF. Pass a plane through AC and AF meeting S and T in BG and CF. Pass a plane through AF and DF meeting S and R in GE and AD.

1. Why can this be done?

2. $AD \parallel GE$, $BG \parallel CF$

2. Why?

3. $\dfrac{AB}{BC} = \dfrac{AG}{GF}, \dfrac{AG}{GF} = \dfrac{DE}{EF}$

3. Why?

4. $\dfrac{AB}{BC} = \dfrac{DE}{EF}$

4. Why?

OUTLINE OF CHAPTER 14

This chapter introduces the following terms:

ratio	proportional division
terms of a ratio	internal division
proportion	external division
extremes	harmonic division
means	extreme and mean ratio
fourth proportional	Golden Section
mean proportional	

This chapter presents information concerning the following:

1. The relation between the products of extremes and means of a proportion. Page 349
2. The relation between inverted ratios of a proportion. Page 350
3. The relation between ratios composed of alternate terms of a proportion. Page 350

4. The relation between ratios composed of the factors of equal products. Page 350

5. The relation between the fourth terms of two proportions that have three terms of one equal respectively to three terms of the other. Page 351

6. The relation of the parts of two sides of a triangle made by a line parallel to the third side. Page 353

7. The relation of the segments intercepted on transversals by a number of parallels. Page 354

8. The method of constructing the fourth proportional. Page 355

9. The method of dividing a segment into parts proportional to given segments. Page 357

10. The relation of one side of a triangle to a line that divides the other two sides proportionally. Page 358

11. The ratio of the segments intercepted on a side of a triangle by a line that bisects an interior angle or exterior angle of the triangle. Pages 359, 360

REVIEW

1. What is a ratio? Illustrate.

2. What is a proportion? Illustrate.

3. What are the terms of a proportion? Point out the terms of the proportion that you used as an illustration in Ex. 2.

4. What is a mean proportional? Illustrate.

5. Solve the proportion $\dfrac{3}{x} = \dfrac{5}{2}$.

6. Solve $\dfrac{4}{x} = \dfrac{x}{9}$.

7. What is meant by internal division of a line segment? What is meant by external division?

8. A line segment 4 centimeters long is divided internally in the ratio $\frac{5}{3}$. Find the length of each part.

9. Theorem. If a line is parallel to one side of a triangle and intersects the other two sides, it divides proportionally the sides that it intersects. Give a demonstration.

10. *ABC* is a triangle. *AB* = 6 in., *AC* = 8 in. *D* is a point on *AB* two inches from *B*. *DE* is parallel to *BC*. Find the lengths of the segments in which *E* divides *AC*.

11. Draw a line segment and divide it by construction into parts whose ratio is 2:3:4.

12. Given three unequal segments, construct the fourth proportional. Describe the steps in the construction and prove that the constructed segment is the fourth proportional.

13. In $\triangle ABC$, *D* is a point on *AB*, and *E* is a point on *AC*. *AD* = 3 cm., *DB* = 1 cm., *AE* = 2 cm., *EC* = $\frac{2}{3}$ cm. $\angle ABC$ = 41°. $\angle A$ = 62°. How many degrees has $\angle AED$? Prove the steps by which you arrive at your answer.

14. In $\triangle RST$, *RS* = 5 in., *RT* = 8 in., *ST* = 10 in. *V* is on *ST*, and *RV* bisects $\angle SRT$. Find the length of *SV*.

YES–NO TEST

Approximately 30 minutes

Copy on your paper the numbers of the following questions. If the answer to a question is *yes* under all conditions, place a plus sign (+) after its number. If the answer is *not yes* under all conditions, place a zero (0) after its number.

1. Is a ratio a fraction?

2. Is the first term of a ratio an extreme?

3. Do the ratios $\frac{3}{5}$ and $\frac{4}{7}$ make a proportion?

4. Do the ratios $\frac{9}{15}$ and $\frac{15}{25}$ make a proportion?

5. Are *b* and *c* the means of the proportion $\frac{a}{b} = \frac{c}{d}$?

6. If $xz = yw$, does $\frac{x}{w} = \frac{z}{y}$?

7. If $ab = cd$, does $\frac{d}{b} = \frac{a}{c}$?

8. If $\frac{r}{s} = \frac{s}{t}$, is *s* the mean proportional between *r* and *t*?

9. If $\frac{x}{y} = \frac{x}{z}$, is *x* the mean proportional between *y* and *z*?

10. If $\dfrac{h}{12} = \dfrac{5}{6}$, does $h = 10$?

11. If $\dfrac{a}{b} = \dfrac{c}{d}$, and $a = 7$, $b = 42$, and $d = 36$, does $c = 6$?

12. If $\dfrac{x}{y} = \dfrac{z}{w}$, does $\dfrac{x+y}{y} = \dfrac{z-w}{w}$?

13. If $\dfrac{5}{x} = \dfrac{x}{7}$, does $x^2 = 12$?

14. If $\dfrac{ab}{2} = xy$, does $\dfrac{a}{x} = \dfrac{2y}{b}$?

15. Is the expression $3x^2 - 2x$ a proportion?

16. Can equal line segments be proportionally divided?

17. If a line intersects two sides of a triangle, does it divide them proportionally?

18. If a line is parallel to the base of a triangle and divides one side into segments 3 inches and 5 inches long, does it divide the other side, which is 12 inches long, into segments having lengths $4\frac{1}{2}$ inches and $7\frac{1}{2}$ inches?

19. If a line divides one side of a triangle into segments 8 inches and 12 inches, and divides another side into corresponding segments 12 inches and 18 inches, is it parallel to the third side?

20. If three parallels cut off segments the lengths of which are a and b on one transversal and corresponding segments the lengths of which are respectively c and d on another transversal, does $\dfrac{a}{b} = \dfrac{c}{d}$?

21. If two sides of a triangle are 24 inches and 30 inches and if the angle included by them is bisected and if the third side is 18 inches, is the third side divided by the angle bisector into segments the lengths of which are 8 and 10 inches?

22. If x and y are line segments that are parts of a segment that has been divided in extreme and mean ratio, does $\dfrac{2x}{y} = 1 - \sqrt{5}$?

23. Do the bisectors of the interior and exterior angles at a vertex of a scalene triangle divide the intersected side harmonically?

24. Through the point of intersection of the medians of a given triangle a parallel is constructed to each of the three sides. Do these three lines trisect each of the three sides?

Copy on your paper the numbers of the following statements and questions. After each number write a word, or letters, or number which, if written in the blank, would complete the statement and make it true, or answer the question.

1. $BD = $ _____

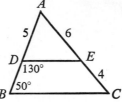

2. $XZ = 28$; $YZ = 25$; $VZ = 21$; $VW \parallel XY$. $WZ = $ _____

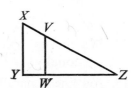

3. $x = $ _____

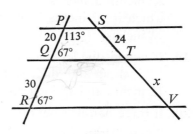

4. $\angle ADE = $ _____ °

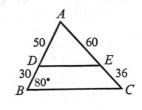

5. Is $ST \parallel PR$? _____

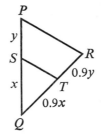

6. $BD = $ _____

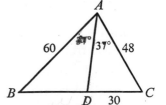

7. $\angle XZY = \underline{\hspace{1cm}}^{\circ}$

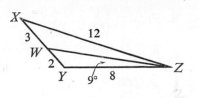

8. $QS = \underline{\hspace{1cm}}$

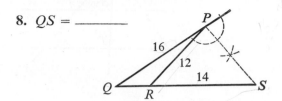

SUPPLEMENTARY EXERCISES

C.

1. If $AD = 8$, $DB = 6$, and $AE = 6$, find EC.

2. If $AD = 150$, $DB = 120$, and $EC = 100$, find AE.

3. If $AB = 7.2$, $AD = 3.2$, and $AE = 2.8$, find EC.

B.

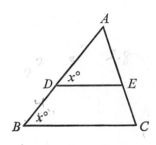

4. Is $JK \parallel GH$? Why?

5. Hyp. $QR = 150$
$\quad\quad QS = \underline{\hspace{1cm}}$ Why?

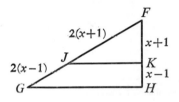

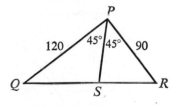

6. $CD = \underline{\hspace{1cm}}$

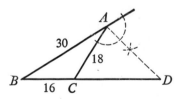

7. Hyp. $FH \parallel GK$
$\quad$ Does $\dfrac{EF}{EG} = \dfrac{EH}{EK}$? Why?

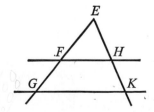

8. Prove: $\dfrac{PQ}{QR} = \dfrac{PX}{XY}$

9. Prove: $\dfrac{QS}{SX} = \dfrac{RT}{TY}$, if
$\angle QPS = \angle SPX$

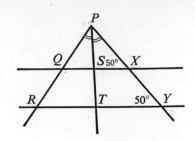

10. Hyp. $EF \parallel AC$; $GF \parallel BC$
Con. $AE \cdot DG = DE \cdot BG$

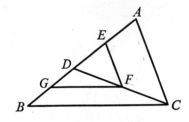

11. Hyp. $JR \parallel HP$; $RL \parallel PM$
Con. $\dfrac{HK}{JK} = \dfrac{MK}{LK}$

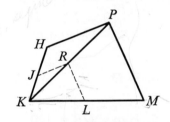

12. Hyp. $FG \parallel BC$; $GH \parallel CD$;
$HK \parallel DE$
Con. $AB \cdot EK = BF \cdot AE$

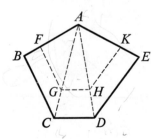

13. Hyp. $RV \parallel ST$; $RS \parallel VT$
Con. $\dfrac{PT}{WT} = \dfrac{PS}{VT}$

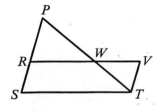

14. Prove: $\dfrac{FE}{EA} = \dfrac{FC}{AB}$

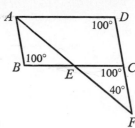

15. *GHJK* is a square.

Prove $\dfrac{GH}{GL} = \dfrac{KP}{GM}$.

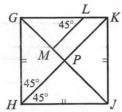

16. Hyp. $RS = 2ST$;

$\angle RTS = 90°$

Con. $\dfrac{RS}{TV} = \dfrac{SX}{XV}$

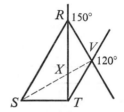

17. Draw a circle and construct the segment x, so that diameter:radius = radius:x.

18. Draw any quadrilateral and divide a 2-inch line into parts proportional to its sides.

19. Divide a 3-inch segment internally into parts the ratio of which is 3:4.

20. Divide a 2-inch segment externally into parts the ratio of which is $2:3\frac{1}{2}$.

A.

21. Draw a scalene triangle and construct the fourth proportional to its sides.   Show all possible cases.

22. Prove: Segments of two parallels intercepted by three lines concurrent at a point outside the parallels are proportional.

23. Prove: If a line from a vertex of a triangle to a point on the opposite side divides this side into segments respectively proportional to the adjacent sides, it is an angle bisector. (This is a converse of Sec. 14–15.)

24. If a line drawn from a vertex of a triangle to an exterior point of the opposite side divides this side externally in the ratio equal to that of the other two sides, it is a bisector of the exterior angle at the vertex. (This is a converse of Sec. 14–16.)

CHAPTER | 15

SIMILARITY

You have seen and perhaps have built model airplanes, model houses, model engines, or model bridges. You have seen a four-inch statue of a six-foot man. You have seen large and small drawings of the same building. The original and the model, the statue and the man, the large drawing and the small one look alike. Generally speaking we say the measurements of the model are proportional to the measurements of the actual object. It is obvious that the model and the object are not the same size, and yet some characteristics have been kept unchanged.

Geometric figures can have this same relation. The relation is one called similarity and is very useful in geometry. The subject of trigonometry is based in part upon geometric similarity. The measurement of distances and angles inaccessible for direct measurement is made possible by the use of similarity. This chapter is devoted to a systematic study of similarity.

A photograph is another example of how some characteristics of an object are retained although the object usually has three dimensions whereas the photograph has only two. The proportions of length and breadth are preserved in the picture while those relating to depth are not. As you know, the photograph can be larger than the object, smaller, or the same size.

15–1   Correspondence of Points in Polygons   If two polygons have the same number of vertices, we establish a correspondence between them by associating each vertex of one polygon with one and only one vertex of the other polygon.   To show this we write the letters symbolizing the vertices of each polygon in the order in which the vertices are made to correspond.

In the figure if we write *ABCDE corresponds to A'B'C'D'E'* we mean *A* corresponds to *A'*, *B* to *B'*, and so on.   In referring to two quadrilaterals *RSTV* and *XYZW* if we write *RSTV corresponds to XYZW*, this would mean that *R* corresponds to *X*, *S* to *Y*, and so on in the order given.

In the figure, then, it is easy to see that side *AB* corresponds to *A'B'*, *BC* to *B'C'*, and so on, and of course ∠*ABC* corresponds to ∠*A'B'C'*, etc.

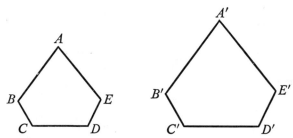

Similar Polygons   Let a one-to-one correspondence between the vertices of two polygons of the same number of sides be established.   Further, let it be given that the ratio of any two corresponding sides is the same number *k* greater than zero.   Finally let it be given that all pairs of corresponding angles are equal.   We then say the polygons are <u>similar</u> and that *k* is the ratio of similitude.

The symbol of "similar to" is "∼."   Thus $\triangle ABC \sim \triangle DEF$ means point *A* corresponds to *D*, *B* to *E*, and *C* to *F*; $\dfrac{AB}{DE} = \dfrac{BC}{EF} = \dfrac{CA}{FD} = k$; ∠*A* = ∠*D*; ∠*B* = ∠*E*, ∠*C* = ∠*F*.

Question.   Are congruent triangles similar?

Using the definition for similar polygons, it is evident that all congruent triangles are similar with the ratio *k* = 1.   Now we have the following relations for similar polygons.

(1) Any polygon is similar to itself.

(2) If one polygon is similar to a second then the second polygon is similar to the first.

(3) If one polygon is similar to a second, and the second polygon is similar to a third, then the first polygon is similar to the third.

C.

1. Is $\triangle ABC \sim \triangle DEF$? Why?

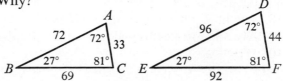

2. Is $\triangle GHI \sim \triangle JKL$? Why?

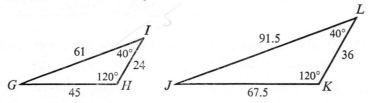

3. If these triangles are similar, write this in symbols.

4. Is $\triangle UVW \sim \triangle XYZ$? Why?

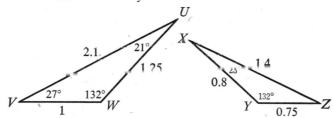

5. Is it correct to say $\triangle GHI \sim \triangle JKL$? Why or why not? What is the value of k?

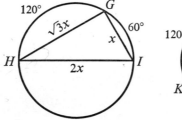
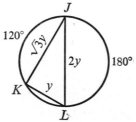

6. Is a square ~ a rhombus? Are the sides proportional? Are the angles equal?

7. Is a square ~ a rectangle? Are the angles equal? Are the sides proportional?

8. Are all equilateral triangles similar? Explain.

9. Are all isosceles triangles similar? Explain.

10. Hyp. $ae = bd$
        $af = cd$
  Con. $\triangle ABC \sim \triangle DEF$

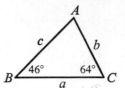 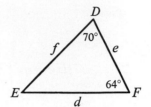

15–2 THEOREM If two angles of one triangle are equal respectively to two angles of another, the triangles are similar.

Hypothesis $\triangle ABC$ and $\triangle DEF$;
            $\angle A = \angle D;\ \angle B = \angle E$

Conclusion $\triangle ABC \sim \triangle DEF$

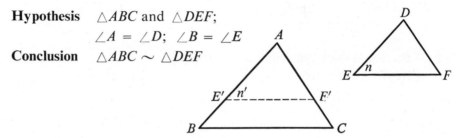

The plan is to measure on two sides of one triangle segments equal to corresponding sides of the other triangle, connect the ends of the segments, and prove that the resulting triangle is similar to one of the given triangles and congruent to the other.

Proof

1. On AB measure $AE' = DE$; on AC measure $AF' = DF$. Draw $E'F'$.	1. Give reason.
2. $\angle D = \angle A;\ \angle B = \angle E;\ \angle C = \angle F$	2. Why?
3. $AE' = DE$	3. Why?
4. $AF' = DF$	4. Why?
5. $\triangle AE'F' \cong \triangle DEF$	5. Why?
6. $\angle n' = \angle n$	6. Why?
7. $\angle n' = \angle B$	7. Why?
8. $E'F' \parallel BC$	8. Why?
9. $\dfrac{AE'}{AB} = \dfrac{AF'}{AC}$	9. Sec. 14–10
10. $\therefore\ \dfrac{DE}{AB} = \dfrac{DF}{AC}$	10. Why?

Now, if we measure $BD' = ED$, $BF' = EF$, and connect D' and F', we can repeat the sequence of steps above and prove:

11. $\dfrac{DE}{AB} = \dfrac{EF}{BC}$

Then we can combine (10) and (11) and get

12. $\dfrac{DF}{AC} = \dfrac{EF}{BC} = \dfrac{DE}{AB}$

Hence $\triangle ABC \sim \triangle DEF$ by definition. (See Sec. 15–1.)

15–3 Corollary If two isosceles triangles have equal vertex angles, the triangles are similar.

15–4 Corollary If an acute angle of one right triangle equals an acute angle of another, the triangles are similar.

15–5 Corollary If two triangles have their sides respectively parallel, the triangles are similar.

15–6 Corollary If two triangles have their sides respectively perpendicular, the triangles are similar.

EXERCISES

C. Oral

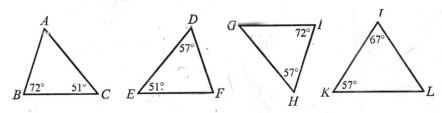

1. Name the triangles above that are similar. Give reasons for your statements.

2. Is $\triangle PQR \sim \triangle SVT$? Why?

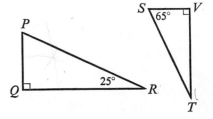

B. Written

3. On a given line segment corresponding to a given side of a given triangle construct a triangle similar to the given triangle.

   Suggestion. Use Sec. 15–2.

A.

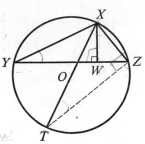

4. Prove: In any triangle the product of two sides equals the product of the altitude on the third side times the diameter of the circumscribed circle.

   Suggestion. Draw *TZ.*
   Prove $\triangle XYW \sim \triangle XTZ$.

15–7 THEOREM If two triangles have an angle of one equal to an angle of the other and the including sides proportional, they are similar.

Hypothesis $\triangle ABC$ and $\triangle DEF$; $\angle A = \angle D$; $\dfrac{DE}{AB} = \dfrac{DF}{AC}$

Conclusion $\triangle ABC \sim \triangle DEF$

The plan is the same as that for Sec. 15–2.

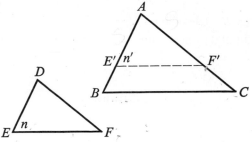

Proof

1. On *AB* measure $AE' = DE$, and on *AC* measure $AF' = DF$. Draw *E'F'*.
2. $\triangle AE'F' \cong \triangle DEF$
3. $\therefore \angle n' = \angle n$
4. $\dfrac{DE}{AB} = \dfrac{DF}{AC}$
5. $\therefore \dfrac{AE'}{AB} = \dfrac{AF'}{AC}$
6. $E'F' \parallel BC$
7. $\therefore \angle n' = \angle B$
8. $\therefore \angle n = \angle B$
9. $\angle D = \angle A$
10. $\therefore \triangle ABC \sim \triangle DEF$

1. Give reason.

2. Prove this.
3. Why?
4. Why?

5. Why?

6. Sec. 14–14
7. Why?
8. Why?
9. Why?
10. Sec. 15–2

378   GEOMETRY

EXERCISES

C. Oral

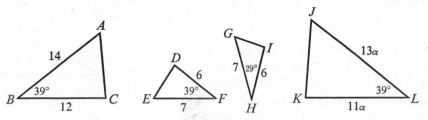

1. Name the triangles above that are similar. Give reasons for your statements.

B. Written

2. What must be the length of TV to make $\triangle STV \sim \triangle QPR$?

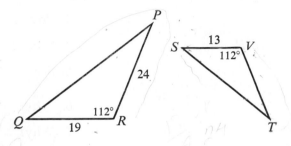

3. What must be the size of $\angle E$ to make $\triangle DEF \sim \triangle CAB$?

4. $\triangle GHI \sim \triangle JLK$
   $KL = $ _____

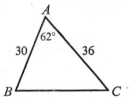

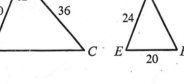

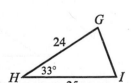

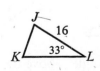

15-8 THEOREM If two triangles have their sides proportional, they are similar.

Hypothesis $\triangle ABC$ and $\triangle DEF$; $\dfrac{AB}{DE} = \dfrac{AC}{DF} = \dfrac{BC}{EF}$

Conclusion $\triangle ABC \sim \triangle DEF$

The plan is to construct on one given triangle a triangle that has two sides equal to two sides of the second given triangle and prove the constructed triangle similar to one given triangle and congruent to the other.

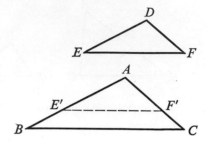

Proof

1. (*a*) On AB mark off $AE' = DE$.
   (*b*) On AC mark off $AF' = DF$.
   (*c*) Draw $E'F'$.

2. $\dfrac{AB}{DE} = \dfrac{AC}{DF}$

3. $\dfrac{AB}{AE'} = \dfrac{AC}{AF'}$

4. $\triangle ABC \sim \triangle AE'F'$

5. $\dfrac{AB}{AE'} = \dfrac{BC}{E'F'}$

6. $\dfrac{AB}{DE} = \dfrac{BC}{EF}$

7. $AE' = DE$

8. $E'F' = EF$

9. $\triangle AE'F' \cong \triangle DEF$

10. $\therefore$ $\triangle ABC \sim \triangle DEF$

1. Give reasons.

2. Why?

3. Post. 2

4. Sec. 15-7

5. Sec. 15-1

6. Why?

7. Why?

8. Sec. 14-8

9. s s s

10. Sec. 15-1

WRITTEN EXERCISES

C.

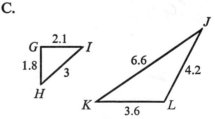

1. Name the triangles above that are similar to each other. Give reasons.

2. What must be the length of XZ and YZ to make $\triangle XYZ \sim \triangle PQR$?

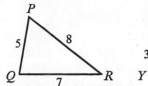
B.

3. $\angle D$ = _____ °
   $\angle E$ = _____ °
   $\angle F$ = _____ ° Why?

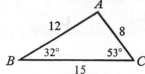
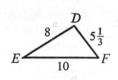

4. $JL \parallel HI$; $JK \parallel GI$; $KL \parallel GH$
   JK = _____ KL = _____
   $\angle J$ = _____ ° $\angle K$ = _____ °
   $\angle L$ = _____ °   Why?

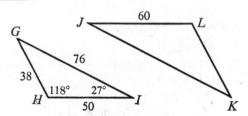

5. The sides of $\triangle XYZ$ are $x = .7n$, $y = 1.2n$ and $z = .9n$. The sides of $\triangle RST$ are $r = 2.7v$, $s = 2.1v$, and $t = 3.6v$. Are the triangles similar? If so, what is the ratio of similitude? If $\angle X = 36°$ and $\angle Z = 48°$, find $\angle R$, $\angle S$, and $\angle T$ if possible.

6. In $\triangle ABC$ if $a = 217$, $b = 372$, $c = 279$, is $\triangle ABC \sim \triangle XYZ$ of Ex. 5? If so, find $\angle A$, $\angle B$, $\angle C$.

DISCOVERY EXERCISES

$\angle RST = \angle RVS$ = a rt. $\angle$

1. Prove $\triangle RSV \sim \triangle STV \sim \triangle RTS$.
2. Prove $\dfrac{RV}{VS} = \dfrac{VS}{VT}$.
3. Prove $\dfrac{RT}{RS} = \dfrac{RS}{RV}$.
4. Prove $\dfrac{RT}{ST} = \dfrac{ST}{TV}$.

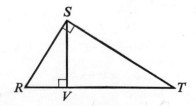

15–9   THEOREM   If in a right triangle the altitude upon the hypotenuse is drawn:

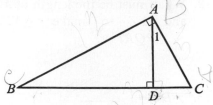

1. The triangles thus formed are similar to the given triangle and to each other.
2. The altitude is the mean proportional between the parts of the hypotenuse.
3. Each side of the given triangle is the mean proportional between the hypotenuse and its adjacent part.

Hypothesis $\triangle ABC$; $\angle BAC$ is a rt. $\angle$; $AD \perp BC$.

Conclusion   (1) $\triangle ADB \sim \triangle CDA \sim \triangle CAB$ (2) $\dfrac{BD}{AD} = \dfrac{AD}{DC}$

(3) $\dfrac{BC}{AB} = \dfrac{AB}{BD}$ (4) $\dfrac{BC}{AC} = \dfrac{AC}{DC}$

Proof

1. $\angle 1 = \angle B$	1. Sec. 6–12
2. $\triangle ADB \sim \triangle CDA \sim \triangle CAB$	2. Sec. 15–4
3. $\dfrac{BD}{AD} = \dfrac{AD}{DC}$	3. Def. of $\sim$ polygons
4. $\dfrac{BC}{AB} = \dfrac{AB}{BD}$, and $\dfrac{BC}{AC} = \dfrac{AC}{DC}$	4. Def. of $\sim$ polygons

15–10   The Pythagorean Theorem and its Converse.   **THEOREM**   In a right triangle, the square of the hypotenuse is equal to the sum of the squares of the arms.

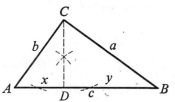

Hypothesis $\angle C = 90°$, sides a, b, and c.

Conclusion $c^2 = a^2 + b^2$.

Construction.   Draw $CD \perp AB$ dividing it into segments x and y.

Proof

1. $\dfrac{y}{a} = \dfrac{a}{c}, \dfrac{x}{b} = \dfrac{b}{c}$	1. Sec. 15–9
2. $cy = a^2$; $cx = b^2$	2. Sec. 14–4
3. $a^2 + b^2 = cx + cy$	3. Why?
4. $cx + cy = c(x + y)$	4. Distributive law
5. $x + y = c$; $c(x + y) = c^2$	5. Substitution
6. $a^2 + b^2 = c^2$	6. Why?

Converse   If in a triangle, the square of one side equals the sum of the squares of the other two sides, the triangle is a right triangle.

Hypothesis $\triangle ABC$, $c^2 = a^2 + b^2$

Conclusion $\angle ACB = 90°$

Construction.   Draw $CD \perp BC$ and of length b. Connect B to D.

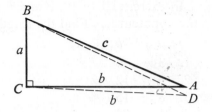

Proof

1. BCD is a right triangle.	1. Construction
2. $\overline{BD}^2 = a^2 + b^2$	2. Sec. 15–10
3. $c^2 = a^2 + b^2$	3. Given
4. $c = BD$	4. If $c^2 = \overline{BD}^2$, then $c = BD$
5. $\triangle BCD \cong \triangle BCA$	5. s s s
6. $\angle ACB = 90°$	6. $\angle ACB = \angle BCD$

NOTE: Throughout the remainder of this course and in later experiences you will need to know how to find or compute square roots of numbers. In your study of arithmetic and algebra you have learned to do this. Also, a Table of Squares and Square Roots is on page 556.

15–11   Corollary   If a line segment is drawn perpendicular to a diameter of a circle from any point on the circle, it is the mean proportional between the parts of the diameter.

Problem   To construct the mean proportional to two segments.

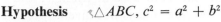

Given   Segments m and n

Required   To construct a segment x such that $\dfrac{m}{x} = \dfrac{x}{n}$.

Construction.   (1) Draw a line AB and on it mark off $AC = m$ and $CB = n$. (2) On AB as diameter construct a semicircle. (3) At C construct a perpendicular to AB and let it intersect the semicircle at D. Then CD is the required segment x, and $\dfrac{m}{x} = \dfrac{x}{n}$. Give the proof.

WRITTEN EXERCISES

C.

In exercises 1 to 10, a and b are the arms of a right triangle, and c is the hypotenuse. Find the length of the side that is not given.

	a	b	c			a	b	c
1.	3	4			6.	55	132	
2.	5	12			7.	24	45	
3.	8	15			8.	40	75	
4.	21	28			9.	12		20
5.	25	60			10.	32		68

11. $CD =$ _____ Why?

12. $GH =$ _____ Why?

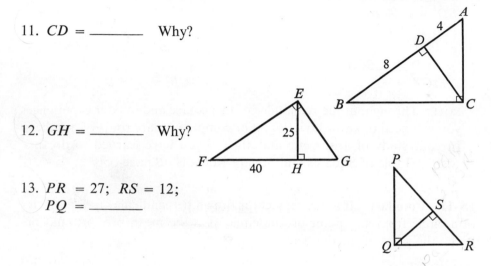

13. $PR = 27$; $RS = 12$;
    $PQ =$ _____

B.

14. Find the diameter of $\odot O$.

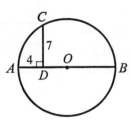

15. Prove: MR is the mean proportional to MS and MN.

16. Find MR if $MQ = 6$ and $NS = 9$.

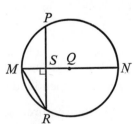

A.

17. Prove: AB is the mean proportional to AC and AD.
18. Find AB if $AC = 12$ and
$AD = 9$.

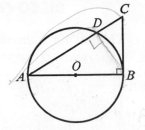

19. Prove: $\overline{XY}^2 = XL \cdot XZ$.

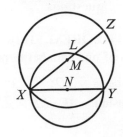

Optional Topic

Primitive Pythagorean Integers   Pythagorean integers are any three integers that satisfy the Pythagorean formula.   For example, 3, 4, and 5 are Pythagorean integers because $3^2 + 4^2 = 5^2$.   These numbers are primitive Pythagorean integers because they have no common factor.

There is a simple method for finding primitive Pythagorean integers. Let $a = x^2 - y^2$, $b = 2xy$, and $c = x^2 + y^2$.   Select x and y any integers that satisfy these conditions: x is greater than y, x and y have no common factors, and either x or y is an even number and the other is odd.   Then a, b, and c are primitive Pythagorean integers.   Verify the sets of numbers given in this table and extend the table by computing other values.

x	y	a	b	c
2	1	3	4	5
3	2	5	12	13
4	1	15	8	17
4	3	7	24	25
5	2	21	20	29
5	4	?	?	?
6	1	?	?	?
6	5	?	?	?
7	2	?	?	?
?	?	33	56	65

DISCOVERY EXERCISES

HJ and *KL* are chords intersecting at *M*.

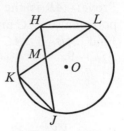

1. Prove $\triangle LMH \sim \triangle JMK$.
2. Does $\dfrac{HM}{LM} = \dfrac{KM}{JM}$? Why?
3. Does $HM \times JM = LM \times KM$? Why?
4. State a theorem based upon your answers to these questions.

15–12 THEOREM If two chords intersect in a circle, the product of the segments of one equals the product of the segments of the other.

Hypothesis $\odot O$; *AB* and *CD* are chords that intersect at *E*.

Conclusion $AE \cdot EB = CE \cdot ED$.

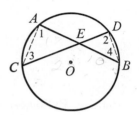

The plan is to connect the ends of the chords, forming triangles that have vertical angles, and prove the triangles similar.

Proof

1. Draw *AC* and *DB*.
2. $\angle 1 = \angle 2$, $\angle 3 = \angle 4$
3. $\triangle ACE \sim \triangle DBE$
4. $\dfrac{AE}{CE} = \dfrac{ED}{EB}$
5. $\therefore AE \cdot EB = CE \cdot ED$

1. Give reasons.
2. Sec. 12–20
3. Why?
4. Sec. 15–1
5. Why?

WRITTEN EXERCISES

C.

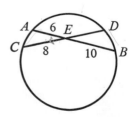

1. $DE = $ _____ Why?

2. $GH = 52$. $GK = $ _____

3. Find CE.

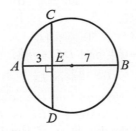

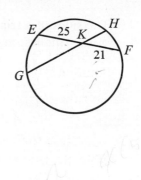

In Ex. 4–7 use the figure of Sec. 15–12. You will find it helpful to reproduce the figure for each exercise and on it write the lengths of the given segments as in Ex. 1–3 above.

4. If $AE = 12.4$, $BE = 16.3$, and $CE = 11.5$, find DE.
5. If $AB = 27$, $BE = 10$, and $DE = 14$, find CE.
6. If $BE = 0.16$, $CE = 1.09$, and $DE = 0.98$, find AE.
7. If $AE = 2x$, $BE = 3x$, $AB = 45$, and $CE = 16$, find DE.
8. Two concentric circles have radii 3 inches and 4 inches respectively. Find the length of a chord of one that is tangent to the other.
9. Repeat Ex. 8 with radii of 26 inches and 45 inches.

A.

10. Prove: In any triangle the square of the bisector of an angle equals the product of the sides that include the bisected angle decreased by the product of the segments made by the bisector on the third side of the triangle. Write a complete demonstration.

    Suggestion. Circumscribe a circle about $\triangle ABC$. Extend AD, the bisector of $\angle BAC$, to intersect the circle at E. Draw CE.

    Is $\triangle ABD \sim \triangle AEC$? Does $AB \cdot AC = AD \cdot AE$?
    Does $AD \cdot AE = AD(AD + DE)$
    $$= \overline{AD}^2 + AD \cdot DE?$$
    Does $\overline{AD}^2 = AD \cdot AE - AD \cdot DE$?
    Does $AD \cdot DE = BD \cdot CD$?
    Does $\overline{AD}^2 = AB \cdot AC - BD \cdot CD$?

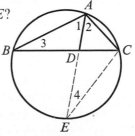

NOTE: This theorem with Sec. 14–15 enables us to calculate the length of the bisector of an angle of a triangle if the three sides are given.

11. The sides of a triangle are 5, 6, and 7. Find the length of the bisector of the smallest angle.

Solution. $\dfrac{AD}{DC} = \dfrac{AB}{BC}$, or $\dfrac{AD}{5 - AD} = \dfrac{6}{7}$.

Then, $7AD = 30 - 6AD$.

$\therefore AD = \frac{30}{13}$, and $DC = \frac{35}{13}$.

$\overline{BD}^2 = 6 \times 7 - \frac{30}{13} \times \frac{35}{13} = \frac{6048}{169}$

Now divide 6048 by 169 and find the square root of the result.

Question. How do we know $\angle ABC$ is the smallest angle of $\triangle ABC$?

12. Find the length of the bisector of the largest angle in the triangle given in Ex. 11.

13. The sides of a triangle are 3, 4, and 5. Find the length of the bisector of the largest angle.

14. Prove: In any triangle the square of the bisector of an exterior angle equals the product of the segments made by the bisector on the opposite side decreased by the product of the other two sides.

Hyp. AD bisects $\angle CAB'$.

Con. $\overline{AD}^2 = BD \cdot CD - AB \cdot AC$

Construction. Circumscribe a circle about $\triangle ABC$. Extend DA to E. Draw EC.

Proof

Does $\angle 3 = \angle 4$?

Does $\angle 1 = \angle 2 = \angle 6$?

Does $\angle 1 + \angle 5 = \angle 6 + \angle 5$?

Is $\triangle ABD \sim \triangle AEC$? Does $AB \cdot AC = AD \cdot AE$?

Does $AD \cdot AE = AD(DE - AD) = AD \cdot DE - \overline{AD}^2$?

Does $\overline{AD}^2 = AD \cdot DE - AD \cdot AE$? Does $AD \cdot DE = BD \cdot CD$?

Does $\overline{AD}^2 = BD \cdot DC - AB \cdot AC$? Write out the complete proof.

NOTE: This theorem with Sec. 14–16 enables us to find the length of the bisector of an exterior angle of a triangle if the three sides are given.

15. The sides of a triangle are 2, 3, and 4. Find the length of the bisector of the smallest exterior angle.

16. Find the length of the bisector of the largest exterior angle of the triangle given in Ex. 15.

17. The sides of a triangle are 6, 6, and 4. Can you compute the length of the bisector of one of the largest exterior angles? Explain.

EG is tangent to ⊙*O*, and *EHK* is a secant.

1. What angle equals ∠*K*? Why?
2. Is △*EGH* ~ △*EKG*? Why?
3. Does $\dfrac{EH}{EG} = \dfrac{EG}{EK}$? Why?

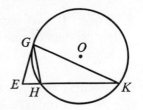

15–13 THEOREM If a secant and a tangent are drawn to a circle from the same external point, the tangent is the mean proportional between the secant and its external part.

Hypothesis ⊙*O*; *AC* is a tangent and *AB* is a secant.

Conclusion $\dfrac{AB}{AC} = \dfrac{AC}{AD}$

The plan is to draw chords from the points of intersection of the secant with the circle to the point of tangency and prove a pair of resulting triangles similar.

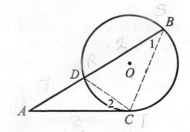

Proof

1. Draw *BC* and *DC*.
2. $\angle 1 \stackrel{\circ}{=} \frac{1}{2}\overset{\frown}{DC}$
3. $\angle 2 \stackrel{\circ}{=} \frac{1}{2}\overset{\frown}{DC}$
4. ∠1 = ∠2
5. ∠*A* = ∠*A*
6. △*ABC* ~ △*ACD*
7. ∴ $\dfrac{AB}{AC} = \dfrac{AC}{AD}$

1. Give reasons.
2. Why?
3. Why?
4. Why?
5. Why?
6. Why?
7. Why?

WRITTEN EXERCISES

C.

In Ex. 1–4, use the figure of Sec. 15–13.

1. Given: *AB* = 4.5; *AC* = 3. Find *AD*.
2. Given: *AB* = 16; *AC* = 1. Find *AD* and *BD*.
3. Given: *AD* = 40; *BD* = 50. Find *AC*.
4. Given: *AB* = 100; *AC* = 40. Find *AD*.

5. Prove: If two secants are drawn from an external point to a circle, the product of one secant and its external part equals the product of the other secant and its external part.

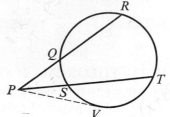

6. Given: $PQ = 7$; $QR = 5$; $PS = 9$.
   Find ST.

7. Given: $PR = 125$; $QR = 70$; $ST = 80$.
   Find PT.

15–14 Optional **Problem** **To divide a line segment in extreme and mean ratio.** The Golden Section. (See Sec. 14–18.)

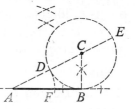

Given   Segment AB

Required   To locate F and F' on AB so that
$$\frac{AB}{AF} = \frac{AF}{FB}, \text{ and } \frac{AB}{AF'} = \frac{AF'}{F'B}$$

Construction. (1) Bisect AB. (2) Construct $BC \perp AB$, and mark off $BC = \frac{1}{2}AB$. (3) With C as center and BC as radius draw a circle. (4) From A draw secant AC intersecting $\odot C$ at D and E. (5) On AB mark off $AF = AD$, and $AF' = AE$. Then $\dfrac{AB}{AF} = \dfrac{AF}{FB}$, and $\dfrac{AB}{AF'} = \dfrac{AF'}{F'B}$

Proof Designate the length of AB by $2a$. Then $CB = a$. By the Pythagorean Theorem $\overline{CA}^2 = 4a^2 + a^2 = 5a^2$. Hence $CA = a\sqrt{5}$. Since $CD = a$, $AD = a\sqrt{5} - a$ or $a(\sqrt{5} - 1)$. $AE = a\sqrt{5} + a = a(\sqrt{5} + 1)$. $AF = AD$, and hence $AF = a(\sqrt{5} - 1)$ and $FB = 2a - a(\sqrt{5} - 1)$ or $a(3 - \sqrt{5})$.

$$\frac{AB}{AF} = \frac{2a}{a(\sqrt{5} - 1)} = \frac{2}{(\sqrt{5} - 1)} \cdot \frac{(\sqrt{5} + 1)}{(\sqrt{5} + 1)} = \frac{2(\sqrt{5} + 1)}{4} = \frac{\sqrt{5} + 1}{2}$$

$$\frac{AF}{FB} = \frac{a(\sqrt{5} - 1)}{a(3 - \sqrt{5})} = \frac{(\sqrt{5} - 1)(3 + \sqrt{5})}{(3 - \sqrt{5})(3 + \sqrt{5})} = \frac{2\sqrt{5} + 2}{4} = \frac{\sqrt{5} + 1}{2}$$

$\therefore \dfrac{AB}{AF} = \dfrac{AF}{FB}$ and F divides AB internally into extreme and mean ratio.

Similarly

$$\frac{AB}{AF'} = \frac{2d}{d(\sqrt{5}+1)} = \frac{2(\sqrt{5}-1)}{4} = \frac{\sqrt{5}-1}{2}$$

$$\frac{AF'}{F'B} = \frac{d(\sqrt{5}+1)}{d(3+\sqrt{5})} = \frac{(\sqrt{5}+1)(3-\sqrt{5})}{4} = \frac{2\sqrt{5}-2}{4} = \frac{\sqrt{5}-1}{2}$$

$\dfrac{AB}{AF'} = \dfrac{AF'}{F'B}$ and F' divides AB externally into extreme and mean ratio.

EXERCISE (Optional)

Divide a 3-inch line in extreme and mean ratio. Check the accuracy of your construction by measurement and calculation.

15–15 Optional **Problem** **To construct an angle of 36°.**

Construction. (1) Draw any segment AB.
(2) Divide AB at F in extreme and mean
ratio making $\dfrac{AB}{AF} = \dfrac{AF}{FB}$. (3) Construct

$\triangle ABG$ having $AG = AB$ and $BG = AF$.
Then $\angle A = 36°$. Draw FG.

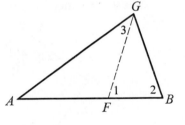

Proof

1. $\dfrac{AB}{AF} = \dfrac{AF}{FB}$	1. Why?
2. $\dfrac{AB}{BG} = \dfrac{BG}{FB}$	2. Why?
3. $\triangle BFG \sim \triangle BGA$	3. Sec. 15–7
4. $\dfrac{BG}{FG} = \dfrac{AB}{AG}$	4. Why?
5. $BG = FG$	5. Why?
6. $\angle 1 = \angle 2$	6. Why?
7. $AF = FG$	7. Each equals BG.
8. $\angle A = \angle 3$	8. Why?
9. $\angle 1 = 2\angle A$	9. Why?
10. $\angle 2 = 2\angle A$	10. Why?
11. $\angle BGA = 2\angle A$	11. Why?
12. $\angle 2 + \angle BGA + \angle A = 5\angle A = 180°$	12. Why?
13. $\therefore \ \angle A = 36°$	13. Why?

This construction enables us to construct a regular pentagon.

15–16 Perimeter   The perimeter of a polygon is the sum of the lengths of its sides.

ORAL EXERCISES

1. What is the perimeter of a square if one side is 100 yards?
2. What is the perimeter of an equiangular triangle if one side is 2 inches?
3. What is the perimeter of a parallelogram if two of its sides are 2 feet and 3 feet respectively?

15–17 THEOREM   **If two polygons are similar, the ratio of their perimeters equals the ratio of any pair of corresponding sides.**

Hypothesis   Polygon $ABCDE \sim$ polygon $FGHIJ$; their perimeters are p and q respectively; AB and FG are corresponding sides.

Conclusion $\dfrac{p}{q} = \dfrac{AB}{FG}$

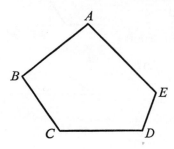 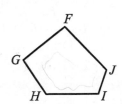

Proof

1. $\dfrac{AB}{FG} = \dfrac{BC}{GH} = \dfrac{CD}{HI} = \dfrac{DE}{IJ} = \dfrac{AE}{FJ}$ 1. Sec. 15–1

2. Let the ratio $\dfrac{AB}{FG} = r$. Then   2. Post. 4

   $AB = r \cdot FG$. Also,
   $BC = r \cdot GH,\ CD = r \cdot HI,$
   $DE = r \cdot IJ,\ AE = r \cdot FJ.$

3. $AB + BC + CD + DE + AE$ 3. Explain.
   $= r(FG + GH + HI + IJ + FJ)$

4. $\therefore \dfrac{AB + BC + CD + DE + AE}{FG + GH + HI + IJ + FJ} = r$ 4. Post. 3

   $= \dfrac{AB}{FG}$, or $\dfrac{p}{q} = \dfrac{AB}{FG}$

1. Hyp. $P \sim P'$; the perimeter of P is 64; the perimeter of P' is 48. Find $A'B'$.

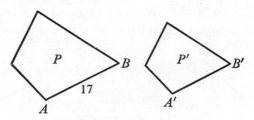

2. Hyp. $Q \sim Q'$; the perimeter of Q is 28. Find the perimeter of Q', CD and $C'D'$ being corresponding sides.

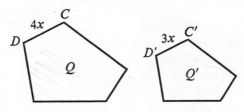

3. Hyp. $\dfrac{a}{b} = \dfrac{c}{d} = \dfrac{e}{f}$ Prove $\dfrac{a}{b} + \dfrac{c}{d} + \dfrac{e}{f} = \dfrac{a}{b}.$

4. Hyp. $\dfrac{a}{b} = \dfrac{c}{d}$ Prove $\dfrac{a+c}{b+d} = \dfrac{c-d}{b-d} = \dfrac{a}{b}.$

5. $T \sim T'$. Find the perimeter of T'.

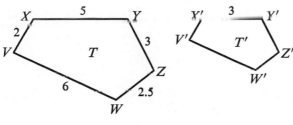

6. $\odot OA$ and $\odot OA'$ are concentric. $OA = 10$; $OA' = 4$. Find the perimeter of $A'B'C'D'E'$.

15–18 THEOREM If two polygons are similar, they can be divided into the same number of triangles, respectively similar and similarly placed.

Hypothesis Polygon *ABCDE* ∼ polygon *FGHIJ*

Conclusion *ABCDE* and *FGHIJ* can be divided into the same number of triangles respectively similar and similarly placed.

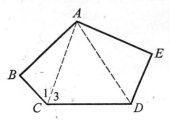 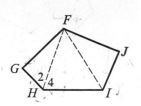

Proof

1. Let *A* and *F* be corresponding vertices. From *A* and *F* draw all possible diagonals.	1. Give reasons.
2. The number of triangles in the polygons is the same, because each polygon has as many triangles as it has sides less 2.	2. Definition of triangle.
3. $\dfrac{AB}{BC} = \dfrac{FG}{GH}$	3. Sec. 15–1
4. ∠*B* = ∠*G*	4. Sec. 15–1
5. △*ABC* ∼ △*FGH*	5. Why?
6. $\dfrac{BC}{GH} = \dfrac{AC}{FH}$	6. Why?
7. $\dfrac{BC}{GH} = \dfrac{CD}{HI}$	7. Why?
8. $\dfrac{AC}{FH} = \dfrac{CD}{HI}$	8. Why?
9. ∠*BCD* = ∠*GHI*	9. Why?
10. ∠1 = ∠2	10. Why?
11. ∴ ∠3 = ∠4	11. =s − =s
12. △*ACD* ∼ △*FHI*	12. Sec. 15–7
13. Similarly we can continue around the entire polygon.	

NOTE: Nothing in the statement of this theorem suggests that the triangles must be made by diagonals from only one vertex. Make a different drawing and suggest how it can be used in the demonstration.

B.

1. Prove: If two polygons are similar, the ratio of two corresponding diagonals equals the ratio of any two corresponding sides.
2. Prove: If two polygons are similar, the ratio of two corresponding diagonals equals the ratio of the perimeters of the polygons.

3. $P \sim P'$. Find CD.

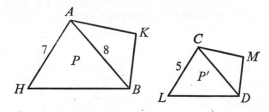

15–19 THEOREM If two polygons can be divided into the same number of triangles, respectively similar and similarly placed, the polygons are similar.

Hypothesis Polygons $ABCDE$ and $FGHIJ$; $\triangle ABC \sim \triangle FGH$; $\triangle ACD \sim \triangle FHI$; $\triangle ADE \sim \triangle FIJ$

Conclusion $ABCDE \sim FGHIJ$

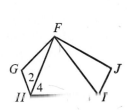
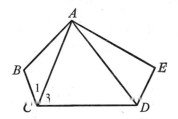

Proof

1. $\dfrac{BC}{GH} = \dfrac{AC}{FH} = \dfrac{AB}{FG}$ 1. Sec. 15–1

2. $\dfrac{AC}{FH} = \dfrac{CD}{HI}$ 2. Why?

3. $\dfrac{AB}{FG} = \dfrac{BC}{GH} = \dfrac{CD}{HI}$ 3. Why?

4. Likewise, $\dfrac{CD}{HI} = \dfrac{DE}{JI}$, etc.

5. $\angle 1 = \angle 2$, $\angle 3 = \angle 4$ 5. Why?
6. $\angle BCD = \angle GHI$ 6. $=$s $+$ $=$s
7. Likewise, $\angle CDE = \angle HIJ$, etc.
8. $\therefore ABCDE \sim FGHIJ$ 8. Sec. 15–1

Optional Topics

Light The understanding of mirrors, lenses, cameras, and other instruments that make use of light depends largely upon the application of the principles of geometry. A few of these applications will be pointed out.

How the artist determines the size of an object in a picture. You may have seen an artist who is working on a landscape painting hold a pencil or brush at arm's length, close one eye, and adjust the thumb on the pencil so that the pencil just covers some object that he is putting into the picture. Having done this, he turns to the paper or canvas on which he is working and sketches the object the length indicated on the pencil. He is using the principle of similar and congruent triangles. The paper is

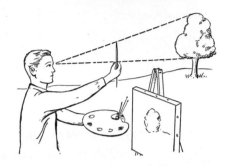

at arm's length from his eye and hence if he paints the object the same length as the indicated part of the pencil, the angle made by the object equals the angle made by the picture of the object: and it is this angle that gives an object or a picture of the object its apparent size.

Parallax If you look at two objects in line, one near and the other far away, and close first one eye then the other, the distant object seems to shift from side to side. This effect is called parallax. It is an apparent change of position of an object due to an actual change of the position of the observation.

One can tell the approximate distance of an object by using the parallax principle, provided the size of the object is known. Let *P* be a distant object, *O* an object near the observer the distance of which is known, *E* and *E'* the eyes of the observer. Suppose the object *P* to shift its apparent position from *P* to *P'* and back again as first one eye then the other is closed. By comparing the known

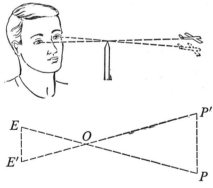

size of the object with the distance *PP'*, one can tell approximately the length of *PP'*. Now, $PP'/PO = EE'/EO$. Why? Since EE' and EO are known, the distance *PO* can be determined. How?

1. What triangles are similar when the artist determines the length of an object by the method described above?
2. How could the artist use the principle of similar triangles in making the sketch?
3. How far away is an automobile if its apparent position is shifted approximately 5 times the length of the car when first one eye then the other is closed and it is observed with reference to an object 40 feet away? Assume the length of the car to be 16 feet and the distance between the eyes to be 2.5 inches.
4. How far away is a house if it shifts an apparent distance equal to 10 times its width as the observer moves a distance of 40 feet and observes the house with respect to a tree that is 60 feet from each observation point? Assume the width of the house to be 50 feet.

The Plane Mirror The law of the reflection of light is: *the angle of incidence equals the angle of reflection.* The angle of incidence is the angle between a line that is perpendicular to the mirror and a ray of light that strikes it. The angle of reflection is the angle between a line that is perpendicular to the mirror and the reflected ray.

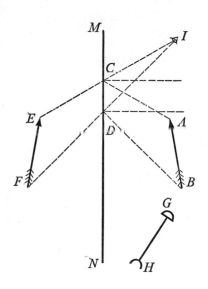

The image EF of an object AB seen in a mirror MN appears to be as far back of the mirror as the object is in front of it. It can be shown that $ABDC \cong CDFE$ and therefore $EF = AB$; that is, as seen in the mirror, an object has the same size as if it were at the distance of EF from the eye, which it is, so far as the distances traveled by the rays of light are concerned. Hence it is seen that a plane mirror neither magnifies nor makes the object appear smaller. The image of GH can be constructed by drawing $GJ \perp MN$ and $HK \perp MN$ and extending these perpendiculars to R and S respectively, making $JR = GJ$ and $KS = HK$. Draw RS.

5. Prove $IC + CA = IC + CE$. Draw any needed lines.
6. Prove $ABCD \cong CDFE$.
7. Draw a line XY and construct its image ZW as seen in a plane mirror PQ from a point T.

Refraction When a ray of light passes from the air into glass or water at an oblique angle, it is refracted (bent) to make the angle of refraction y less than the angle of incidence x. If it again passes from the glass or water into the air, it is once more refracted to make the angle of refraction w greater than the angle of incidence z. If the glass has parallel surfaces as here shown, then AB is parallel to CD.

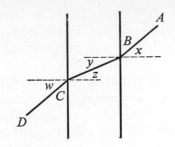

NOTE: In this discussion, it is assumed that the angle of incidence is less than the critical angle, the least angle at which the ray of light will not enter the glass but will be reflected.

8. EF is an incident ray of light. Reproduce this figure and construct the ray after it leaves the glass at G.

9. A fish at W is seen by a man with his eye at X. The lines show the path of the ray of light coming to his eye. Reproduce this figure and draw in lines to show the fish in the position where it appears to the man to be. If the man wants to shoot the fish, how should he take account of refraction so that he will not shoot over or under the fish?

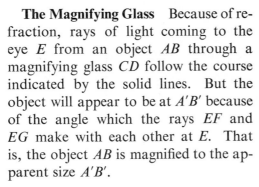

The Magnifying Glass Because of refraction, rays of light coming to the eye E from an object AB through a magnifying glass CD follow the course indicated by the solid lines. But the object will appear to be at A'B' because of the angle which the rays EF and EG make with each other at E. That is, the object AB is magnified to the apparent size A'B'.

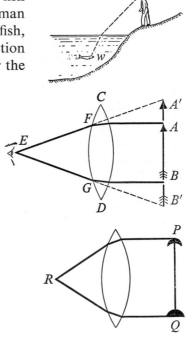

10. Reproduce this figure and draw PQ as it will appear to an eye at R.

WRITTEN EXERCISE

A.

On a given line segment construct a polygon similar to a given polygon.

Let *ABCDE* be the given polygon and *C'D'* a given segment corresponding to *CD*.

At *D'* construct ∠2 = ∠1. At *C'* construct ∠4 = ∠3. Then △*C'D'E'* ~ △*CDE*. Why?

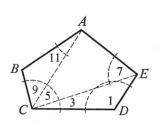 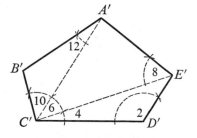

Let the pupil complete the description of the construction and give the proof.

B.

1. Prove: The greatest distance, d miles, at which an object is visible on the level surface of the earth or at sea from a height h feet is given approximately by the formula $d = \sqrt{\dfrac{3h}{2}}$.

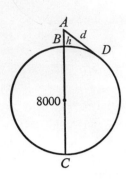

Solution. Let A be the point from which observation is made. $AB = h$ feet, $AD = d$ miles, and $BC = 8000$ miles, the diameter of the earth. Then the secant $AC = 8000 + \dfrac{h}{5280}$ miles. Explain.

Now, $\dfrac{AB}{AD} = \dfrac{AD}{AC}$. Why? Then, $AB \cdot AC = \overline{AD}^2$, or $AD = \sqrt{AB \cdot AC}$.

Why? That is, $d = \sqrt{\dfrac{h}{5280}\left(8000 + \dfrac{h}{5280}\right)} = \sqrt{\dfrac{8000h}{5280} + \dfrac{h^2}{(5280)^2}}$.

Since h will generally be small, $\dfrac{h^2}{5280^2}$ will be so small that it can be left out without making an appreciable error. This gives $d = \sqrt{\dfrac{8000h}{5280}}$, or $d = \sqrt{\dfrac{3h}{2}}$, approximately.

2. How far can an officer on a battleship see from the crow's nest 80 feet above the surface of the sea?

3. How far can a ship be seen from the top of the Woolworth Building in New York City if the observer at the top of the building is 775 feet above sea level?

4. Lighthouses are seldom higher than 250 feet. How far can a sailor see the light of such a house? (Assume the observation to be made from the surface of the sea.)

5. Thales, a mathematician of ancient Greece, surprised the Egyptians by finding the height of one of the great pyramids by measuring the length of its shadow and comparing this with the length of the shadow of his staff. Explain how this could be done.

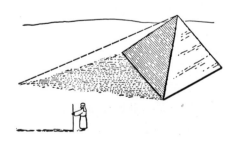

6. How far can one see across a plain from the top of a mountain peak which rises ¾ of a mile above the level of the plain?

7. A tree casts a shadow 80 feet long at the same time that a post 5 feet high casts a shadow 4 feet long. How high is the tree?

8. The shadow of a cliff extends 470 feet across a valley at the same time that the shadow of a man 6 feet high is $4\frac{1}{2}$ feet long. How high is the cliff?

9. Prove: If one base of a trapezoid is twice the other, the diagonals trisect each other.

10. Prove: If a line segment is parallel to the bases of a trapezoid, passes through the intersection point of the diagonals, and is terminated by the nonparallel sides, it is bisected at the point where it intersects the diagonals.

A.

11. *ABCD* is a parallelogram. *AG* is drawn cutting the diagonal *BD* at *E*, the side *BC* at *F*, and the side *DC* extended at *G*. Prove: *AE* is the mean proportional between *EF* and *EG*.

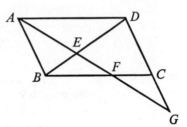

12. *ABC* is any triangle. *DK* is any line intersecting *AB* at *F*, *AC* at *E*, and *BC* extended at *D*. Prove: $AF \times BD \times CE = AE \times BF \times CD$. (The Theorem of Menelaus.)

Suggestions. Prove that $\dfrac{AF}{BF} = \dfrac{AH}{BK}$, $\dfrac{BD}{CD} = \dfrac{BK}{CL}$, and $\dfrac{CE}{AE} = \dfrac{CL}{AH}$. Multiply the members of these equations together.

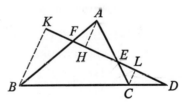

13. Prove: The tangents to two intersecting circles from any point on the common chord extended are equal.

NOTE: The line *ACD* is the radical axis of circles *O* and *Q*.

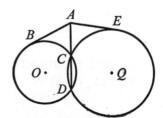

14. Find a point such that tangents from it to two given circles are equal.

   NOTE: *P* is a point on the radical axis of circles *O* and *Q*. See Ex. 13.

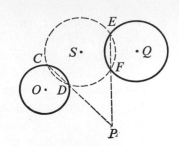

15. *PQR* is any triangle. *O* is any point inside the triangle. *PO* is drawn intersecting *QR* at *X*; *QO* is drawn intersecting *PR* at *Y*; *RO* is drawn intersecting *PQ* at *Z*. Prove:

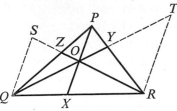

   $PZ \times QX \times RY = PY \times QZ \times RX$.
   (Ceva's Theorem.)

   Suggestions. Draw $QS \parallel PX$ intersecting RZ extended at S; draw $RT \parallel PX$ intersecting QY extended at T. Prove $\triangle QXO \sim \triangle QRT$, $\triangle RXO \sim \triangle RQS$, $\triangle RTY \sim \triangle POY$, $\triangle POZ \sim \triangle QSZ$. Then, $\dfrac{QS}{OX} = \dfrac{QR}{XR}$, and $\dfrac{OX}{TR} = \dfrac{QX}{QR}$. Multiplying these equations we have $\dfrac{QS}{TR} = \dfrac{QX}{RX}$, also $\dfrac{TR}{PO} = \dfrac{RY}{PY}$, and $\dfrac{PO}{QS} = \dfrac{PZ}{QZ}$. Multiply the last three equations, left sides by left, and right sides by right.

16. *AD* and *BE* are two altitudes of $\triangle ABC$.
   Prove: $\dfrac{AD}{BE} = \dfrac{AC}{BC}$

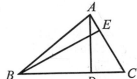

17. The bisector *AD* of $\angle BAC$ of $\triangle ABC$ intersects the circumscribed circle at *E*.
   Prove: $\dfrac{AD}{AC} = \dfrac{AB}{AE}$

   Suggestion. Prove $\triangle ABD \sim \triangle AEC$.

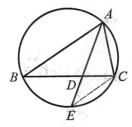

18. *RS* and *QT* are altitudes of $\triangle PQR$.
   Prove: $\triangle PST \sim \triangle PRQ$.

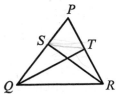

19. Two circles are tangent at P. AA', BB', and CC' are drawn through P.
Prove: $\triangle ABC \sim \triangle A'B'C'$.

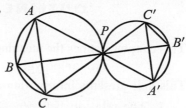

20. Given a line AB and two points C and D not on and not separated by the line. Construct a circle that passes through C and D and is tangent to AB.

Suggestions. Draw the line determined by C and D. Let E be the intersection point of this line with AB. Suppose the circle has been constructed. Let F be the point of tangency. Then EF is the mean proportional between EC and ED.

21. Given two lines AB and CD and a point E not on either line. Construct a circle that passes through E and is tangent to AB and CD.

Suggestions. Bisect the angle formed by AB and CD. Construct a perpendicular to this angle bisector through E. Locate F on this perpendicular so that the angle bisector also bisects EF. Now construct a circle through E and F and tangent to AB.

Question. If AB and CD are parallel, how will this construction be changed?

22. The hypsometer is an instrument for getting the length of an inaccessible line by using the principle of similar triangles. It can be made by tacking a piece of cross-ruled paper to a board and suspending a weight at A'. Prove $\triangle ABC \sim \triangle A'B'C'$ and show how to find BC by use of the instrument.

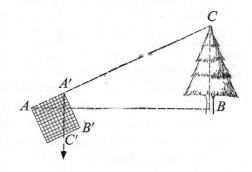

23. A clinometer is an instrument for measuring an angle of inclination. Show how to construct and use one as illustrated in this drawing.

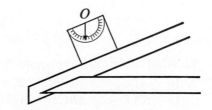

OUTLINE OF CHAPTER 15

This chapter defines the meanings of the terms:

similar polygons   perimeters

This unit presents information concerning:

1. The relation between two triangles that have two angles of one equal respectively to two angles of the other. Page 376
2. The relation between two triangles that have their sides respectively parallel or perpendicular. Page 377
3. The relation between two triangles that have an angle of one equal to an angle of the other and the including sides proportional. Page 378
4. The relation between two triangles that have proportional sides. Page 380
5. Proportions resulting from drawing the altitude to the hypotenuse of a right triangle. Page 382
6. The Pythagorean Theorem and its converse. Pages 382, 383
7. The construction of the mean proportional to two segments. Page 383
8. The relation between the segments of two chords that intersect in a circle. Page 386
9. The relation between a tangent, a secant that intersects the tangent, and the external part of the secant. Page 389
10. The method of dividing a line segment in extreme and mean ratio. Page 390
11. The method of constructing an angle of 36°. Page 391
12. The ratio of the perimeters of similar polygons. Page 392
13. The relation between the similarly placed triangles formed by corresponding diagonals of similar polygons. Page 394
14. Similarity of polygons as a consequence of similarity of component triangles. Page 395

REVIEW

1. What are similar polygons? Illustrate.
2. In $\triangle ABC$, $\angle A = 49°$, $\angle B = 73°$. In $\triangle RST$, $\angle T = 58°$, $\angle S = 73°$. Is $\triangle RST \sim \triangle ABC$? Why?

3. The sides of $\triangle DEF$ are 3 in., 4 in., and 5 in. The sides of $\triangle GHK$ are 8 in., 10 in., and 6 in. Are the triangles similar? Why?

4. Draw a scalene triangle XYZ. Draw a line segment $X'Y'$ which is longer than XY. On $X'Y'$ construct $\triangle X'Y'Z'$ similar to $\triangle XYZ$. Describe the steps and prove that the triangles are similar.

5. In $\triangle ABC$, $AB = 11$ cm., $AC = 15$ cm., $\angle A = 58°$, $\angle B = 65°$. In $\triangle DEF$, $DE = 33$ in., $DF = 45$ in., $\angle D = 58°$. Find $\angle E$. Prove the steps by which you reach your conclusion.

6. $\triangle RST$ is a right triangle with the right angle at R. The point M is on ST. $RM \perp ST$. Prove that $\triangle RSM \sim \triangle TRM$.

7. Construct the mean proportional to two given segments and prove your construction.

8. RS and TV are chords in $\odot O$. They intersect at N. $RN = 4$ cm., $NS = 3$ cm., $TN = 5$ cm. How long is TV?

9. P is a point outside $\odot Q$. PT is a tangent and PRS is a secant. $PR = 4$ in., $RS = 2$ in. Find the length of PT.

10. In pentagon $ABCDE$, $AB = 2$ in., and the perimeter of the pentagon is 15 in. $FGHJK$ is a pentagon similar to $ABCDE$ and with FG corresponding to AB. $FG = 3$ in. What is the perimeter of $FGHJK$?

11. These circles are concentric. AB is tangent to the smaller circle at C. $OB = 130$. Find the length of OC.

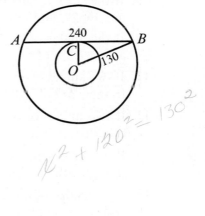

12. Find DF.

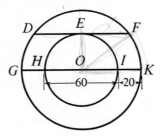

$x^2 + 120^2 = 130^2$

13. The radius of one circle is double that of another circle concentric to it. A chord of one is tangent to the other and is 420 inches long. Find the radius of each circle.

14. The radius of one circle is $\frac{5}{13}$ that of another that is concentric to it. A tangent of one is a chord of the other and is 120 cm. long. Find the radius of each circle.

YES-NO TEST

Approximately 20 minutes

Copy on your paper the numbers of the following questions. If the answer to a question is *yes* under all conditions, place a plus sign (+) after its number. If the answer is *not yes* under all conditions, place a zero (0) after its number.

1. Is a triangle a polygon?
2. Do similar triangles have the same size?
3. Do similar triangles have the same shape?
4. Are the sides of similar triangles respectively equal?
5. Are the angles of similar triangles respectively equal?
6. If the angles of one triangle are equal respectively to the angles of another, are the corresponding sides proportional?
7. If the corresponding sides of two triangles are proportional, are the corresponding angles equal?
8. If the sides of one triangle are 3, 5, and 5, and the sides of another are 8, 6, and 10, are the triangles similar?
9. If the sides of one triangle are 6, 9, and 12, and the sides of another are 36, 27, and 18, are the triangles similar?
10. If the angles of one triangle are 30°, 65°, and 85°, and the angles of another are 65°, 85°, and 30°, are the triangles similar?
11. If two angles of one triangle are 47° and 61°, and two angles of another triangle are 61° and 47°, are the triangles similar?
12. If two angles of one triangle are 68° and 54°, and two angles of another triangle are 64° and 58°, are the triangles similar?
13. If two angles of one triangle are 52° and 66°, and two angles of another triangle are 66° and 62°, are the triangles similar?
14. If two sides of a triangle are 4.5 and 6 and the included angle is 44°, and if the corresponding sides of another triangle are 9 and 12 and the included angle is 44°, are the triangles similar?
15. If two chords intersect in a circle and the segments of one are 6 and 8, and if one segment of the second chord is 3, is the other segment of the second chord 16?
16. If two polygons are composed of the same number of triangles, are the polygons similar?

COMPLETION TEST

Approximately 30 minutes

Copy on your paper the numbers of the following statements and questions. After each number write a number, or word, or letters which, if written in the blank, would complete the statement and make it true, or answer the question.

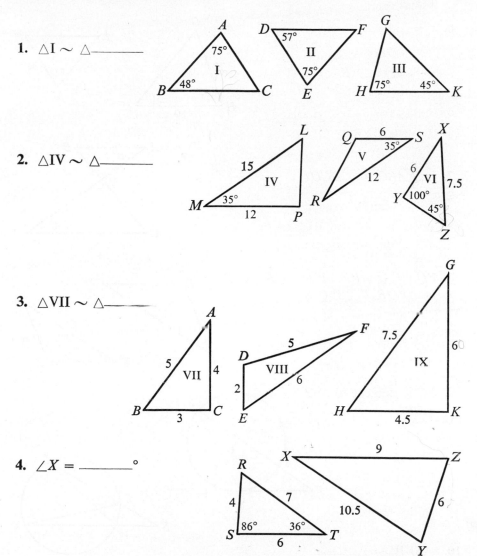

1. △I ~ △————

2. △IV ~ △————

3. △VII ~ △————

4. ∠X = ————°

5. $\triangle I \sim \triangle II$.

$\angle n =$ _____°

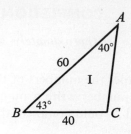

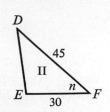

6. $s =$ _____

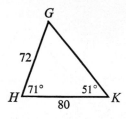

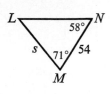

7. Is $\triangle ABO \sim \triangle DCO$?

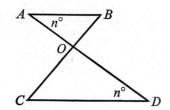

8. $PQ \parallel P'Q'$; $PR \parallel P'R'$; $QR \parallel Q'R'$
Is $\triangle PQR \sim \triangle P'Q'R'$?

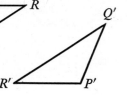

9. PC is tangent to $\odot O$.
$\triangle PBC \sim \triangle$_____

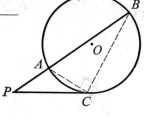

10. $\triangle SVW \sim \triangle$_____

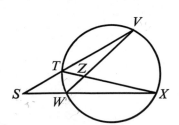

11. $\triangle ADE \sim \triangle$_____

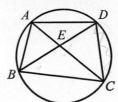

12. $PY =$ _____

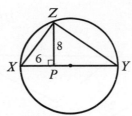

SUPPLEMENTARY EXERCISES

C.

1. Is $\triangle ABC \sim \triangle EFD$? Why?

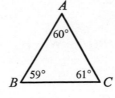

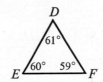

2. Is $\triangle GHI \sim \triangle LKJ$? Why?

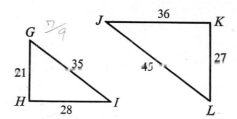

3. Is $\triangle PQR \sim \triangle TVS$? Why?

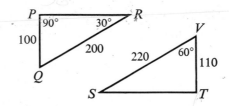

4. Is $\triangle ABC \sim \triangle DFE$? Why?

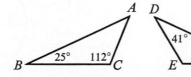

5. Is $\triangle GHI \sim \triangle KLJ$? Why?

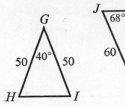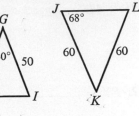

6. $VT = $ _____

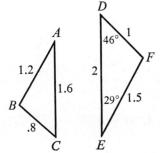

7. $\angle B = $ _____° Why?

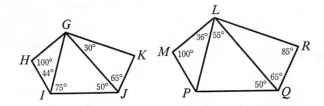

8. Is $GHIJK \sim LMPQR$? Why?

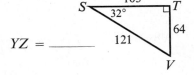

9. $XY = $ _____ $YZ = $ _____
Why?

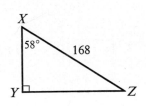

10. $CD = $ _____ Why?

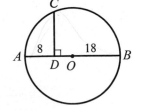

410 **GEOMETRY**

11. $EF =$ _____ Why?

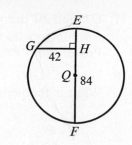

B.

12. Hyp. $JM = 16$; $ML = 4\frac{1}{4}$.
Find JK.

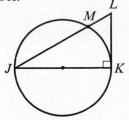

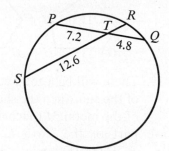

13. $RT =$ _____ Why?

14. Hyp. $XZ = 60$; $XY = 108$;
$ZW = 40$. Find VW.

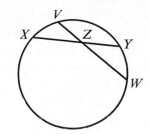

15. Hyp. $AB = 52$; $AC = 39$.
Find CD.

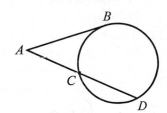

16. $XY =$ _____

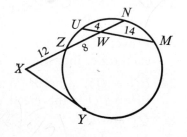

17. *OR* and *PT* are parallel tangents. *OT* and *PR* intersect on the circle.
Prove: $OR \cdot PT = \overline{OP}^2$

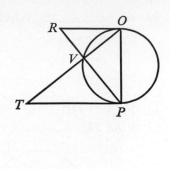

18. Hyp. *EFGHI* ∼ *E'F'G'H'I'*.
What is the perimeter of *E'F'G'H'I'*?

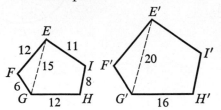

19. There will be a total eclipse of the sun when the shadow of the moon *M* touches any part of the earth *E*. *SX* = 93,000,000 miles, the radius of the sun is 400,000 miles and the radius of the moon is 1000 miles. What is the greatest possible distance *XM* of the moon from the earth for a total solar eclipse?

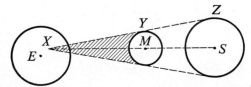

20. A boy sees in a pool of water the reflection of a balloon anchored to a building. He knows the building to be $\frac{1}{2}$ mile away. He knows from his study of physics that $\angle a = \angle b$. His eyes are 5 feet from the ground and he is $16\frac{1}{2}$ feet from the pool. How high is the balloon?

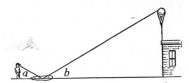

21. Two boys at *A* and *B* are watching an airplane at *C*. When the plane is directly over *B*, *A* estimates that the angle of elevation is 30°. The distance *AB* is a mile. How high is the plane?

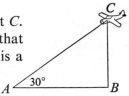

22. In △*XYZ*, $\angle XYZ = 2 \angle X$, and *YW* bisects $\angle XYZ$. Prove $\overline{YZ}^2 = XZ \cdot ZW$.

23. Prove: The diagonals of a trapezoid divide each other into proportional segments.

24. $\overarc{PQ} = \overarc{QS}$. Chords *PS* and *QR* intersect at *T*. Prove *PQ* is the mean proportional between *QT* and *QR*.

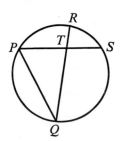

25. Two circles are tangent externally. Prove that the chords formed by a line through the point of contact have the same ratio as the radii.

26. What is the ratio of the arms of a right triangle if one acute angle is 45°?

27. What is the ratio of the hypotenuse of a right triangle to the shorter arm if one acute angle is 60°?

28. The radius of a circle is 18 inches. A chord 27 inches long is drawn through a point 12 inches from the center. Find the lengths of the segments into which the chord is divided.

29. A chord 6 inches long is drawn through a point $7\frac{3}{4}$ inches from the center of a circle the diameter of which is $16\frac{1}{2}$ inches. Find the lengths of the segments into which the chord is divided.

30. Construct an isosceles triangle having its vertex angle 36°.

31. Two angles of one triangle are 26° and 58°, and two angles of another are 58° and 96°. Are the triangles similar?

32. An acute angle of one right triangle is 41°, and an acute angle of another right triangle is 49°. Are the triangles similar?

33. An acute angle of one right triangle is 27°, and an acute angle of another right triangle is 73°. Are the triangles similar?

34. Are congruent triangles similar?

35. The sides of one triangle are 5 inches, 7 inches, and 11 inches, and the sides of another are 7 feet, 5 feet, and 11 feet. Are the triangles similar?

36. The sides of one triangle are 12 centimeters, 15 centimeters, and 18 centimeters, and the sides of another triangle are 3 centimeters, 2.2 centimeters, and 3.6 centimeters. Are the triangles similar?

A.

37. A house is 30 feet wide and the height of the gable is 9 feet. What is the length of the rafters used?

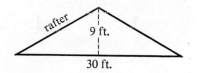

38. Show that the lengths of BO, CO, DO, and EO are correctly given. Find the lengths of FO and GO.

39. Construct $\sqrt{8}$.

40. Construct $\sqrt{17}$. Find the shortest way you can to do this.

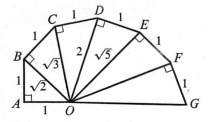

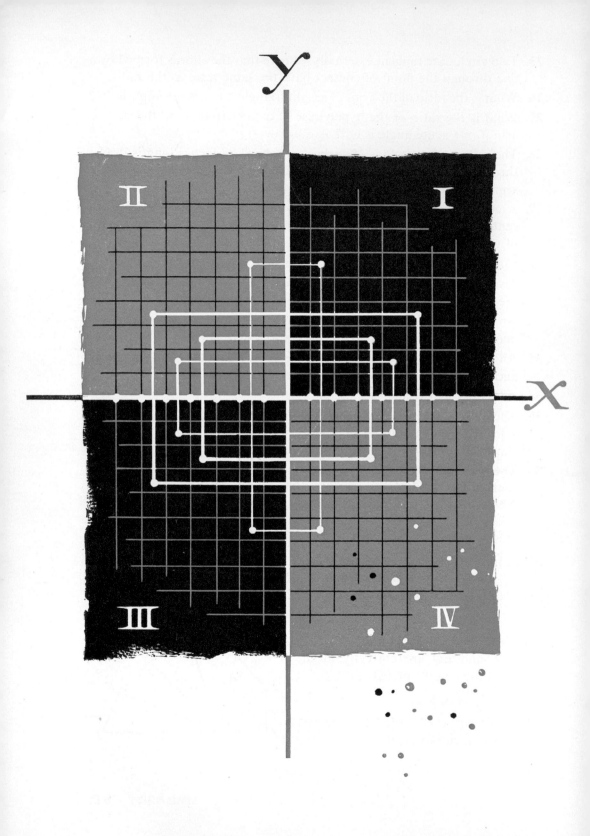

CHAPTER | 16

COORDINATE GEOMETRY

16–1   Numbers and Points on a Line   In our work on geometry so far we have talked for the most part only in terms of points, lines, segments, circles, and polygons. The only use of numbers has been in measuring distances. Now we shall study geometry by the use of number and variable in a manner similar to that used in the study of graphs in algebra.

Geometry and algebra are first united on a number scale. Recall, from your study of algebra, the number scale. This scale is obtained by taking *two points* on a line, such as *O* and *I*, and designating them by the *two numbers* 0 and +1 respectively. Point *O* is called the origin and point *I* is called the unit point. The segment *OI* is then used to divide the line into equal segments both to the right of *I* and the left of *O*. The division points are then labeled by the sequence of positive and negative integers. Thus *to each of certain points on the line there is a certain integer and to each integer there is only one point.*

$$
\begin{array}{c}
\quad\quad\quad\quad\quad\quad\quad\quad\quad O \quad I \\
\hline
-8\ -7\ -6\ -5\ -4\ -3\ -2\ -1 \quad 0\ +1\ +2\ +3\ +4\ +5\ +6\ +7\ +8
\end{array}
$$

By dividing each interval into halves, thirds, fourths, and so on forever, we obtain many more points of the line which can be named by the posi-

415

tive and negative fractions. In this way, for example, to $-3\frac{10}{19}$ there is only *one point*, and to the point B, where the interval 1 to 2 has been divided into 57 parts and B is the 35th, there is only one number, namely $1\frac{35}{57}$. All the positive and negative fractions, including zero and fractions with denominator 1, are called the rational numbers. Having selected a *zero* point and a *one* point on a line we can now say: *For every rational number there is only one point on the line corresponding to the number.* Thus we can speak of the point $3\frac{1}{2}$ or $-2\frac{3}{5}$, and so on, using numbers to represent points.

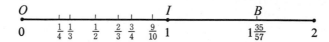

In the above division of the line there are still many points left unnamed. For example, in the figure shown, if $BA \perp OA$, and $OA = AB = 1$, then $OB = \sqrt{2}$. If $OQ = OB$, then Q is a point on the number scale which has the irrational number $\sqrt{2}$ as its name. Since $\sqrt{2}$ is not a rational number, it is

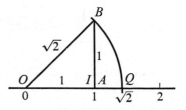

clear that point Q was not named in the process of the preceding paragraph. The irrational numbers and rational numbers form the real numbers. The real numbers correspond to all the points on a line, which is then called the real number line. Thus we have the Postulate:

POSTULATE 36 **Having selected a zero point and a one point on a line, each point on the line corresponds to only one real number, and to any real number there is only one point on the line.** The number is called the coordinate of the point.

We can now use the real numbers to study relations between points of the line.

16–2 Distance between Points. Absolute Value The distance between two points on a line is the length of the segment joining the two points. The direction, that is from P to Q or Q to P, is not considered. The distance is thus an arithmetic number which tells the size of the segment. The distance from P to Q is the same as from Q to P.

On a number scale, the number assigned to the point gives the length of the segment from the origin to the point, if we use the arithmetic value of this number. By the arithmetic value of a number we mean only the size represented by the number without regard to the direction from zero. Thus the arithmetic value of $+3$ is 3, and the arithmetic value of -3 is also 3. Also the absolute value of a real number is its arithmetic value. We use vertical bars to show the absolute value, e.g. $|-3| = 3$; $|+3| = 3$; $|-\sqrt{2}| = \sqrt{2}$, etc. In general if x is a variable which is replaced by any real number, the absolute value of x is the number without regard to its sign and it is represented by $|x|$.

Thus if x_2 is -4 and x_1 is $+3$ $|x_2 - x_1| = |-4 - +3| = |-7| = 7$. Note that we carry out the operation between the bars before we give the absolute value.

EXERCISES

1. Give the absolute value of (a) $+3$ (b) $-2\frac{3}{5}$ (c) $-4\frac{7}{8}$ (d) $-\sqrt{2}$ (e) $-3 + -2$ (f) $-5 - +3$ (g) $-5 - -3$ (h) $+5 - -3$ (i) $(+5 - +3)$

2. Evaluate $x_2 - x_1$ if (a) $x_2 = +4$, $x_1 = -3$, (b) $x_2 = -4$, $x_1 = -2\frac{1}{2}$ (c) $x_2 = \sqrt{3}$, $x_1 = -\sqrt{2}$ (d) $x_2 = 1.414$, $x_1 = +1.732$.

3. Show that in every case $|x_2 - x_1| = |x_1 - x_2|$. Express this rule in words.

4. Show that if x_1 and x_2 are oppositely signed then $|x_1| + |x_2| = |x_2 - x_1|$.

We can now find a simple formula for the distance between any two points P and Q on the real number line. Note that absolute values of the numbers of P and Q also give the lengths of the segments OP and OQ. There are two cases

(1) When P and Q are on the same side of the origin
(2) When P and Q are on opposite sides of the origin

Case 1. Let the points be on the same side of the origin. Then both coordinates have the same sign and the distance between P and Q is given by

$$|PQ_1| = |OQ_1 - OP| = |x_2 - x_1|$$

Example: Find the distance between $P, -2\frac{3}{4}$ and $Q, -5\frac{1}{4}$.

Solution. $PQ = |-5\frac{1}{4} - -2\frac{3}{4}| = |-5\frac{1}{4} + 2\frac{3}{4}| = |-2\frac{1}{2}| = 2\frac{1}{2}$

Case 2. Let P and Q be points on opposite sides of the origin. Then the coordinates have opposite signs. Then

$$|PQ| = |OQ| + |OP| = |x_2| + |x_1|$$

However, since x_1 and x_2 have opposite signs we note that $|x_2| + |x_1| = |x_2 - x_1|$, for a positive number minus a negative number is equal to the sum of the two positive numbers. Thus in Case 2 we also have

$$|PQ| = |OP - OQ| = |x_2 - x_1|$$

In the algebra of real numbers, $\sqrt{}$ always indicates the positive, or the arithmetic, square root. Since $(x_2 - x_1)^2$ or $(x_1 - x_2)^2$ always yields the same number, we can also write the distance as $\sqrt{(x_2 - x_1)^2}$. Hence

$$d = |x_2 - x_1| = \sqrt{(x_2 - x_1)^2}$$

EXERCISES

1. Draw a number scale and locate the following points: (a) -2 (b) $2\frac{3}{4}$ (c) $\frac{3}{8}$ (d) $-4\frac{3}{4}$ (e) $-2\frac{3}{16}$

2. How is the point $1\frac{16}{25}$ located on a number scale given points 0 and 1?

3. If the distance between two points whose coordinates are x_1 and x_2 is designated by d, show that $d = \sqrt{(x_2 - x_1)^2}$ (a) when both x_2 and x_1 are negative, (b) when one is negative and the other positive, (c) when both are positive.

4. Find the distance between the following points: (a) P is 2, Q is -3 (b) P is -3, Q is -7 (c) P is $2\frac{3}{4}$, Q is $-3\frac{3}{8}$ (d) P is $-3\frac{1}{3}$, Q is $-7\frac{3}{4}$

16–3 Number Pairs and Points in a Plane To locate a point in a plane we may use two number scales. While these scales can be given in many different positions, the easiest system is one in which they are perpendicular to each other at their origin, or zero point. One number scale, usually drawn in a horizontal position, is called the *x*-axis, or axis of abscissas. The other axis is called the *y*-axis, or axis of ordinates.

In our coordinate geometry, the scale on each axis is the same. If this were not so, then a distance on the y-axis could yield the same number as one on the x-axis and yet the lengths would not be the same.

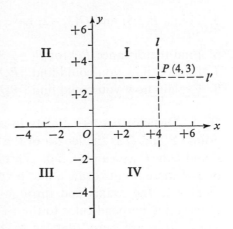

The two axes divide the plane into four regions called quadrants. Beginning with the upper right quadrant and counting counterclockwise, these quadrants are numbered I, II, III, and IV. The entire system is called a rectangular coordinate system because the axes are perpendicular.

We can relate any point P to these axes by *first* finding its abscissa, that is, its distance to the left or right of the origin on the x-axis. Next we find its ordinate, that is, its distance above or below the origin on the y-axis. To do this, we merely draw lines *l* and *l'* through P parallel to the y-axis and x-axis respectively. The points where these lines intersect the axes give us the abscissa and ordinate of the point P. We write these numbers as an ordered pair of real numbers enclosed in parentheses and separated by a comma. This ordered pair of numbers is called the coordinates of the point P and we write it (4,3). The order in which numbers are given is very significant; the abscissa is always given first. Note well that (3,4) is an entirely different point. In general, any given point has only one abscissa and one ordinate and hence only one ordered pair of numbers.

Conversely, for any ordered pair of numbers (x,y) there is only one point in the plane. Prove this.

EXERCISES

1. Locate the following points in the plane: $A(3,4)$; $B(-2,+5)$; $C(-3,-6)$; $D(-2\frac{1}{2},+3\frac{1}{2})$; $E(+3\frac{1}{3},-2\frac{2}{3})$; $F(-1,+1)$.

2. In the figure, find the coordinates of the points shown.

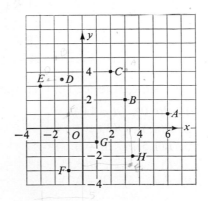

3. Where are all the points having the same abscissa but different ordinates?
4. Where are all the points having the same ordinate but different abscissas?
5. Points $P(3,5)$ and $Q(3,-2)$ have the same abscissa. Find the distance PQ.
6. Find the distance PQ for $P(-2,8)$ and $Q(+4,8)$.
7. Explain how you could find $|PQ|$ for $P(4,0)$ and $Q(0,3)$.
8. Explain how you could find $|PQ|$ for $P(-3,2)$ and $Q(1,-1)$.

16–4 Distance between Points in a Plane The distance d between two points P and Q is the length of the segment PQ. Let the coordinates of P and Q be (x_1,y_1) and (x_2,y_2). Through one of these points draw a line perpendicular to the x-axis and through the other a line perpendicular to the y-axis. These lines are perpendicular to each other and meet at a point A. Why? The coordinates of point A are (x_1,y_2). Why? The length of PA is $|y_2 - y_1|$ and the length of QA is $|x_2 - x_1|$. Why? $d^2 = \overline{QA}^2 + \overline{AP}^2$. Why? Thus, since $|y_2 - y_1|^2 = (y_2 - y_1)^2$, etc., $d^2 = (x_2 - x_1)^2 + (y_2 - y_1)^2$ or

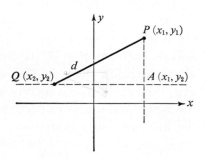

$$d = \sqrt{(x_2 - x_1)^2 + (y_2 - y_1)^2}$$

Example: Find the distance between $P(3,1)$ and $Q(-2,-11)$.
Solution. Here $x_1 = 3$, $y_1 = 1$, $x_2 = -2$, $y_2 = -11$.
Substituting in the formula,

$$d = \sqrt{(-2 - 3)^2 + (-11 - 1)^2} = \sqrt{-5^2 + (-12)^2} = \sqrt{169} = 13$$

EXERCISES

Find the distance between the following pairs of points.

1. $P(6,0)$, $Q(-4,0)$
2. $P(-1,-1)$, $Q(5,5)$
3. $P(8,3)$, $Q(3,8)$
4. $P(-2,4)$, $Q(-3,-5)$
5. $P(1,5)$, $Q(6,-7)$
6. $P(2,-5)$, $Q(-4,3)$
7. $P(-1,-2)$, $Q(3,1)$
8. $P(a,a)$, $Q(4a,5a)$
9. $P(4,-5)$, $Q(-3,2)$
10. $P(6,1)$, $Q(-6,6)$

11. Find the length of the three sides of the triangle with vertices (0,0), (5,3), (3,5). What kind of triangle is this?
12. Show that the quadrilateral $ABCD$ with $A(1,1)$, $B(7,1)$, $C(4,4)$, and $D(-2,4)$ is a parallelogram.
13. Show that the triangle with vertices (3,2), (7,5), and (0,6) is a right triangle.

16–5   Division of a Line Segment   A point in the interior of a line segment divides it into two segments. The ratio of these two segments is the ratio of the lengths of the two segments. If we are given the coordinates of an interior point, it is easy to find the length of the two parts, and hence the ratio of these segments. The reverse problem, that is, given a ratio to find the point of division, is solved by the following theorem.

THEOREM   If a point R divides the line segment PQ in the ratio $\dfrac{PR}{RQ} = \dfrac{r_1}{r_2}$, then the coordinates of point R are $\left(\dfrac{r_1x_2 + r_2x_1}{r_1 + r_2}, \dfrac{r_1y_2 + r_2y_1}{r_1 + r_2}\right)$, where the coordinates of P are (x_1,y_1) and of Q are (x_2,y_2).

Proof   Let the coordinates of point R be (x_r,y_r). In the figure drop perpendiculars from P, R, and Q to the x-axis meeting it at P', R', and Q' respectively. Then the coordinates of these three points are respectively $(x_1,0)$, $(x_r,0)$, and $(x_2,0)$.

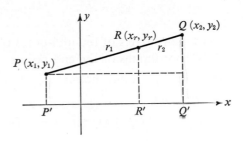

By Sec. 15–1 we have

$$\frac{PR}{RQ} = \frac{P'R'}{R'Q'} \tag{A}$$

It is given that $\dfrac{PR}{RQ} = \dfrac{r_1}{r_2}$. The length of the segment $P'R' = x_r - x_1$ and that of $R'Q' = x_2 - x_r$. (Note that both these lengths are positive numbers.) Substituting in (A) we obtain:

$$\frac{r_1}{r_2} = \frac{x_r - x_1}{x_2 - x_r} \quad \text{or} \quad r_1(x_2 - x_r) = r_2(x_r - x_1)$$

Solving this equation for x_r we obtain:

$$x_r = \frac{r_1x_2 + r_2x_1}{r_1 + r_2}$$

Similarly by dropping perpendiculars from P, R, and Q to the y-axis, we obtain

$$y_r = \frac{r_1 y_2 + r_2 y_1}{r_1 + r_2}$$

Therefore the coordinates of R are $\left(\dfrac{r_1 x_2 + r_2 x_1}{r_1 + r_2}, \dfrac{r_1 y_2 + r_2 y_1}{r_1 + r_2} \right)$

Example 1: Find the point that divides the segment joining $(-3, -1)$ to $(-1, 8)$ in the ratio $2 : 1$.

Solution. Here $x_1 = -3$, $x_2 = -1$, $y_1 = -1$, $y_2 = 8$, $r_1 = 2$, $r_2 = 1$.

Hence $x_r = \dfrac{2(-1) + 1(-3)}{2 + 1} = -1\tfrac{2}{3}$. $\qquad y_r = \dfrac{2(8) + 1(-1)}{3} = 5$

The coordinates are $(-1\tfrac{2}{3}, 5)$.

If $r_1 = r_2$, then the point R bisects the segment, or is the mid-point of the segment. In this case, substituting r_1 for r_2 we obtain for the coordinates of the mid-point

$$x_m = \frac{r_1 x_2 + r_1 x_1}{r_1 + r_1} = \frac{r_1(x_2 + x_1)}{2r_1} = \frac{x_2 + x_1}{2}$$

$$y_m = \frac{r_1 y_2 + r_1 y_1}{r_1 + r_1} = \frac{r_1(y_2 + y_1)}{2r_1} = \frac{y_2 + y_1}{2}$$

The coordinates of the mid-point of a segment are the arithmetic means of the coordinates of the end points.

Example 2: Find the mid-point M of the segment AB joining $A(-3, 1)$ and $B(1, -7)$.

Solution. The abscissa is $\dfrac{-3 + 1}{2} = -1$; the ordinate is $\dfrac{1 + (-7)}{2}$ $= -3$. The point M is $(-1, -3)$.

EXERCISES

C.

In exercises 1 to 6, find the coordinates of the mid-point.
1. $C(3, 5)$, $D(5, 7)$
2. $E(2, 3)$, $F(1, 9)$
3. $G(-4, 1)$, $H(2, -3)$
4. $J(-1, -1)$, $K(4, -2)$
5. $L(1.5, 2.1)$, $M(2.1, -3.1)$
6. $P(-2, 5)$, $Q(2, -5)$

B.

In exercises 7 to 14, $k = \dfrac{r_1}{r_2}$. Find the coordinates of the point that divides the segment in this ratio.

7. $A(1,2)$, $B(4,8)$, $k = \frac{1}{2}$
8. $A(-3,-4)$, $B(2,1)$, $k = \frac{3}{2}$
9. $A(-1,6)$, $B(5,-3)$, $k = \frac{2}{1}$
10. $A(4,5)$, $B(-3,8)$, $k = \frac{5}{3}$
11. $A(1,-4)$, $B(6,1)$, $k = \frac{2}{3}$
12. $A(8,-5)$, $B(-7,5)$, $k = \frac{3}{7}$
13. $A(2,-4)$, $B(-6,4)$, $k = \frac{3}{5}$
14. $A(4,8)$, $B(\frac{1}{2},-1)$, $k = \frac{4}{5}$

A.

15. Find the points that trisect the segment $A(-4,5)$, $B(5,-1)$.
16. Find the formula for the coordinates of point R in terms of k, if

$$k = \frac{r_1}{r_2}. \quad \text{(Sec. 16–5)}$$

Hint. Solve for r_1 and substitute.

17. Using the formula of Ex. 16, do exercises 7 to 14.
18. Find the coordinates of the point that divides $A(2,4)$, $B(8,4)$ in the ratio $-\frac{1}{2}$. Draw a figure and explain the result. Is there more than one point that satisfies the given condition?
19. Find the coordinates of the point that divides $C(-5,7)$, $D(0,-2)$ in the ratio $-\frac{2}{3}$. Is there more than one point? Draw a figure.
20. Find the coordinates of 2 points that divide the line $A(1,1)$, $B(4,4)$ in 3 equal parts. What is the length of AB? What angle does AB make with the x-axis?

16–6 Slope of a Line. Directed Distance On a line, the distance of a segment PQ is $|x_2 - x_1|$. However, the distance given by the real number $x_2 - x_1$ may be positive or negative and is called the directed distance. In finding the directed distance we begin with the coordinate of the terminal point and subtract the coordinate of the initial point of the segment. In the figure $PQ = x_2 - x_1$ and is positive, while $QP = x_1 - x_2$, which is negative. In the following discussion we shall use directed distances.

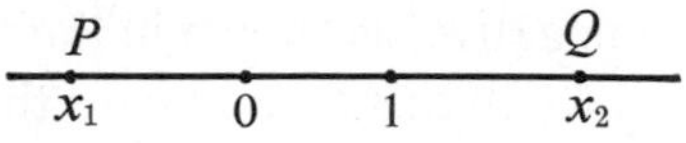

In this figure, l is a line oblique to both coordinate axes. Through A we draw a line parallel to the x-axis and mark off a fixed distance AC. (It can be positive or negative as shown in the figure.) At C draw a parallel to the y-axis meeting the line l again at B. Then the directed distance AC is called the <u>run</u> from point A to B and the directed distance CB is called the <u>rise</u> from point A to B.

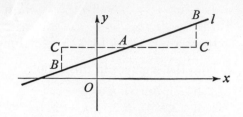

The ratio $\dfrac{CB}{AC} = \dfrac{\text{rise}}{\text{run}}$ is called the <u>slope</u> of the line l. The slope of a given line is constant, for no matter what points A and B are selected, for any other set of points A' and B', the triangles formed will be similar and hence the ratio of the rise and run will be the same in every case.

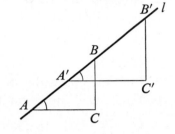

Let the coordinates of points A and B be (x_1, y_1) and (x_2, y_2) respectively. The coordinates of C are (x_2, y_1). Then the directed distance AC is $x_2 - x_1$ and the directed distance CB is $y_2 - y_1$. The symbol usually used for the slope of a line is m. Hence, the slope of line l is given by the formula:

$$m = \frac{y_2 - y_1}{x_2 - x_1}$$

Note that the rise, $y_2 - y_1$, is in the numerator.

The slope is independent of the order of the end points. This is true because

$$\frac{y_2 - y_1}{x_2 - x_1} = \frac{y_1 - y_2}{x_1 - x_2}$$

The slope of a line may be positive, as shown in the figures above. It may be negative, as shown in the figure at the right. In this second case the run AC is positive but the rise CB is negative. It is easy to show that if B is taken on the other side of A on line l, then the run will be negative and the rise will be positive and the slope is still negative.

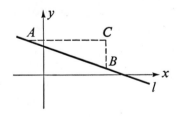

If a line is parallel to the x-axis, the rise is zero and the slope is zero. If the line is parallel to the y-axis, then the run is zero. Since division by zero is not permitted, there is no slope for such a line. These cases are illustrated below.

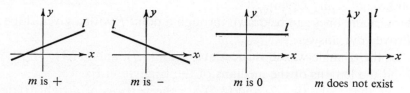

| m is $+$ | m is $-$ | m is 0 | m does not exist |

16–7 THEOREM **If two lines are parallel, their slopes are equal.**

Proof In the figure $l_1 \parallel l_2$. Let A and B be any two points on l_1. Draw a line through $A \parallel x$-axis and a line through $B \parallel y$-axis, the two lines meeting at C. Line l_2 meets BC at B' and AC at A'. Then $\triangle ABC \sim \triangle A'B'C$. Why? Hence

$$\frac{CB}{AC} = \frac{CB'}{A'C} \quad \text{or} \quad m_1 = m_2$$

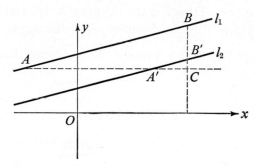

To prove that two lines are parallel, prove that their slopes are equal. This follows from Ex. 9 below.

EXERCISES

C.

1–8. Find the slopes of the lines through the given points in exercises 7–14 of Sec. 16–5.

B.

9. Prove that if two lines have the same slope they are parallel. This is the converse of Sec. 16–7.

In exercises 10–13 tell whether the pairs of lines *AB* and *CD* are parallel.

10. $A(1,3)$, $B(4,6)$; $C(3,1)$, $D(6,4)$
11. $A(-1,4)$, $B(5,6)$; $C(-3,2)$, $D(-6,1)$
12. $A(8,4)$, $B(0,-2)$; $C(-2,0)$, $D(4,8)$
13. $A(3,8)$, $B(-1,2)$; $C(9,6)$, $D(1,-6)$
14. How many lines can be drawn through a point *P* with a given slope *m*? Prove your answer.
15. Plot the triangle whose vertices are $(2,3)$, $(5,7)$, and $(17,11)$.
16. Find the lengths of the medians of the triangle in Ex. 15.
17. Show that $(3,1)$, $(9,-2)$ and $(5,5)$ are the vertices of a right triangle.
18. What sort of quadrilateral is *ABCD* when the coordinates are respectively $(36,25)$, $(16,55)$, $(-17,33)$, and $(3,3)$?

16–8   Reciprocal of a Number   If the product of two numbers is 1, then each number is called the <u>reciprocal</u> of the other.   Thus $\frac{1}{2}$ and 2, or $-1\frac{1}{2}$ and $-\frac{2}{3}$, and so on, are reciprocals.   The reciprocal of *m* is $\dfrac{1}{m}$.

If the product of two numbers is -1, then one number is the negative reciprocal of the other.   Thus 2 is the negative reciprocal of $-\frac{1}{2}$, and $-\frac{1}{2}$ is the negative reciprocal of 2.   Similarly $\frac{2}{3}$ is the negative reciprocal of $-\frac{3}{2}$, and $-\frac{2}{3}$ is the negative reciprocal of $\frac{3}{2}$.   Note that $\dfrac{1}{\frac{2}{3}}$ can also be written as $\frac{3}{2}$.

EXERCISES

1. Give the reciprocal of each of the following numbers.   (a) $\frac{5}{7}$, (b) $\frac{19}{5}$, (c) -11, (d) .3, (e) $-.5$, (f) $1\frac{3}{4}$, (g) *r*, (h) $-\dfrac{2}{k}$

2. Give the negative reciprocal of each number in Ex. 1.

16–9   THEOREM   **If two lines are perpendicular, the slope of one is the negative reciprocal of the slope of the other.**

Hypothesis $l_1 \perp l_2$, slope of $l_1 = m$, slope of $l_2 = m'$

Conclusion $-m' = \dfrac{1}{m}$

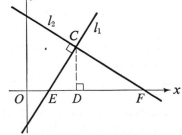

Proof

1. Let the lines meet the x-axis at E and F and intersect at C. Then $\triangle ECF$ is a right triangle. Draw the altitude CD.

2. The slope of l_1 is $\dfrac{DC}{ED}$. (Note that ED, FD, and DC are directed distances.)

3. $\triangle EDC \sim \triangle CDF$ and $\dfrac{ED}{DC} = \dfrac{DC}{DF}$, or $\dfrac{1}{\dfrac{DC}{ED}} = \dfrac{DC}{DF}$. Why?

4. $\dfrac{DC}{DF} = -\dfrac{DC}{FD}$ (since the denominator DF is the negative of FD)

5. $\dfrac{1}{\dfrac{DC}{ED}} = -\dfrac{DC}{FD}$, or $\dfrac{1}{m} = -m'$

Example: Are the lines determined by $A(3,8)$, $B(1,5)$ and $C(1,6)$, $D(4,4)$ perpendicular?

Solution. Slope of $AB = \dfrac{5-8}{1-3} = \dfrac{3}{2}$; slope of $CD = \dfrac{4-6}{4-1} = -\dfrac{2}{3}$.
Since $\frac{3}{2}(-\frac{2}{3}) = -1$, the slopes are negative reciprocals and the lines are perpendicular.

EXERCISES

Give the slope of a line $\perp$ a line having the slope:

1. 2   2. -3 3. $\frac{1}{2}$ 4. $-\frac{2}{3}$ 5. $-3\frac{1}{2}$

6. k 7. $-\dfrac{1}{r}$ 8. $\dfrac{c}{d}$ 9. $-\dfrac{3}{r}$ 10. -1

16–10 Proving Theorems in Coordinate Geometry Using the theorems and formulas proved in this chapter, we can prove by coordinate geometry many of the theorems of Euclidean plane geometry. We shall prove some of these theorems to show how coordinate geometry may be employed to advantage.

Coordinate geometry is not, however, recommended as a replacement for Euclidean geometry. Each has its place. The methods of coordinate geometry have advantages for some purposes while the methods of Euclidean geometry have advantages for others. The greatest benefits are obtained when we select the method which is best suited to the problem being considered.

Example 1: Prove that the diagonals of a parallelogram bisect each other.

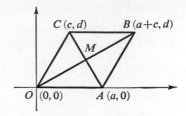

Proof. Let the base of the parallelogram be $O(0,0)$, $A(a,0)$, and let the coordinates of C be (c,d). Then the coordinates of B are $(a + c, d)$. Using the mid-point formula of Sec. 16–5, the mid-point of OB is

$$\left(\frac{0 + a + c}{2}, \frac{0 + d}{2}\right) \quad \text{or} \quad \left(\frac{a + c}{2}, \frac{d}{2}\right)$$

The mid-point of CA is $\left(\dfrac{c + a}{2}, \dfrac{d + 0}{2}\right)$ or $\left(\dfrac{a + c}{2}, \dfrac{d}{2}\right)$. Since these mid-points have the same coordinates, they are the same point, and the lines intersect at this point.

Example 2: Prove that the line segment joining the mid-points of two sides of a triangle is parallel to the third side and equal to one half of it.

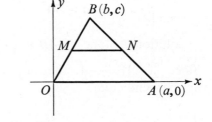

Proof. Let one side of the triangle be on the x-axis with a vertex at the origin. Let the coordinates of the other vertices be $A(a,0)$ and $B(b,c)$.

Then the coordinates of the mid-point M are $\left(\dfrac{b}{2}, \dfrac{c}{2}\right)$ and of the mid-point N they are $\left(\dfrac{b + a}{2}, \dfrac{c}{2}\right)$. The slope of MN is:

$$\frac{\dfrac{c}{2} - \dfrac{c}{2}}{\dfrac{b + a}{2} - \dfrac{b}{2}} = 0$$

The slope of OA is 0. $\therefore MN \parallel OA$. The length of OA is a. The length of

$$MN = \sqrt{\left(\frac{c}{2} - \frac{c}{2}\right)^2 + \left(\frac{b + a}{2} - \frac{b}{2}\right)^2} = \sqrt{\frac{a^2}{4}} = \frac{a}{2}. \quad \text{Hence } MN = \tfrac{1}{2}OA.$$

EXERCISES

Prove the following theorems by coordinate geometry.

1. The diagonals of a rectangle are equal.

2. The medians of an isosceles triangle drawn from the end points of the base are equal.
3. The median from the vertex of an isosceles triangle is perpendicular to the base.
4. The medians of a triangle meet in a point which is two thirds the distance from any vertex to the opposite side.

Hint. First find the coordinates of the mid-points of the sides; then for each median use the ratio formula for a point the ratio of whose distances from the vertex and the opposite mid-point is 2:1.

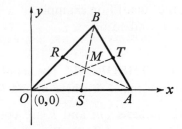

16–11 Equation of a Straight Line If a geometrical figure is a straight line, then it has a constant slope. That is, the slope of any of its segments always has the same value m. We shall now study what condition must be imposed upon a variable point (x,y) in order that it lie in a given line.

A given point is usually indicated by using subscripts for its coordinates, for example, (x_1,y_1) or (x_i,y_i). Such a point is a constant in a given discussion. We shall also speak of a variable point P with coordinates (x,y).

Suppose a line passes through a given point (x_1,y_1) and has a slope m. What restrictions must we place on x and y so that the variable point $P(x,y)$ lies on the line? This is answered by the following theorem.

THEOREM If the point $P(x,y)$ lies on the straight line passing through $A(x_1,y_1)$ and having slope m, then $(y - y_1) = m(x - x_1)$.

Hypothesis Straight line l, point $A(x_1,y_1)$ on l, slope of $l = m$. $P(x,y)$ is any point on the line other than A.

Conclusion $(y - y_1) = m(x - x_1)$

Proof

1. The slope of AP is $\dfrac{y - y_1}{x - x_1}$. See Sec. 16–6.

2. But the slope of AP is the slope of l, which is m.

3. $\therefore \dfrac{y - y_1}{x - x_1} = m$, or $(y - y_1) = m(x - x_1)$

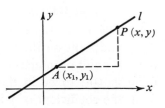

In the last equation we may select any value for x (or y) but then the value of y (or x) is determined. We say that $(y - y_1) = m(x - x_1)$ is the point-slope form of the equation of a straight line.

Example: Find the equation of a line through $(3,5)$ with slope -2.

Solution. Here $x_1 = 3$, $y_1 = 5$, $m = -2$. $\therefore$ the equation of the line is $y - 5 = -2(x - 3)$. Now we can find coordinates of many points on the line. For example, if $x = 4$, substitution gives $y = 3$. If $x = 5$, $y = 1$, and so on.

16–12 THEOREM The set of points whose coordinates satisfy the equation $y = mx + b$ where m and b are given constants is a straight line.

Hypothesis m and b are constants; P_1, P_2, P_3 are points with coordinates (x_1,y_1), (x_2,y_2), (x_3,y_3) respectively satisfying the equation $y = mx + b$.

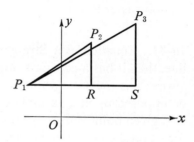

Conclusion P_1, P_2, P_3 are on a straight line.

Proof

1. $y_1 = mx_1 + b$; $\quad y_2 = mx_2 + b$; $\quad y_3 = mx_3 + b$

2. $y_2 - y_1 = m(x_2 - x_1)$; $\quad y_3 - y_1 = m(x_3 - x_1)$

3. $\dfrac{y_2 - y_1}{x_2 - x_1} = m$; $\quad \dfrac{y_3 - y_1}{x_3 - x_1} = m$

4. $\therefore \dfrac{y_2 - y_1}{x_2 - x_1} = \dfrac{y_3 - y_1}{x_3 - x_1}$, or the slope of $P_2 P_1$ = slope of $P_3 P_1$

1. Given

2. Sec. 16–11

3. Post. 3

4. Post. 2

5. Hence lines determined by $P_3 P_1$ and $P_2 P_1$ coincide, and P_1, P_2, and P_3 are on the same straight line.

16–13 Slope-Intercept Form of an Equation

Corollary In the equation $y = mx + b$, m is the slope of the line and $(0,b)$ is a point on the line. The number b is called the y-intercept, since it is the point of intersection of the y-axis and the line. An equation in this form is said to be in the slope-intercept form. Remember that in this form the coefficient of y is 1.

16-14 Plotting the Straight Line

If we are given an equation such as $y = -3x + 7$ which expresses a relation between the abscissa and ordinate of a variable point (x,y), then we can select values of x and determine corresponding values of y, to find points on the line.

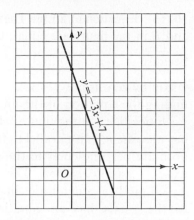

By plotting two of the points whose coordinates are the ordered pairs (x,y) thus found and drawing a straight line through them, we get the graph of the given equation. Finding the coordinates of a third point and plotting give a check on the work.

$y = -3x + 7$
(x,y)
$(2,1)$
$(0,+7)$
$(1,4)$

EXERCISES

1. Does the point $C(0,\frac{3}{2})$ lie on $3x + 2y = 3$?
2. Does the point $D(3,0)$ lie on this line?
3. The abscissa of E is -2 and E lies on the line $3x + 2y = 3$. What is the ordinate of E?
4. The ordinate of F is 5 and F lies on the line $3x + 2y = 3$. What is the abscissa of F?
5. Find the equation that represents the relation between the coordinates of the set of points that lie on the straight line that passes through $G(-1,1)$ and $H(1,-2)$. *Hint.* Find the slope first.
6. Find the equation of the set of points that lie on the straight line through $J(0,0)$ and $K(-2,-3)$.
7. Find the equation of the set of points that lie on the line that is parallel to (*a*) $x + y = 1$ and passes through $M(2,3)$.

   Suggestions. What is the slope of (*a*)? What is the slope of the required line? What is the slope of a line through $M(2,3)$ and $P(x,y)$?

Graph each equation and find the slope of the line.

8. $y = 3x + 2$ 9. $y = -x - 1$ 10. $x + 2y = 6$
11. $3x - 4y = 12$ 12. $2x + 3y = 6$ 13. $2x - \frac{1}{2}y = 0$
14. $x = y$ 15. $y = 1$ 16. $y = -1$

16–15 Equation of a Line That Has No Slope If the abscissas of points A and B in the figure are equal, then the line through A and B has no slope because $x_1 - x_2 = 0$ and the ratio $\dfrac{y_1 - y_2}{x_1 - x_2}$ has no meaning because division by zero is not possible. In this case we need a different method for finding the equation of the line.

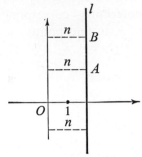

Notice line l in the figure. Every point on it has abscissa n. l is parallel to the y-axis because both are perpendicular to the same line, the x-axis. l has no slope. The equation of l is $x = n$, and in general any line that is parallel to the y-axis has an equation of the form $x = k$, where k is a constant. This fact enables us to write the equation of a line that has no slope.

Example 1: Give the slope and y-intercept of the line whose equation is $y = 2x - 1$.

Solution. Since the equation is given in the slope-intercept form, one can write at once: slope $= 2$, y-intercept $= -1$.

Example 2: Find the slope and y-intercept of a line whose equation is $3x + 4y = 5$.

Solution. First, we transform the equation to the slope-intercept form. This gives $y = -\tfrac{3}{4}x + 1\tfrac{1}{4}$. Hence the slope is $-\tfrac{3}{4}$, and the y-intercept is $1\tfrac{1}{4}$.

Example 3: What is the equation of a line that passes through $A(3, -1)$ and $B(3,1)$?

Solution. Since $3 - 3 = 0$, the line has no slope. Its equation is $x = 3$.

Example 4: Discuss the slope and y-intercept of the line whose equation is $x = -5$.

Solution. The equation has no y-term. Hence, for any value we choose for y, $x = -5$. For example, if $y = 3$, $x = -5$, and if $y = 7$, $x = -5$.

If the line has a slope, it is $\dfrac{7 - 3}{-5 - (-5)} = \dfrac{4}{0}$, but since division by zero is impossible, the line has no slope.

The equation of the y-axis is $x = 0$, but the given equation is $x = -5$, and hence the line has no y-intercept.

Compare the equation and graph of Example 4 with those of Ex. 15 or Ex. 16, page 431 with regard to slope and y-intercept. Do the lines in Ex. 15 and Ex. 16 have y-intercepts? Does the line in Ex. 14 page 431 have a y-intercept? If so, what is it? Does it have an x-intercept?

Find the slope and y-intercept of each line whose equation is given. Graph the line.

1. $y = 3x + 7$
2. $y = -x + 3$
3. $x = -y - 2$
4. $2y = 6x - 8$
5. $3y = x - 4$
6. $2x + y = 3$
7. $\dfrac{x}{2y} = 4$
8. $\dfrac{3x - 1}{y} = 2$
9. $\dfrac{2x + 3}{3y - 1} = 5$
10. $y = 3$
11. $x = 3$
12. $x = 0$

16–16 Parallel Lines If two lines have the same slope, they are parallel, and conversely. (See page 425.)

Example 1: Are the lines whose equations are (*a*) $2x - 5y = 0$ and (*b*) $6x = 15y - 4$ parallel?

Solution. We transform each equation to the slope-intercept form.

$$(a)\ y = \tfrac{2}{5}x$$
$$(b)\ y = \tfrac{2}{5}x + \tfrac{4}{15}$$

The slope of each line is $\tfrac{2}{5}$, and hence the lines are parallel.

Example 2: Find the equation of the line that is parallel to the line whose equation is $5x - y = 3$ and passes through the point whose co-ordinates are $(-2, -3)$.

Solution. The given equation can be written in the form $y = 5x - 3$. Hence the slope of its graph is 5. The equation of a line that is parallel to the given line is of the form $y = 5x + b$. Since this line is to pass through $(-2, -3)$, we substitute -2 for x and -3 for y. We get $-3 = 5(-2) + b$. Whence $b = 7$. Then the required equation is $y = 5x + 7$.

1. Are the lines whose equations are $3x = y - 9$ and $6x = 2y - 7$ parallel?
2. Are the lines whose equations are $9x = 4y + 7$ and $4x = 9y - 7$ parallel?
3. Find the equation of the line that passes through the point whose co-ordinates are $(-5, 0)$ and is parallel to the line whose equation is $2y - 5x - 7 = 0$.
4. Find the equation of the line that passes through the point whose co-ordinates are $(7, -1)$ and is parallel to the line whose equation is $x = y$.

5. Find the equation of the line that passes through $(5, -5)$ and is parallel to the y-axis.
6. Find the equation of the line that passes through $(-1, 4)$ and is parallel to the x-axis.
7. Find the equation of the line that passes through $(4, -2)$ and is parallel to $x - 2y = 0$.

16–17 Line through Two Points

Given two points $H(x_1, y_1)$ and $K(x_2, y_2)$, we can write the equation of a straight line that passes through them. The two points enable us to find the slope. Then we can use either point with this slope to find the equation of the line.

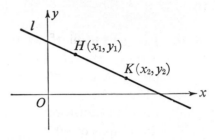

Example 1: What is the equation of the line that passes through $H(-2, 3)$ and $K(0, -4)$?

Solution. The slope is $\dfrac{3 - (-4)}{-2 - 0}$ or $-\dfrac{7}{2}$. Use the point $K(0, -4)$.
Then $y - (-4) = -\frac{7}{2}(x - 0)$ or $2y + 8 = -7x$. Hence the equation is $7x + 2y = -8$. (See Sec. 16–11.)

Example 2: What is the slope of a line that is perpendicular to the line whose equation is $4x - 7y = 11$?

Solution. The slope of the given line is $\frac{4}{7}$. Then the slope of a line that is perpendicular to it is $-\frac{7}{4}$.

Example 3: Are the graphs of lines whose equations are given by (a) $2x = 3y + 3$ and (b) $6x + 4y - 11 = 0$ perpendicular to each other?

Solution. The slope of (a) is $\frac{2}{3}$. The slope of (b) is $-\frac{3}{2}$. Since the slope of each line is the negative reciprocal of the slope of the other, the lines are perpendicular.

Example 4: Find the equation of the line perpendicular to $2x - y = 4$ and passing through $P(2, -2)$.

Solution. The slope of the given line is 2. Then the slope of the required line is $-\frac{1}{2}$. The general form of its equation is $y = -\frac{1}{2}x + b$. (See page 430.) Since this line passes through P, the equation must be satisfied by $x = 2$, $y = -2$. Substituting these values in the equation, we have $-2 = -\frac{1}{2}(2) + b$, or $b = -1$. Then the required equation is $y = -\frac{1}{2}x - 1$. We can eliminate the fraction and give this equation in the form: $x + 2y + 2 = 0$.

EXERCISES

Find the equation of the line that passes through each pair of points whose coordinates are given. Plot the points and draw the line.

1. $A(0,0)$, $B(3,3)$
2. $C(0,2)$, $D(4,4)$
3. $E(2,5)$, $F(4,-1)$
4. $G(-2,-3)$, $H(1,-2)$
5. $J(1.5,3.5)$, $K(-2.5,1.5)$
6. $L(\sqrt{2},\sqrt{3})$, $M(\sqrt{3},-\sqrt{2})$
7. $M(1,1)$, $O(3,1)$
8. $V(-2,-3)$, $W(7,-3)$
9. $P(4,4)$, $Q(7,4)$
10. $R(2,3)$, $S(2,4)$

11. Find the equation of the perpendicular bisector of $C(-4,3)$, $D(8,3)$.
    Suggestions. What is the slope of CD? What is the slope of a line $\perp CD$? What are the coordinates of the mid-points of CD?

12. Find the equation of the line that is perpendicular to $3x - y = 1$ and passes through $P(1,1)$.

13. Are the graphs of (a) $3x + 2y = 4$ and (b) $2x = 3y + 4$ perpendicular to each other?

14. Find the equation of the altitude from A of the triangle whose vertices are $A(2,-2)$, $B(-3,5)$, $C(5,-3)$. *Suggestions.* What is the slope of BC? What is the slope of a line $\perp BC$? Through what point does the altitude pass?

15. Find the equation of the line that bisects AB and AC in triangle $A(0,0)$, $B(-7,0)$, $C(-4,3)$.

16. Find the equation of the median from A to the side BC of $\triangle ABC$ of Ex. 15.

Optional Topic

16-18 Locus We can use algebraic methods to solve locus problems. You recall that to establish a locus theorem we must do the following two things:

(1) Prove that every point on the locus satisfies the conditions.
(2) Prove that every point satisfying the conditions is on the locus.

In coordinate geometry we establish our proof in the following steps.

1. Select a convenient set of axes if they are not given.
2. Select a variable point $P(x,y)$ which is restricted to the given conditions.
3. Express these conditions in algebraic form.
4. Simplify the result and identify the locus.
5. Show that any point satisfying the condition found in (4) is on the locus.

Example 1: Find the locus of points equally distant from the points $A(1,1,$ and $B(5,5)$.

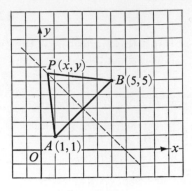

Solution.

(1) The axes are already fixed by the given points.

(2) Let $P(x,y)$ be any point on the locus.

(3) By the given condition, $PA = PB$ and by the distance formula

$$PA = \sqrt{(x-1)^2 + (y-1)^2}, \quad PB = \sqrt{(x-5)^2 + (y-5)^2}.$$

Hence $\sqrt{(x-1)^2 + (y-1)^2} = \sqrt{(x-5)^2 + (y-5)^2}$.

(4) Square each side and simplify. $x^2 - 2x + 1 + y^2 - 2y + 1 = x^2 - 10x + 25 + y^2 - 10y + 25$, or $8x + 8y = 48$. $x + y = 6$.

(5) If a point $P_i(x_i,y_i)$ satisfies $x + y = 6$, then the steps (3) and (4) can be reversed and $P_iA = P_iB$.

Thus the locus is a straight line. Show that this line is $\perp AB$ and passes through its mid-point.

Example 2: Find the locus of points whose coordinates satisfy both equations $3x + 2y = 5$ and $2x - 3y = 12$.

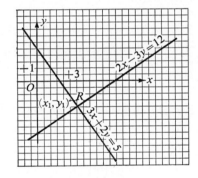

Solution. Let (x_1,y_1) be the coordinates of a point on the locus. Then $3x_1 + 2y_1 = 5$ and $2x_1 - 3y_1 = 12$.

$$
\begin{aligned}
6x_1 + 4y_1 &= 10 \\
6x_1 - 9y_1 &= 36 \\
\hline
13y_1 &= -26 \\
y_1 &= -2
\end{aligned}
\qquad
\begin{aligned}
6x_1 + 4(-2) &= 10 \\
6x_1 &= 18 \\
x_1 &= 3
\end{aligned}
$$

The locus is the point $R(3,-2)$. This is shown in the graph. Note that in subtracting the equalities, x_1 has the same value in both equations, and y_1 has the same value in both. If this were not so, $6x_1 - 6x_1$ would not be 0, etc.

EXERCISES

1. Find the locus of points equally distant from $A(-3,2)$ and $B(7,1)$.
2. Find the locus of points that are on a line that is parallel to $y = 3x + 4$ and contains the point $(4,5)$.
3. Find the locus of points that are on a line that is perpendicular to $y = \frac{1}{2}x - 3$ and contains the point $(3,-3)$.
4. Given the points $A(0,0)$ and $B(8,0)$. Find the locus of points P for which $\overline{PA}^2 - \overline{PB}^2 = 32$. Describe the locus.
5. Find the locus of points common to the medians of triangle $A(0,0)$, $B(9,0)$, $C(3,6)$.
6. Find the equations of the altitudes of triangle $A(0,0)$, $B(8,0)$, $C(2,6)$.

In the following, find the locus of points common to both lines.

7. $2x + y = 4$
   $x - y = -1$

8. $x + 2y = 4$
   $2x - y = 3$

9. $5x + 2y = 1$
   $4x + 3y = -2$

10. $2x + y = 6$
    $2x + y = 4$

11. $2x + y = 4$
    $4x + 2y = 8$

12. $5y - 2x = 24$
    $2y - 3x = 14$

OUTLINE OF CHAPTER 16

This chapter introduces the following terms:

line coordinates
absolute value
rectangular coordinates
abscissa
ordinate
origin
axes

quadrants
ordered pair of numbers
reciprocal
slope
intercept
point-slope equation
slope-intercept equation

This chapter presents information concerning:

1. Points on a line represented by real number coordinates. Page 415
2. The meaning of distance and directed distance between two points on a line. Page 416, 423
3. How to represent a point in a plane by an ordered pair of numbers called its coordinates. Page 418
4. How to find the coordinates of a point dividing a line segment in a given ratio. Page 421

5. The meaning and relation of slope to parallel lines and perpendicular lines. Pages 425, 426, 433
6. The formula for the distance between two points in a plane. Page 420
7. How to use algebra to prove geometric relations. Page 427
8. The equation of a straight line in its several forms. Pages 429, 430
9. The use of algebra in solving locus problems. Page 435

REVIEW

1. What is the real number scale?
2. What is the distance between points $+3$ and -2 on a number scale?
3. What is the directed distance from $+3$ to -2? From -2 to $+3$?
4. What is the distinction between $x_2 - x_1$ and $|x_2 - x_1|$ if x_2 and x_1 are the line coordinates of two points?
5. What is a rectangular coordinate system?
6. Name the quadrants and give the signs of x and y in each of these quadrants.
7. What is an ordered pair of numbers? What names are given to these numbers?
8. How is the point (a,b) located in the coordinate axis system?
9. What are the coordinates of the mid-point of a line segment joining two given points $A(x_1,y_1)$, $B(x_2,y_2)$?
10. What are the coordinates of the point that divides a segment AB in a given ratio $r_1:r_2$?
11. Find the mid-point of $A(3,1)$, $B(7,-5)$.
12. Find the point that divides AB of Ex. 11 in the ratio $2:3$.
13. Define slope of a line. Find the slope of AB of Ex. 11.
14. Prove the formula for the distance between two points. Use this formula to find the length of AB in Ex. 11.
15. How are the slopes of parallel lines related? Of perpendicular lines?
16. What is the negative reciprocal of a number?
17. Prove by analytic geometry that the median of a trapezoid is parallel to the base and equal to one half the sum of the bases.
18. What is the point-slope form of the equation of a straight line?
19. Find the equation of a straight line passing through $(3,-4)$ and having slope 5.

20. Find the equation of a line passing through $(2, -5)$ and $(-4,1)$.
21. Find the equation of a line with slope 3 and y-intercept -2.
22. What is the locus of points equally distant from $A(0,0)$ and $B(10,0)$?
23. Prove that the locus of points whose coordinates satisfy $ax + by = c$
    and $dx + ey = f$ is the point $\dfrac{ce - bf}{ae - bd}$, $\dfrac{af - cd}{ae - bd}$ if $ae - bd \neq 0$.
24. Prove that triangle ABC with $A(1,1)$, $B(8,25)$, and $C(17,13)$ is a right triangle.
25. Find the equation of a line meeting the x-axis at $(a,0)$ and the y-axis at $(0,b)$.

TEST

1. (a) If x_2 and x_1 are line coordinates of two points when x_2 is negative and x_1 is positive, prove that the distance between these points is $|x_2 - x_1|$ or $|x_1 - x_2|$.
   (b) Give the meaning of $x_1 - x_2$, $x_2 - x_1$, and $|x_2 - x_1|$ and illustrate each using -2 and $+4$ for x_1 and x_2 respectively.
2. Derive the formulas for the x- and y-coordinates of a point that divides the segment $P(x_1,y_1)$, $Q(x_2,y_2)$ in the ratio $r_1:r_2$.
3. Given the points $A(3,1)$ and $B(7,7)$. Find:
   (a) the coordinates of the mid-point of AB
   (b) the length of AB
   (c) the slope of AB
   (d) the equation of the line containing A and B
   (e) the equation of the perpendicular bisector of AB

4. Prove by analytic geometry that the line from C to the mid-point M of side AB in parallelogram $OABC$ trisects the diagonal OB. Use the coordinates given in the figure.

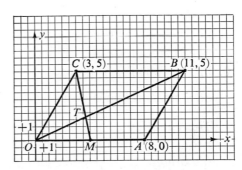

5. A variable point $P(x,y)$ moves under the restriction that the square of its distance from $A(-1,-2)$ is equal to the square of its distance from the origin. Find the locus of P and illustrate on a graph.

MISCELLANEOUS EXERCISES

1. Draw the graph of $y = 0$. Of $x = 0$.
2. Find the fourth vertex of a parallelogram with vertices (0,0), (6,0), and (3,0). There are three solutions.
3. Find the length of the sides of the triangle ABC, given $A(-5,0)$, $B(-4,-1)$, $C(2,3)$.
4. Prove that $A(-4,-1)$, $B(-2,3)$, $C(1,-1)$ are the vertices of an isosceles triangle.
5. Prove that $A(-3,-1)$, $B(-5,3)$, $C(7,4)$ are the vertices of a right triangle.
6. Prove that $A(-1,-2)$, $B(0,1)$, $C(-3,2)$, $D(-4,-1)$ are vertices of a parallelogram.
7. Find the point P such that $PA:PB = 2:5$, given the points $A(-2,0)$ and $B(5,-4)$.
8. Prove that the lines joining in order the mid-points of any quadrilateral form a parallelogram. Use the coordinates given in the figure.

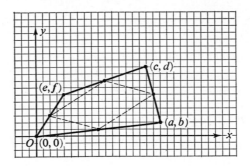

9. Prove that there is only one point equally distant from the three points $A(0,0)$, $B(4,4)$, $C(2,8)$.
10. Prove: The locus of points passing through $(a,0)$ and $(0,b)$ and lying on a straight line is given by $\dfrac{x}{a} + \dfrac{y}{b} = 1$.
11. The equation of Ex. 10 can be written in the form $bx + ay = ab$. From this, show that if the x-intercept is 0, then the line passes through the origin.
12. What values of a and b must be excluded in the equation of Ex. 10?
13. The x-intercept of a line is -3 and its y-intercept is 7. Find its equation.

14. A thermometer is doubly scaled to read both centigrade and Fahrenheit temperature. (*a*) Show that the two scales *C* and *F* are related by the linear formula $F = mC + b$. (*b*) Find the numeral values of *m* and *b* given the ordered pairs $(32,0), (212,100)$ of (F,C).

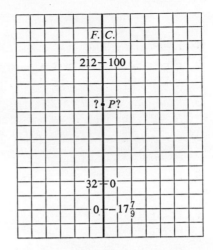

15. The vertices of a quadrilateral are $A(a,b)$, $B(c,d)$, $C(e,f)$, $D(g,h)$. *E* is the mid-point of *AB*, *F* is the mid-point of *BC*, *G* is the mid-point of *CD*, and *H* is the mid-point of *AD*. Show that *EG* and *FH* bisect each other.

16. In the figure of Ex. 15 show that $EH = FG$.

17. Draw a circle with radius 5 and center at the origin. Choose any point on the circle and call it $P(x,y)$. Using the Pythagorean theorem can you show that the equation for this circle is $x^2 + y^2 = 25$?

18. Draw a circle the same size as the one in Ex. 17 but with center at (1,1). Can you find the equation for this circle?

19. Describe the graph of the equation $(x - 2)^2 + (y - 3)^2 = 4$.

CHAPTER | **17**

AREA

I<small>N</small> ancient Egypt, one of the most important practical duties of the priests was the determination of the areas of farms and home sites, and from that day to this the subject of area has increased in importance. We buy farms and building lots by area. Factory and store rental is often based upon the floor area. In building airplanes, wing area is one of the most important factors. The painter, the plasterer, the roofer, the concrete mason, the paper hanger, the surveyor, the map maker must understand the calculation of the areas of all kinds of geometric figures.

One of the most remarkable of the simpler mathematical instruments is one for measuring the area of a surface bounded by an irregular outline. It is called the planimeter. By tracing with one of these instruments the outline of any figure drawn on a piece of paper, the area is calculated by using the numbers registered on the instrument. However, for nearly all practical purposes, simple geometric principles are sufficient for the calculation of areas. These principles as applied to straight-line figures are studied in this chapter.

Just as the measurement of line segments and of angles require an agreement about units of measure, so measurement of area requires an agreement about a unit of area. Can you think of units other than the one suggested on page 444?

17-1 Unit of Area To measure length one uses a unit of length, such as an inch, a mile, or a centimeter. To measure an angle one uses a unit angle, such as a degree. To measure the area of a surface one uses a unit of area. The unit of area can be any definite part of a surface which we find it convenient to use. Unless otherwise indicated, the <u>unit of area</u> is the part of a plane enclosed by a square, a side of which is one unit of length.

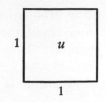

17-2 Area of a Geometric Figure The *area of a geometric figure* is the area of the surface bounded by the line or lines that form the figure. Thus, the area of a rectangle is the area of the surface enclosed by its sides, and the area of a circle is the area of the surface bounded by the curved line which we call the circle. The <u>area of a geometric figure</u> is the *number* of units of area it contains.

17-3 Base and Altitude In studying area we shall frequently have to use the words *base* and *altitude*. You have already used these words in the study of the triangle. You know that an altitude of a triangle can refer to either a line segment or to the length of the line segment. The context in which the word is used tells you which meaning is to be given to the word. The same will be true in the study of polygons.

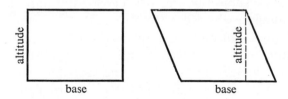

An <u>altitude</u> of a rectangle, a parallelogram, or a triangle is the perpendicular distance from any vertex to the opposite side or this side extended. The side to which the altitude is drawn is also referred to as a <u>base</u>. Since two parallel lines are everywhere equally distant (Sec. 7-16), an altitude of a rectangle is the perpendicular distance from any point on one side to the opposite side. The <u>altitude of a trapezoid</u> is the perpendicular distance between the parallel sides, called the bases.

In general we do not speak of the altitudes of plane geometric figures other than the four mentioned here. Draw a pentagon and consider the meaning of altitude as applied to it. Would there be any meaning to the expression *altitude of a circle?*

17–4 The Area of a Rectangle In the rectangle shown here, there are 4 squares in each row, and there are 3 rows. The rectangle therefore contains $3 \times 4 = 12$ squares. We say its area is 12 square units.

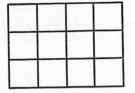

If the base of the rectangle is given by any number (e.g., 3, $2\frac{4}{5}$, $\sqrt{15}$), and the altitude of the rectangle is given by another number (e.g., 2, $1\frac{3}{5}$, $\sqrt{10}$), then we assume that the number of square units bounded by the rectangle is given by the product of these two numbers (e.g., 3×2; $2\frac{4}{5} \times 1\frac{2}{5}$; $\sqrt{15} \times \sqrt{10}$).

POSTULATE 37 **The area of a rectangle equals the product of its base and altitude.**

WRITTEN EXERCISES

B.

1. What is the area of a rectangle 12 cm. long and 9 cm. wide?
2. What is the area of a rectangle 2 in. long and 3 in. wide?
3. The area of a rectangle is 480 square feet and its width is 96 feet. What is its length?
4. The area of a square is 625 sq. cm. Find the length of a side.
5. $ABCD$ is a rectangle.
   $AB =$ _____ $AD =$ _____

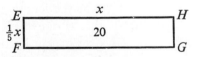

6. $EFGH$ is a rectangle.
   $EF =$ _____ $EH =$ _____

7. $PQRS$ is a rectangle; $TVWX$ is a square. $PQRS = TVWX$.
   $PQ =$ _____ $PS =$ _____

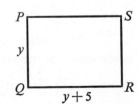
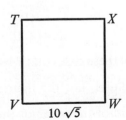

8. Show geometrically that
$(a + b)^2 = a^2 + 2ab + b^2.$

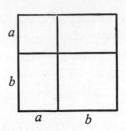

9. Show geometrically that
$(a - b)^2 = a^2 - 2ab + b^2.$

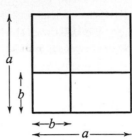

10. Show geometrically that
$(a + b)(a - b) = a^2 - b^2.$

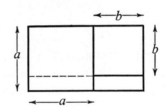

11. Use Ex. 8 to square 43. *Hint.* Let $a = 40, b = 3.$
12. Use Ex. 9 to square 68. *Hint.* Let $a = 70, b = 2.$
13. Use Ex. 10 to factor $(169 - 25)$. *Hint.* $169 = (?)^2; 25 = (?)^2.$
14. Factor $95 = 144 - 49 = 12^2 - 7^2.$
15. Given two squares such that one has twice the area of the other, can you determine the length of a side of the larger if the length of a side of the smaller is one?
16. Repeat Ex. 15 except let the area of the larger be 4 times the area of the smaller.

In the following discussions we shall use sentences such as

$$\triangle ABC = \triangle DEF$$
$$\square ABCD = \square MNOP.$$

It is evident in all these cases that what is meant is that the areas bounded by the figures are equal, not the figures themselves. Similarly $\dfrac{\triangle ABC}{\triangle EFG} = \dfrac{4}{9}$ refers to the ratio of the areas of the triangles.

17–5 THEOREM The area of a parallelogram equals the product of its base and altitude.

Formula: $A = ab$

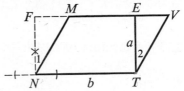

Hypothesis $\square MNTV$ having altitude a, base b, and area A.

Conclusion $A = ab$

The plan is to form a rectangle whose sides are a and b and prove that its area equals the area of the parallelogram.

Proof

1. Construct $NF \perp NT$, and extend VM to meet NF at F.	1. Give reasons.
2. $\angle\rule{1cm}{0.4pt} = \angle 2$	2. Sec. 5–18
3. $MN = \rule{1cm}{0.4pt}$; $\rule{1cm}{0.4pt} = ET$	3. Opp. sides of $\square$
4. $\triangle MNF \cong \triangle TVE$	4. Why?
5. $\square MNTV =$ trapezoid $MNTE + \triangle TVE$ $= $ trapezoid $MNTE + \triangle MNF$ $= FNTE$	5. Explain.
6. $FNTE$ is a rectangle.	6. Prove this.
7. Area $FNTE = ab$.	7. Why?
8. $\therefore \square MNTV = ab$, or $A = ab$	8. Post. 2

17–6 Corollary If two parallelograms have equal bases and equal altitudes, they have equal areas.

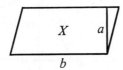
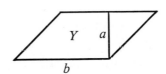

17–7 Corollary If two parallelograms have equal bases, the ratio of their areas equals the ratio of their altitudes.

17–8 Corollary If two parallelograms have equal altitudes, the ratio of their areas equals the ratio of their bases.

17–9 Corollary The ratio of the areas of two parallelograms equals the ratio of the products of their bases and altitudes.

C.

1. Find the area of □*ABCD*.

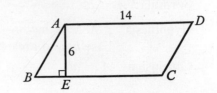

2. Find the area of □*PQRS*.

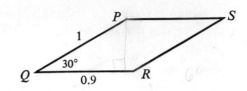

3. Find the altitude of □*ABCD*.

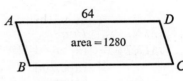

4. The area of □*XYZW* is 93.5.
   XW = ____

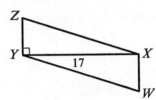

B.

5. *ABCD* is a □. Find *AF*.

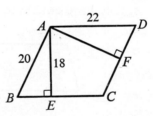

6. Find the area of a parallelogram if two sides are 62 and 96 respectively and the included angle is 150°.

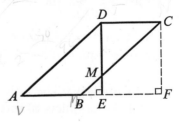

7. Prove the Theorem of Sec. 17–5 using the diagram shown.

8. What is the area of *RSTV*?
   What kind of figure is *RSTV*?
   Why? What is the length of
   the base? What is the length
   of the altitude?

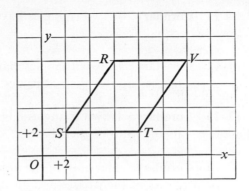

DISCOVERY EXERCISE

Draw △*MNT*. Construct the altitude *MW*. Through *M* construct
MV ∥ *NT*. Through *N* construct *NV* ∥ *MT*. What kind of quadrilateral
is *MVNT*? What is the area of the quadrilateral? What part of the
area of the quadrilateral is included in △*MNT*? Write an expression
for the area of △*MNT*.

If ∠*N* or ∠*T* were obtuse,
would the same steps apply?

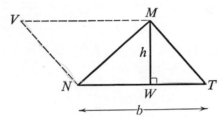

17–10 THEOREM **The area of a triangle equals one half the product
of a side and the altitude to that side.**

Formula. $A = \frac{1}{2}hb$

Hypothesis △*MNT* having altitude *h*, base *b*, and area *A*

Conclusion $A = \frac{1}{2}hb$

The plan is to form a parallelogram two sides of which are sides of the
triangle and show that the given triangle is half the parallelogram.

Proof

1. Construct *MV* ∥ *NT*, and
   NV ∥ *MT*.
2. *MVNT* is a ▱.
3. Area *MVNT* = *hb*.
4. △*MNT* = $\frac{1}{2}$▱*MVNT*
5. ∴ $A = \frac{1}{2}hb$

1. Give reasons.

2. Why?
3. Why?
4. △*MNT* ≅ △*MNV*
5. Post. 3 and 2

17–11 Corollary If two triangles have equal bases and equal altitudes, they have equal areas.

17–12 Corollary If two triangles have equal bases, the ratio of their areas equals the ratio of their altitudes.

17–13 Corollary If two triangles have equal altitudes, the ratio of their areas equals the ratio of their bases.

17–14 Corollary The ratio of the areas of two triangles equals the ratio of the products of their bases and altitudes.

WRITTEN EXERCISES

C.

1. Find the area of △ABC.

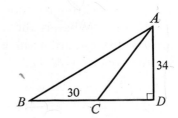

B.

2. Find the area of △XYZ.

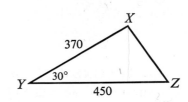

3. Find the altitude of △PQR.

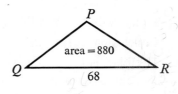

4. The area of △ABC = 96
   BC = _____

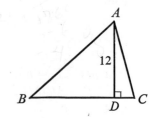

5. Find the length of XY.

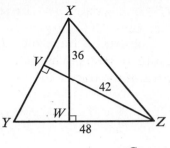

6. How does the area of $\triangle GHK$ compare with the area of $\triangle LHK$. Why?

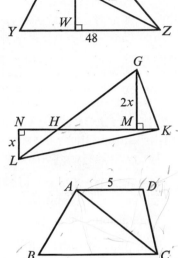

7. $ABCD$ is a trapezoid. How does the area of $\triangle ABC$ compare with the area of $\triangle ACD$? Why?

8. Find the area of $\triangle RST$.

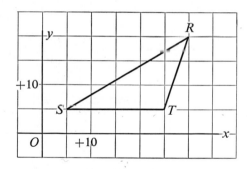

9. Find the area of triangle $A(5,6)$, $B(11,6)$, $C(7,9)$. Draw the figure on graph paper.

10. On graph paper draw the pentagon $R(0,0)$, $S(12,0)$, $T(14,3)$, $V(8,6)$, $W(3,2)$. Find its area. *Hint.* Divide it into triangles.

11. Find the area of the triangle bounded by the equations: $y = x$; $y = -x$; and $x = 3$.

Construct a trapezoid *MNTV* with *MV* ∥ *NT*. Draw *MT*. Construct altitude *MW*. What is the area of △*MNT*? Of △*MTV*? What is the area of the trapezoid?

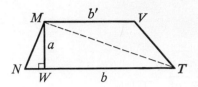

17–15 THEOREM The area of a trapezoid equals one half the product of its altitude times the sum of its bases.

Formula. $A = \frac{1}{2}a(b + b')$

Hypothesis Trapezoid *MNTV* with area *A*, altitude *a*, and bases *b* and *b'*.

Conclusion $A = \frac{1}{2}a(b + b')$

The plan is to draw a diagonal and show that the area of the trapezoid equals the sum of the areas of the resulting triangles.

Proof

1. Draw *MT*.	1. Give reasons.
2. △*MNT* = $\frac{1}{2}ab$	2. Why?
3. △*MTV* = $\frac{1}{2}ab'$	3. Why?
4. △*MNT* + △*MTV* = $\frac{1}{2}ab + \frac{1}{2}ab'$	4. Why?
5. ∴ $A = \frac{1}{2}a(b + b')$	5. Explain.

17–16 Corollary The area of a trapezoid equals the product of its altitude and median.

WRITTEN EXERCISES

C.

1. Find the area of trapezoid *ABCD*.

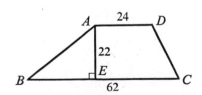

B.

2. Find the area of trapezoid *XYZW*.

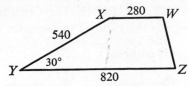

3. Find the area of *MNTV*.

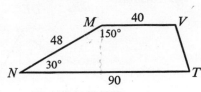

4. The area of trapezoid *PQRS* is 326.8. Find the length of the median.

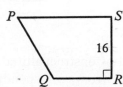

5. The area of *ABCD* is 110. Find *x*.

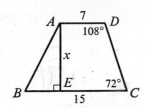

6. Find *y*.

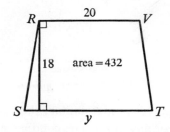

7. What is the area of *HJKL*?

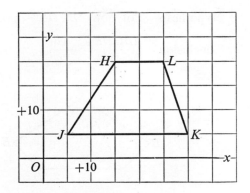

17–17 THEOREM If two triangles are similar, the ratio of their areas equals the ratio of the squares of any two corresponding sides.

Hypothesis $\triangle ABC \sim \triangle DEF$

Conclusion $\dfrac{\triangle ABC}{\triangle DEF} = \dfrac{\overline{AB}^2}{\overline{DE}^2}$

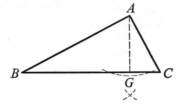 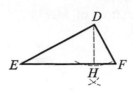

Proof

1. Construct altitudes AG and DH from corresponding vertices.

2. $\triangle ABC = \frac{1}{2}AG \cdot BC,$
   $\triangle DEF = \frac{1}{2}DH \cdot EF$

3. $\dfrac{\triangle ABC}{\triangle DEF} = \dfrac{\frac{1}{2}AG \cdot BC}{\frac{1}{2}DH \cdot EF}$
   $= \dfrac{AG \cdot BC}{DH \cdot EF}$

4. $\triangle ABG \sim \triangle DEH$

5. $\dfrac{AB}{DE} = \dfrac{AG}{DH}$, and $\dfrac{AB}{DE} = \dfrac{BC}{EF}$

6. $\dfrac{\triangle ABC}{\triangle DEF} = \dfrac{\overline{AB}^2}{\overline{DE}^2}$

1. Give reasons.

2. Why?

3. Why?

4. Prove this.

5. Why?

6. Post. 2

17–18 THEOREM If two polygons are similar, the ratio of their areas equals the ratio of the squares of any two corresponding sides.

Hypothesis Polygon $ABCDE \sim$ polygon $FGHIJ$

Conclusion $\dfrac{ABCDE}{FGHIJ} = \dfrac{\overline{AB}^2}{\overline{FG}^2}$

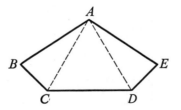 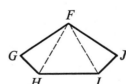

The plan is to divide the polygons into similar triangles, express the proportions involving the areas of the triangles, and combine these proportions so as to get the ratio of the areas of the polygons.

Proof

1. Divide the polygons into similar triangles.

1. Sec. 15–17

2. $\dfrac{\triangle ABC}{\triangle FGH} = \dfrac{\overline{AB}^2}{\overline{FG}^2}; \dfrac{\triangle ACD}{\triangle FHI}$

 $= \dfrac{\overline{AC}^2}{\overline{FH}^2}; \dfrac{\triangle ADE}{\triangle FIJ} = \dfrac{\overline{AE}^2}{\overline{FJ}^2}$

2. Why?

3. $\dfrac{AB}{FG} = \dfrac{AC}{FH} = \dfrac{AE}{FJ}$

3. Sec. 15–1

4. $\dfrac{\overline{AB}^2}{\overline{FG}^2} = \dfrac{\overline{AC}^2}{\overline{FH}^2} = \dfrac{\overline{AE}^2}{\overline{FJ}^2}$

4. ·Post. 4

5. $\dfrac{\triangle ABC}{\triangle FGH} = \dfrac{\triangle ACD}{\triangle FHI} = \dfrac{\triangle ADE}{\triangle FIJ}$

5. Post. 2

6. $\dfrac{\triangle ABC + \triangle ACD + \triangle ADE}{\triangle FGH + \triangle FHI + \triangle FIJ}$

 $= \dfrac{\triangle ABC}{\triangle FGH}$

6. See proof of Sec. 15–17.

7. $\dfrac{ABCDE}{FGHIJ} = \dfrac{\overline{AB}^2}{\overline{FG}^2}$

7. Post. 2

The proof is similar for polygons of any number of sides.

WRITTEN EXERCISES

C.

1. $\dfrac{\triangle ABC}{\triangle DEF} = \dfrac{?}{?}$

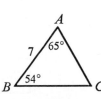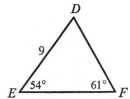

2. $\triangle ABC \sim \triangle DEF$.   *AB* and *DE* are corresponding sides.   *AB* = 1, and *DE* = 2.   What is the ratio of the area of $\triangle ABC$ to the area of $\triangle DEF$?

3. $\triangle PQR = 4\triangle TSV$
   $SV = \underline{\hspace{1cm}}$

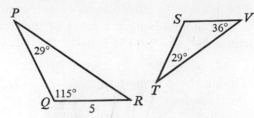

4. $P \sim Q$
   $\dfrac{\text{Area } P}{\text{Area } Q} = \dfrac{?}{?}$

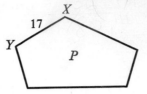
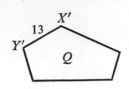

5. Polygon I $\sim$ Polygon II
   $W'Z' = \underline{\hspace{1cm}}$

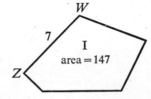
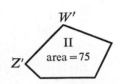

6. $\triangle XYZ \sim \triangle X'Y'Z'$. XY and $X'Y'$ are corresponding sides. $XY = \frac{1}{5}$. The area of $\triangle XYZ$ is 27 and the area of $\triangle X'Y'Z'$ is 75. Find $X'Y'$.

7. Use this figure and areas to prove the square of the hypotenuse of a right triangle equals the sum of the squares of the other two sides.

   Suggestions. $\triangle CBD \sim \triangle ABC \sim \triangle ACD$.

   Then $\dfrac{\triangle CBD}{\triangle ABC} = ?$, etc.

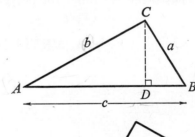

8. Find the area of $\triangle RST$.
9. Find the perimeter of $\triangle RST$.
10. x, y, and z are squares. Find the area of each.

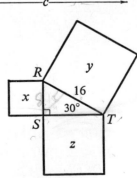

11. $RS =$ _____ $ST =$ _____

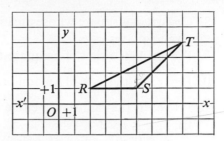

12. A and B are squares whose areas are respectively 16 and 9.

$x =$ _____

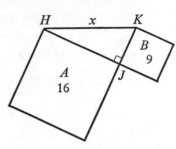

13. $QR =$ _____

14. Find the area of $EFGH$.

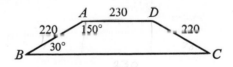

15. Find the area of $ABCD$.

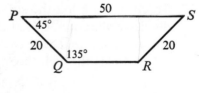

16. Find the area of $PQRS$.

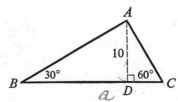

17. Find the area of $\triangle ABC$.

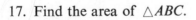

18. Construct a square whose area is equal to the sum of the areas of three given squares.

19. Prove: If the side of a square is s, the diagonal is $s\sqrt{2}$.

20. Prove: If the side of an equilateral triangle is s, the altitude is $\frac{s}{2}\sqrt{3}$.

21. Prove: If the radius of a circle is r, the side of an inscribed equilateral triangle is $r\sqrt{3}$.

22. Prove: If the radius of a circle is r, the side of a circumscribed equilateral triangle is $2r\sqrt{3}$.

23. Prove: The radius of a circle inscribed in an equilateral triangle is one third the altitude.

24. Prove: If s is the side of an equilateral triangle, the area is $\frac{s^2}{4}\sqrt{3}$.

A.

25. $OA = 50$; $OB = 130$; $DE = 300$. Find BE.

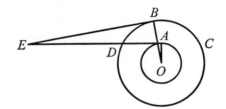

26. From any point O perpendiculars are drawn to the sides of a triangle. Prove $\overline{GJ}^2 + \overline{HK}^2 + \overline{FL}^2 = \overline{GL}^2 + \overline{FK}^2 + \overline{HJ}^2$.

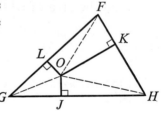

27. To cut from a log the stiffest possible rectangular beam, the sawyer divides a diameter GH at J, O, and K into 4 equal parts. He then constructs JL and KM each $\perp GH$. He draws GM, MH, HL, and GL and cuts through them.

(a) Prove $GMHL$ is a rectangle.

(b) Prove $\dfrac{GM}{MH} = \dfrac{\sqrt{3}}{1}$.

(c) Find the dimensions of such a beam cut from a log the diameter of which is 2 feet.

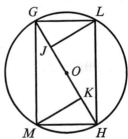

28. To cut from a log the strongest possible rectangular beam, the sawyer trisects diameter *AB* at *C* and *D*. He then constructs *CF* and *DE* each ⊥ *AB*. He draws *AE*, *EB*, *BF*, and *AF* and cuts through these lines.

(*a*) Prove *AEBF* is a rectangle.

(*b*) Prove $\dfrac{AE}{AF} = \dfrac{\sqrt{2}}{1}$.

(*c*) Find the dimensions of such a beam cut from a log the diameter of which is 2 feet.

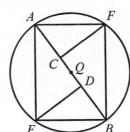

MISCELLANEOUS WRITTEN EXERCISES

C.

1. Find the area of *ABCD*.

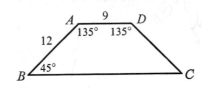

2. Find the area of *EFGH*.

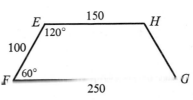

3. Find the altitude of the trapezoid.

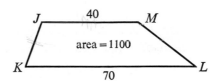

4. Show that the area of ▱*PQRS* is to the area of ▱*QTVR* as $\sqrt{3}$ is to 1.

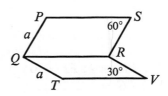

5. Show that the area of rectangle *ABCD* is to the area of ▱*BEFC* as $\sqrt{2}$ is to 1.

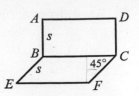

6. Area $\triangle HKL = 10$
   Area $\triangle GHL = $ _____

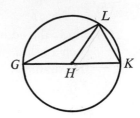

7. Find the area of $\triangle PQR$.

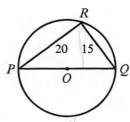

B.

8. Find the area of *SVXZ*.

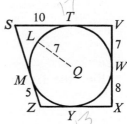

9. *ABCD* is a trapezoid. Find the ratio of the area of $\triangle ABD$ to the area of $\triangle BCD$.

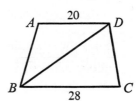

10. $EH = 4$; $FK = 6$
    $EG = $ _____

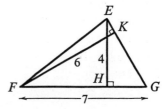

11. Find the area of △PQR.

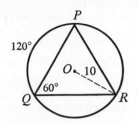

12. What is the ratio of the area of △ABC to the area of △DEF?

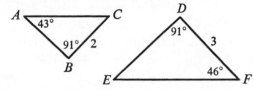

13. The area of △PQR is 490.
Find the area of △GHK.

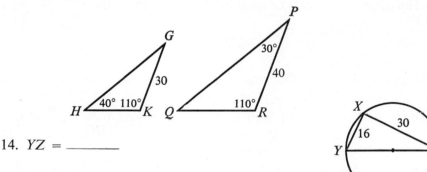

14. YZ = _____

15. The area of a square is 289. What is the length of a side?
16. The arca of a square is 676. What is the length of a diagonal?
17. The area of a square is 900. What is the altitude of a triangle having the same area and a base equal to a side of the square?
18. The arms of a right triangle are 10 and 24. What is the diameter of the circumscribed circle?
19. The sides of a triangle are 8 inches, 15 inches, and 17 inches. What is the radius of the circumscribed circle?
20. The hypotenuse of a right triangle is 41 and one arm is 17. Find the length of the other arm.
21. The arms of a right triangle are 7 centimeters and 11 centimeters. What is the length of the hypotenuse?

OUTLINE OF CHAPTER 17

This chapter introduces the following terms:

unit of area   base   altitude

This chapter presents information concerning:

1. The area of a rectangle. Page 445
2. The area of a parallelogram. Page 447
3. The area of a triangle. Page 449
4. The ratio of the areas of two parallelograms or two triangles having one dimension of one equal to the corresponding dimension of the other. Pages 447, 450
5. The ratio of the areas of any two rectangles, parallelograms, or triangles. Pages 447, 450
6. The area of a trapezoid. Page 452
7. The ratio of the areas of similar polygons. Page 454

REVIEW

1. Theorem. The area of a parallelogram equals the product of its base and altitude. Give a complete demonstration.

2. The base of $\Box$A $=$ 3 in., and its area is 10 square inches. The base of $\Box$B $=$ 3 in., and its area is 16 square inches. What is the ratio of the altitude of $\Box$A to the altitude of $\Box$B?

3. The area of a triangle is 18 square centimeters and its altitude is 9 centimeters. Find the base.

4. Theorem. The area of a trapezoid equals half the product of its altitude and the sum of its bases. Give a complete demonstration.

5. The altitude of a trapezoid is 6 in., one base is 2 in., and its area is 21 square inches. Find the second base.

6. $\triangle ABC$ has an area of 36 square inches, and $\triangle A'B'C'$ has an area of 48 square inches. AB and $A'B'$ are corresponding sides and the triangles are similar. What is the ratio of $A'B'$ to AB?

7. Prove: The ratio of the areas of two similar triangles equals the ratio of the squares of the lengths of any two corresponding altitudes.

8. $\triangle ABC$ is a right triangle with the right angle at C. $AB = 26$ inches, and $AC = 10$ inches. How long is BC?

9. The sides of a rectangle are 21 cm. and 28 cm. Find the diagonal.

10. A diameter of a circle is 39 inches. A chord 36 inches long connects one end of the diameter to a point on the circle, and a second chord is drawn to complete a triangle. Find the length of the second chord. Prove the steps by which you get your answer.

11. An old town in India is surrounded by a circular wall 1 mile in diameter. There are gates in the wall, at both north and south. Between the gates is a straight street which is a diameter. From the north gate a road runs due north. From the south gate a road runs due west. One mile from the north gate on the road is a watchtower. A traveler left the south gate and walked westward until he could just see the tower on a line tangent to the wall. How far had he walked?

YES–NO TEST

Approximately 25 minutes

Copy on your paper the numbers of the following questions. If the answer to a question is *yes* under all conditions, place a plus sign (+) after its number. If the answer is *not yes* under all conditions, place a zero (0) after its number.

1. If two rectangles have the same area, are they similar?
2. If the sides of one rectangle are 12 and 18, and the sides of another are 18 and 30, is the ratio of their areas $\frac{2}{5}$?
3. If the sides of a rectangle are 2 and 3, is its area 5?
4. If the area of a rectangle is 60, and one side is 15, is another side 4?
5. If the sides of a parallelogram are 8 and 10, is its area 80?
6. If the sides of a parallelogram are 80 and 100 and the included angle is 30°, is the area 4000?
7. If the base of a triangle is x and the altitude is y, is the area xy?
8. If the base and altitude of a triangle are respectively 25 and 40, and if the base and altitude of a second triangle are respectively 40 and 25, are the areas equal?
9. Bases of a trapezoid are 12 and 22; the altitude is 6. Is the area 102?
10. If two angles of one triangle are 40° and 70° and the included side is 12, and if two angles of another triangle are 70° and 40° and the included side is 18, is the ratio of the areas $\frac{4}{9}$?

COMPLETION TEST

Copy on your paper the numbers of the following statements. After each number write a word, or letters, or a number, or an expression which, if written in the blank, would complete the statement and make it true.

1. The area of *ABCD* is _____

2. The area of *EFGH* is _____

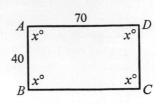

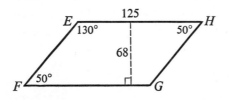

3. The area of △*XYZ* is _____

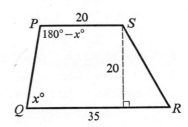

4. The area of *PQRS* is _____

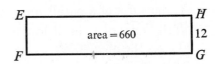

5. The area of rectangle *EFGH* is 660.

EH = _____

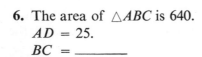

6. The area of △*ABC* is 640.
AD = 25.
BC = _____

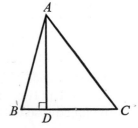

7. *EFGH* is a parallelogram. Its area is _____

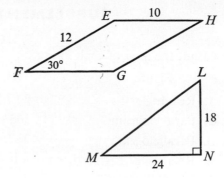

8. △*LMN* is a rt. △.
LM = _____

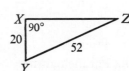

9. *XZ* = _____

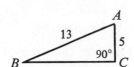

10. The area of △*ABC* = _____

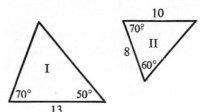

11. The ratio of the area of △I to the area of △II = _____

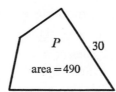

12. *P* ~ *Q*   *x* = _____
13. *n* = _____

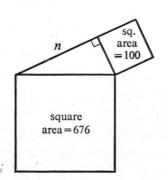

SUPPLEMENTARY EXERCISES

C.

Find the area of each figure.

Figure	Base	Altitude
1. Rectangle	22.7 in.	18.4 in.
2. Parallelogram	$16\frac{2}{3}$ cm.	$31\frac{1}{2}$ cm.
3. Parallelogram	$2\frac{1}{3}$ ft.	$6\frac{3}{4}$ ft.
4. Rectangle	8 ft.	16 in.
5. Triangle	42 cm.	13 cm.
6. Triangle	$12\frac{1}{2}$ ft.	$38\frac{1}{3}$ ft.
7. Triangle	6	12
8. Parallelogram	35	140
9. Rectangle	r	s
10. Triangle	72	46

11. Find the area of a trapezoid with bases of 62 and 3 and altitude of 116.

B.

12. Find the area of a trapezoid if the bases are 148 and 96 and if one of the nonparallel sides is 80 and makes an angle of 30° with the base the length of which is 148.

13. Two sides of a parallelogram inscribed in a circle are 7 and 12. What is its area?

14. One side of a rhombus is 10 and one angle is 150°. Find its area.

15. The diagonals of a rhombus are 12 and 18. Find its area.

16. One arm of an isosceles right triangle is 13. Find its area.

17. One of the equal sides of an isosceles triangle is 82. The vertex angle is 120°. Find the area.

18. The altitude on the hypotenuse of a right triangle divides it into segments with lengths of 6 and 54. Find the area of the triangle.

19. The area of a rectangle is 1225 and its altitude is 120. Find the base.

20. The area of a parallelogram is 1.82 and its base is 0.455. Find the altitude.

21. The area of a triangle is 16 and its base is 8. Find the altitude.

22. The area of a right triangle is 98 and one arm is twice as long as the other. Find each arm.

23. The area of a trapezoid is 1800 and the bases are 52 and 68. Find the altitude.

24. The area of a trapezoid is 3650, one base is 84, and the altitude is 50. Find the other base.

25. Similar triangles have areas 169 square inches and 225 square inches respectively. Find the side of the smaller triangle which corresponds to a 5-inch side of the larger triangle.

26. Similar polygons have corresponding sides 2 and 12. The area of the smaller polygon is 28. What is the area of the larger?

27. The side of an equilateral triangle is 5 and its area is 10.85. Find the side of an equilateral triangle the area of which is 21.70.

28. The arms of a right triangle are 28 and 21. Find the hypotenuse.

29. The arms of a right triangle are 45 and 108. Find the hypotenuse.

30. The arms of a right triangle are 7 and 11. Find the hypotenuse.

31. The hypotenuse of a right triangle is 91 and one arm is 35. Find the other arm.

32. Repeat Ex. 31 if the hypotenuse is 53 and one arm is 41.

33. The hypotenuse of a right triangle is 130 and one arm is three times the other. Find each arm.

34. The diameter of a circle is 120. Find the length of a chord of a 30° inscribed angle.

35. The diameter of a circle is 546. Find the length of a chord of a 60° angle inscribed in the circle.

36. In a circle of radius 10 how long is the chord of a 45° inscribed angle?

A.

37. A 30° central angle in a circle has a chord 14 centimeters long. What is the length of the chord of a 60° angle?

38. A line segment AB can be divided in extreme and mean ratio as follows. Construct a square of which AB is a side. Bisect BD at E. With E as center and AE as radius draw an arc intersecting DB at F. With B as center and BF as radius draw an arc intersecting AB at G.

Prove: $\dfrac{AB}{BG} = \dfrac{BG}{AG}$

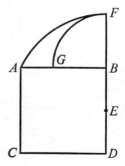

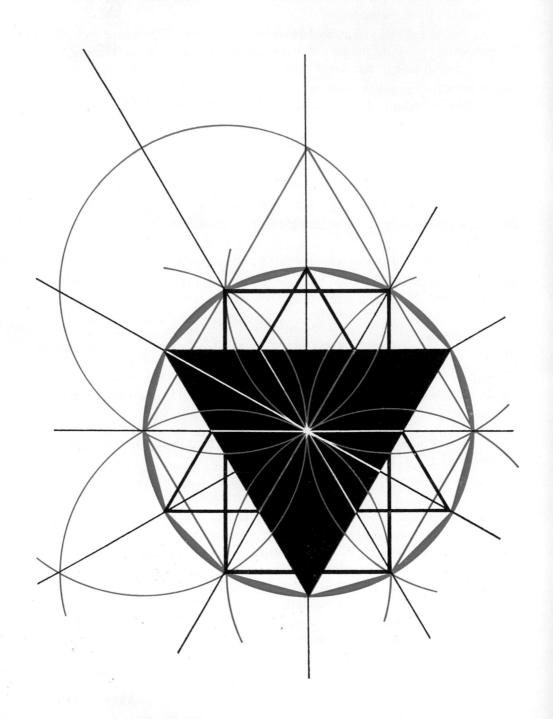

CHAPTER | 18

REGULAR POLYGONS AND CIRCLES

EVERYWHERE you look, you see equilateral triangles, squares, pentagons and hexagons with equal sides and equal angles, star polygons, and circles. In floor designs, advertisements, neon lights, church windows, pavements, tableware, watches, buttons, fruit cans, medicine containers, cosmetics boxes, and machinery you see these figures in hundreds of combinations and sizes. The designer, the engineer, the artist, the carpenter, and the decorator must be familiar with these figures.

Much of the development of mathematics centers about the geometry of regular polygons and circles. Thousands of pages of mathematics have been written about the ratio of the circumference of a circle to its diameter, that is, about π. This number also appears in many connections not related to the circle.

Parts of the subject of this chapter have been completely developed, but not all. For example, it is known that it is possible to construct a regular polygon of 257 sides, but no one has discovered how to do this. In this chapter we are to study a number of elementary facts and concepts related to regular polygons and circles.

18–1 Regular Polygon A regular polygon is a polygon all of whose sides are equal and all of whose angles are equal.

$\triangle HQK$, $\triangle KQL$, $\triangle LQM$, $\triangle MQR$, and $\triangle RQS$ are equilateral triangles by construction. Draw the figure.

1. $\angle HQK + \angle KQL + \angle LQM + \angle MQR + \angle RQS = ?$ Why?
2. What is the sum of all angles around a point such as Q? Why?
3. $\angle SQH = ?$ Why?
4. If segment HS were drawn, what kind of triangle would $\triangle SQH$ be? Why?
5. What would be the length of HS? Why?
6. How would $\angle SHQ$ compare with $\angle KHQ$? Why?
7. How would $\angle HSQ$ compare with $\angle RSQ$? Why?
8. Compare angles HKL, KLM, LMR, MRS, RSH, SHK.
9. What kind of polygon would $SHKLMR$ be? Why?

18–2   Problem To inscribe a regular hexagon in a circle.

   Given $\odot O$

Required   To inscribe a regular hexagon.

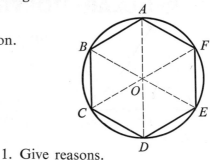

   Proof

1. Open the compass to the length of the radius of the circle; begin at any point such as A, and mark off five other points of division on the circle, B, C, D, E, and F. Draw AB, BC, CD, DE, EF, and AF; AO, BO, CO, DO, EO, and FO.

2. $\triangle$s OAB, OBC, etc. are equilateral.

3. The angles at O total 360°.

4. Then $\angle AOF$ is 60° and $\triangle AOF$ is equilateral.

5. The angles of the hexagon are each 120°.

6. $ABCDEF$ is a regular hexagon.

1. Give reasons.

2. Why?

3. Why?

4. Why?

5. Why?

6. By definition

18–3 THEOREM If a circle is divided into n equal arcs and if chords of these arcs are drawn, the chords form a regular inscribed polygon.

Hypothesis $\odot O$; $\overarc{AB} = \overarc{BC} = \overarc{CD} = \overarc{DE} = \overarc{EF} = \overarc{FG} = \cdots$ to n arcs; chords AB, BC, CD, DE, EF, FG, $\cdots$ to n chords.

Conclusion $ABCDEF \cdots$ is a regular polygon.

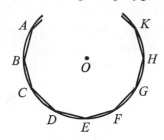

Proof

1. $\overarc{AB} = \overarc{BC} = \overarc{CD} = \overarc{DE} = \overarc{EF}$
   $= \overarc{FG} = \cdots$
2. $\therefore AB = BC = CD = DE$
   $= EF = FG = \cdots$
3. $\angle A \overset{\circ}{=} \frac{1}{2}(\overarc{BC} + \overarc{CD} + \overarc{DE}$
   $+ \overarc{EF} + \cdots$ to $(n - 2)$ arcs$)$
4. $\angle B \overset{\circ}{=} \frac{1}{2}(\overarc{CD} + \overarc{DE} + \overarc{EF}$
   $+ \overarc{AF} + \cdots$ to $(n - 2)$ arcs$)$
5. $\angle A = \angle B$
6. In like manner, $\angle B = \angle C$
   $= \angle D = \angle E = \angle F = \cdots$
7. $ABCDEF \cdots$ is a regular polygon.

1. Why?

2. Sec. 11–17

3. Sec. 12–18

4. Why?

5. Post. 2
6. Show this.

7. Sec. 18–1

18–4 Corollary If chords are drawn from each vertex of a regular inscribed polygon to the mid-points of the intercepted arcs, they form a regular inscribed polygon of double the number of sides of the given polygon.

18–5 Corollary An equilateral polygon inscribed in a circle is regular.

By making use of the theorem of Sec. 18–3 you can construct a number of regular polygons and anticipate some work that is later given in this book. Can you construct regular polygons of 4 sides, 12 sides? What others can you construct?

Oral

Using only the information given in the figure, answer these questions.

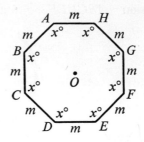

1. Is *O* regular? Why?

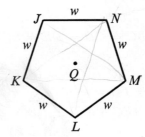

2. Is *Q* regular? Why?

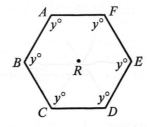

3. Is *R* regular? Why?

4. Is *S* regular? Why?
5. Is *T* regular? Why?

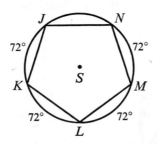

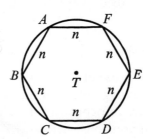

18–6   THEOREM   If a circle is divided into equal arcs, and tangents are drawn at the points of division, the tangents form a regular circumscribed polygon.

   Hypothesis $\odot O$; $\overset{\frown}{AB} = \overset{\frown}{BC} = \overset{\frown}{CD} = \cdots$; tangents PQ, QR, RS, $\cdots$.

   Conclusion $PQR \cdots$ is a regular polygon.

   The plan is to draw chords connecting the points of division of the circle, thus forming a regular inscribed polygon, and use congruent isosceles triangles to prove the sides of the circumscribed polygon equal and the angles equal.

   Sketch the proof.

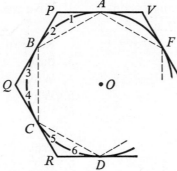

18–7   Corollary   If tangents are drawn at the mid-points of the arcs intercepted by the sides of a regular circumscribed polygon, they form a regular polygon of double the number of sides of the given polygon.

ORAL EXERCISE

AE, ED, etc. are tangent to $\odot K$.
Is $ABCDE$ regular?   Why?

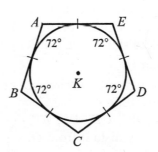

WRITTEN EXERCISE

Circumscribe a regular octagon about a circle.

18–8   THEOREM   A circle can be circumscribed about a regular polygon.

Hypothesis   The regular polygon
$\qquad\qquad$ *ABCDEF* · · ·

Conclusion   A circle can be circumscribed
$\qquad\qquad$ about it.

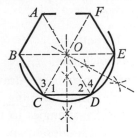

The plan is to construct a circle that passes
through three consecutive vertices of the polygon and prove that the other vertices lie on it.

Proof

1. Construct ⊙*O* through consecutive vertices *C*, *D*, and *E*.
2. *OC* = *OD*
3. ∠1 = ∠2
4. ∠*BCD* = ∠*CDE*
5. ∠3 = ∠4
6. *BC* = *DE*
7. △*BCO* = △*DEO*
8. *BO* = *EO*
9. *B* is on ⊙*O*.

1. Give reasons. See Sec. 11–1.

2. Radii of same ⊙
3. Base ∠s of isos. △
4. Why?
5. Why?
6. Why?
7. Why?
8. Why?
9. Def. of circle

In like manner, prove *A*, *F*, · · · are on ⊙*O*.

18–9   THEOREM   A circle can be inscribed in a regular polygon.

Hypothesis   The regular polygon
$\qquad\qquad$ *ABCDEF* · · ·

Conclusion   A circle can be inscribed in it.

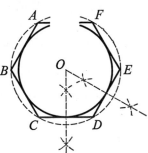

The plan is to circumscribe a circle about the
polygon and show that the sides of the polygon
are equal chords of this circle and therefore
equally distant from the center.

Proof

1. Circumscribe a circle *O* about
ABCDEF · · ·.
2. *AB*, *BC*, *CD*, *DE*, *EF*, · · · are
equally distant from *O*.
3. ∴ the circle with center *O* and
radius equal to the distance
from *O* to *CD* is inscribed in
ABCDEF · · ·.

1. Give reasons.

2. Sec. 11–21

3. Def. of circle

Inscribe a regular hexagon in a circle and then inscribe a circle in the hexagon.

18–10 Center of a Regular Polygon The center of a regular polygon is the common center of the circumscribed and inscribed circles.

18–11 Radius of a Regular Polygon The radius of a regular polygon is the distance from the center to a vertex. It is the radius of the circumscribed circle.

18–12 Apothem of a Regular Polygon The apothem of a regular polygon is the shortest distance from the center to a side. It is the radius of the inscribed circle.

18–13 Central Angle of a Regular Polygon A central angle of a regular polygon is the angle formed by two radii drawn to consecutive vertices.

18–14 THEOREM Each central angle of a regular polygon of n sides is $\frac{2}{n}$ straight angles.

18–15 Corollary If an angle whose size is $\frac{2}{n}$ straight angles can be constructed, a regular polygon of n sides can be constructed.

By constructing n adjacent angles each equal to $\frac{2}{n}$ straight angles, we obtain the n central angles of a regular polygon.

18–16 Corollary Each angle of a regular polygon of n sides is $\frac{n-2}{n}$ straight angles.

18–17 THEOREM A radius of a regular polygon bisects an angle of the polygon.

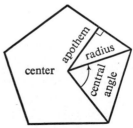

18–18 THEOREM An apothem of a regular polygon is the perpendicular bisector of a side of the polygon.

18–19 Problem To inscribe an equilateral triangle in a circle.

18–20 Corollary Regular polygons of 3×2^n sides can be constructed. (n is 0 or any positive integer. Recall that $2^0 = 1$.)

WRITTEN EXERCISES

C.

1. In the formula $P = 3 \times 2^n$ substitute 0,1,2,3,4,5,6 for n and make a list of the series of regular polygons that can be inscribed as indicated by this formula.
2. Find the side of an equilateral triangle inscribed in a circle of radius 1.
3. Find the side of an equilateral triangle inscribed in a circle of radius r.
4. Find the side of an equilateral triangle if the radius of its inscribed circle is x.
5. Find the radius of a circle inscribed in an equilateral triangle one side of which is 1.
6. Find the radius of a circle circumscribed about an equilateral triangle one side of which is k.

7. $AB =$ _____

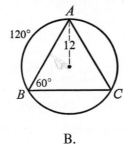

B.

8. $OT =$ _____

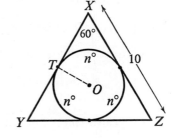

9. $\angle OAB =$ _____° Why?

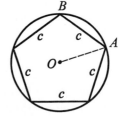

18-21 Problem **To inscribe a square in a circle.**

Describe the construction and give a complete demonstration.

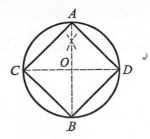

18-22 Corollary Regular polygons of 4×2^n sides can be constructed. (n is 0 or any positive integer.)

WRITTEN EXERCISES

C.

1. In the formula $P = 4 \times 2^n$, substitute 0,1,2,3,4,5,6 for n and make a list of the series of regular polygons that can be constructed as indicated by this formula.
2. Inscribe a circle in a square.

B.

3. The radius of a circle is 16. Find the side and the area of the inscribed square.
4. The radius of a circle is 50. Find the area of the circumscribed square.
5. Find the side of a square inscribed in a circle of radius r.
6. Find the side of a square circumscribed about a circle of radius x.
7. Find the area of a square inscribed in a circle of radius r.
8. Find the radius of a circle inscribed in a square one side of which is s.
9. Find the radius of a square if one side is n.

10. Find x.

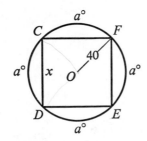

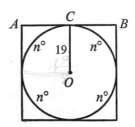

11. $AB = ?$ Why?

12. $OE = 50$. $OA = ?$

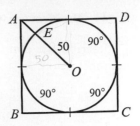

13. Inscribe a regular octagon in a circle.

18–23 Problem Optional To inscribe a regular decagon in a circle.
Suggestion. Construct central angles of 36°. See Sec. 15–15.

18–24 Corollary Optional To inscribe a regular pentagon in a circle.

18–25 Corollary Optional Regular polygons of 5×2^n sides can be constructed. (n is 0 or any positive integer.)

18–26 THEOREM If two regular polygons have the same number of sides, they are similar.

Hypothesis Regular polygons *ABCDE* and *FGHIJ*, each having n sides.

Conclusion $ABCDE \sim FGHIJ$

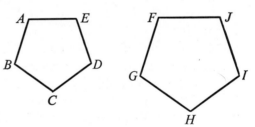

Proof

1. $\angle A = \angle B = \cdots = \dfrac{n-2}{n}$ st. $\angle$s.	1. Sec. 18–16
2. $\angle F = \angle G = \cdots = \dfrac{n-2}{n}$ st. $\angle$s.	2. Why?
3. $\angle A = \angle F$; $\angle B = \angle G$; etc.	3. Why?
4. $AB = BC = CD = \cdots$	4. Why?
5. $FG = GH = HI = \cdots$	5. Why?
6. $\dfrac{AB}{FG} = \dfrac{BC}{GH} = \dfrac{CD}{HI} = \cdots$	6. Why?
7. $\therefore ABCDE \sim FGHIJ$	7. Why?

478 GEOMETRY

18–27   The Regular Polygon of Many Sides and the Circle   Suppose a regular polygon, say a regular hexagon, to be inscribed in a circle.   If chords are drawn from the vertices to the mid-points of the arcs intercepted by the sides of the hexagon, a regular inscribed <u>dodecagon</u> is formed.   It is easily shown that the perimeter of the dodecagon is more than that of the hexagon.

The perimeter of the dodecagon is less than the circumference of the circle.

If still more chords are drawn from the vertices of the dodecagon to the mid-points of the new arcs intercepted by the sides of the dodecagon, and this process is continued indefinitely, then regular polygons of 24, 48, 96, 192, 384, etc. sides are formed. The perimeter of any of these polygons is more than that of the preceding polygon, but less than the length of the circle.

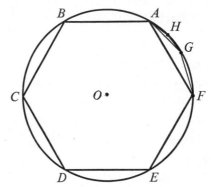

It seems evident that as the number of sides of the inscribed polygon is continually increased, the perimeter of the polygon gets nearer and nearer to the length of the circle, so that we can find very nearly the length of the circle by finding the perimeter of an inscribed polygon of many sides.

18–28   Circumference   The <u>circumference</u> of a circle is the length of the circle.

18–29   Finding Circumference of a Circle   Sec. 18–27 suggests how we can find the approximate perimeter of a circle.   First we must learn how to find the perimeter of a regular polygon inscribed in the circle. From this knowledge we must learn how to find the perimeter of a regular polygon of double the number of sides of the first regular polygon.   We can continue to find perimeters of polygons of double the number of sides of one polygon just evaluated.   The limit, or least boundary number, which none of these perimeters can exceed is the circumference of the circle.

A similar consideration of the areas of these inscribed polygons leads to a method of finding the area bounded by the circle.

Mathematicians of ancient Greece used a method like that suggested here for developing formulas related to the circle.   It is sometimes called the *method of exhaustion.*

18–30 THEOREM If two regular polygons have the same number of sides, the ratio of their perimeters equals the ratio of their apothems or the ratio of their radii.

Hypothesis Regular polygons P and Q having perimeters p and q respectively. P and Q have the same number of sides; PC is the apothem of P; QG is the apothem of Q; PB is the radius of P; QF is the radius of Q.

Conclusion $\dfrac{p}{q} = \dfrac{PC}{QG}, \dfrac{p}{q} = \dfrac{PB}{QF}$

The plan is to prove the triangles similar and show that the ratio of a pair of sides equals the ratio of the perimeters of the polygons.

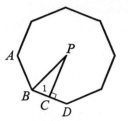 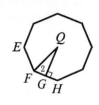

Proof

1. $P \sim Q$ 1. Sec. 18–26
2. $\angle ABC = \angle EFG$ 2. Why?
3. $\angle 1 = \angle 2$ 3. Sec. 18–17, Post. 3
4. $\triangle PBC \sim \triangle QFG$ 4. Sec. 15–4
5. $\dfrac{PB}{QF} = \dfrac{BC}{FG} = \dfrac{PC}{QG}$ 5. Why?
6. $\dfrac{BC}{FG} = \dfrac{2BC}{2FG} = \dfrac{BD}{FH}$ 6. Why?
7. $\dfrac{p}{q} = \dfrac{BD}{FH}$ 7. Sec. 15–17
8. $\dfrac{p}{q} = \dfrac{PC}{QG}$ 8. Post. 2

Let the pupil prove $\dfrac{p}{q} = \dfrac{PB}{QF}$.

NOTE: When capital letters and small letters are used in the same theorem, as here, they are read "P major" and "p minor."

18–31 Corollary If two regular polygons have the same number of sides, the ratio of their areas equals the ratio of the squares of their apothems.

Suggestion. Apply Sec. 17–18.

What other words could replace *apothems* in this corollary and give true statements?

18–32 POSTULATE 38   The ratio of the circumferences of two circles equals the ratio of their radii.

It is clear that for polygons of the same number of sides inscribed in the two circles the theorem of Sec. 18–30 applies.   Then the discussion of Sec. 18–27 and Sec. 18–29 makes the present postulate plausible.

$$\frac{c}{c'} = \frac{r}{r'}$$

18–33   Corollary   The ratio of the circumferences of two circles equals the ratio of their diameters.

$$\frac{c}{c'} = \frac{d}{d'}$$

This follows from Sec. 18–32.

18–34   Corollary   The ratio of the circumference of any circle to its diameter is constant;   that is, it is the same for any two circles.

$$\frac{c}{d} = \frac{c'}{d'}.$$

See Sec. 18–33.

18–35   π   The constant ratio of the circumference of a circle to its diameter is denoted by the Greek letter π (pi).   Thus $\frac{c}{d} = \pi$.   The numerical value of this ratio is an irrational number and is an unending nonrepeating decimal.   It is approximately 3.1416, or $\frac{22}{7}$.

More than 2000 years ago Archimedes proved $3\frac{10}{70} > \pi > 3\frac{10}{71}$.

18–36   THEOREM   If the diameter of a circle is d, the circumference c is given by the formula $c = \pi d$.

18–37   Corollary   The circumference of a circle whose radius is r is given by the formula $c = 2\pi r$.

The famous problem of *squaring the circle* is suggested by this corollary. It can be stated thus: Is it possible to construct a straight line equal to the circumference of a given circle, using compasses and straightedge only?

18–38 Corollary The ratio of the areas of two circles equals the ratio of the squares of their radii or the squares of their diameters.

Hypothesis ⊙O having area A, radius ON, and diameter MN; ⊙O' having area A', radius O'N', and diameter M'N'.

Conclusion $\dfrac{A}{A'} = \dfrac{\overline{ON}^2}{\overline{O'N'}^2} = \dfrac{\overline{MN}^2}{\overline{M'N'}^2}$

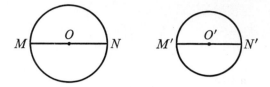

EXERCISES

C.

1. P and Q are regular polygons. Find the ratio of their areas.

2. c and c' are circumferences of ⊙O and ⊙O' respectively. Find the ratio of c to c'.

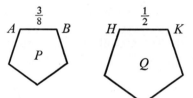

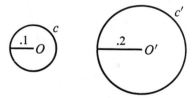

3. DC and HG are tangents. BC = 3; CD = 6; FG = 5; GH = 9. Let x and x' be the circumferences of ⊙R and ⊙S. Find the ratio of x to x'.

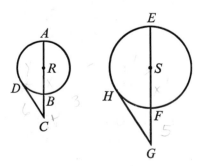

4. Let z be the area of $\odot O$ and z' be the area of $\odot O'$. Find the ratio of z to z'.

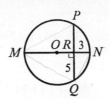 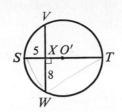

5. The orbit of the moon is a circle (nearly) whose diameter is about 480,000 miles. Find the circumference of its orbit.
6. The radius of the earth's orbit is about 93,000,000 miles. The earth makes a circuit of this orbit in 365 days. What is the speed of the earth in miles per hour? Assume the orbit to be a circle.
7. The diameter of a tire is 26 inches. Find its circumference.
8. The circumference of a circle is 11 inches. Find its radius.

18–39 THEOREM The area of a regular polygon equals one half the product of its apothem and perimeter.

Formula. $A = \frac{1}{2}hp$

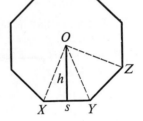

Hypothesis Regular polygon O having n sides; h is the apothem, s is a side, p is the perimeter, and A is the area.

Conclusion $A = \frac{1}{2}hp$

The plan is to draw the radii of the polygon, thus dividing it into congruent triangles, find the areas of the triangles, and add them.

Proof

1. Draw the radii OX, OY, OZ, etc., forming n triangles.
2. $\triangle OXY = \frac{1}{2}hs$; $\triangle OYZ = \frac{1}{2}hs$; etc.
3. $A = \triangle OXY + \triangle OYZ + \cdots$ etc.
4. $A = \frac{1}{2}hs + \frac{1}{2}hs + \cdots$
5. $p = ns$
6. $\therefore A = \frac{1}{2}hp$

1. Give reason.

2. Why?

3. Why?

4. Why?
5. Why?
6. Why?

18–40 Corollary The area of a circle equals one half the product of its radius and circumference.

Formula. $A = \frac{1}{2}cr$

18–41 Corollary The area A of a circle whose radius is r is given by the formula $A = \pi r^2$.

  Suggestion. Use Sec. 18–40 and Sec. 18–37.

WRITTEN EXERCISES

C.

Assume that numerical data are exact.

1. C is a regular polygon. Find its area.

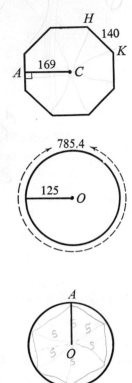

2. The circumference of $\odot O$ is 785.4. Its radius is 125. Find its area.

3. T is a regular hexagon. Find x.

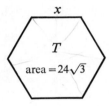

4. The circumference of $\odot O$ is 18.85. The area $= 28.3$. Find OA.

5. Find the area of a circle of radius 2 inches.
6. Find the area of a regular hexagon inscribed in a circle of diameter 10 centimeters.
7. The circumference of a circle is 12 inches. Find its area.
8. The area of a circle is 48 square centimeters.   Find its circumference.
9. Find the area of a circle whose diameter is 10 feet.
10. A circle is inscribed in a square whose area is 81 square centimeters. Find the area of the circle. Find its circumference.
11. Concentric circles have diameters of 1 inch and 2 inches respectively. What is the area of the ring between the circles?

484 GEOMETRY

18–42 Problem Given the side and radius of a regular inscribed polygon, to find the side of a regular inscribed polygon of double the number of sides.

Given $\odot O$ with radius r; $AB = s$, a side of a regular inscribed polygon of n sides; $AC = s_2,*$ a side of the regular inscribed polygon of $2n$ sides.

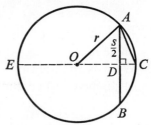

Required To find the length of s_2 in terms of r and s.

The plan is to apply the Pythagorean Theorem to the right triangles.

Construction. Draw the diameter CE intersecting AB at D.

Solution.

1. $AD = \dfrac{s}{2}$

2. $s_2^2 = \dfrac{s^2}{4} + \overline{CD}^2 = \dfrac{s^2}{4} + (r - OD)^2$

3. $s_2^2 = \dfrac{s^2}{4} + \left(r - \sqrt{r^2 - \dfrac{s^2}{4}}\right)^2$

4. $s_2^2 = \dfrac{s^2}{4} + r^2 - 2r\sqrt{r^2 - \dfrac{s^2}{4}} + r^2 - \dfrac{s^2}{4}$

5. $s_2^2 = 2r^2 - 2r\sqrt{r^2 - \dfrac{s^2}{4}}$

6. $s_2^2 = 2r^2 - 2r\dfrac{\sqrt{4r^2 - s^2}}{2} = 2r^2 - r\sqrt{4r^2 - s^2}$

7. $s_2 = \sqrt{2r^2 - r\sqrt{4r^2 - s^2}}$

18–43 Sector A <u>sector</u> of a circle is the set of points consisting of an arc, its radii, and all the interior points of the circle which they bound. The area of a sector is proportional to its central angle; that is, the area of a sector is to the area of the circle as its angle is to 360°.

18–44 Segment A <u>segment</u> of a circle is the set of points interior to a circle and bounded by a chord and its arc. If the central angle is less than a straight angle, the area of a segment can be found by subtracting the area of $\triangle OAB$ from the area of the sector OAB. Give a rule when the central angle is greater than a straight angle.

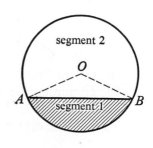

* Note: s_2 is read "s sub 2."

WRITTEN EXERCISES

C.

1. Find the area of a sector of a circle of radius 10 inches if its central angle is 60°.
2. What is the area of a sector having a central angle of 24° in a circle of diameter 14 centimeters?

B.

3. What is the area of a segment whose chord is 10 inches in a circle of 10 inch radius?
4. What is the area of a segment whose chord is $2\sqrt{3}$ centimeters in a circle of diameter 4 centimeters?

MISCELLANEOUS WRITTEN EXERCISES

C.

1. Construct a regular hexagon having each side $1\frac{1}{4}$ inches.
2. Construct a square having each diagonal $1\frac{1}{2}$ inches.
3. Construct a regular octagon in a circle having a diameter of 3 inches.
4. Find the perimeter of a regular hexagon inscribed in a circle whose diameter is 2.25.

B.

5. Find the perimeter of a square inscribed in a circle of radius 6.
6. Find the perimeter of a regular triangle inscribed in a circle whose radius is 100.
7. Find the circumference of a circle if its radius is 300.
8. The radius of the equatorial circle of the earth is 3960 miles. Find its circumference.
9. The diameter of the equatorial circle of the sun is 866,000 miles. Find its circumference.
10. The diameter of the equatorial circle of the moon is 2000 miles. Find its circumference, assuming the moon to be a sphere.
11. The circumference of a wheel is 21 inches. What is its diameter?
12. The circumference of a wheel is 3 centimeters. What is its diameter?
13. The circumference of the (nearly) circular orbit of the planet Mars is 930,000,000 miles. Find the distance from Mars to the sun if the sun is at the center of the orbit.

14. Find the area of a circle if its radius is 1.25.
15. Find the area of a circle if its diameter is 40 inches.
16. Find the area of a circle if its diameter is 8000 miles.
17. The area of a circle is 48 square inches. Find its radius.
18. The area of a circle is 100 square centimeters. Find its diameter.
19. The area of a circle is 620 square inches. Find its circumference.
20. The area of a circle is 64.5 square feet. Find its circumference.
21. The circumference of a circle is 82 inches. Find its area.
22. The circumference of a circle is 8421. Find its area.
23. The apothems of two regular pentagons are respectively 5 and 6. What is the ratio of their perimeters? What is the ratio of areas?
24. The radii of two circles are 10 and 20 respectively. What is the ratio of their circumferences? Of their areas?
25. The diameters of two circles are 144 and 121. What is the ratio of their areas?
26. The areas of two circles are 144 and 121. What is the ratio of their circumferences?
27. The ratio of the areas of two squares is 9:16. What is the ratio of the areas of their circumscribed circles?
28. The ratio of the perimeters of two regular hexagons is 11:12. What is the ratio of the areas of their circumscribed circles?
29. A sector of a circle has a 30° central angle. Find the area of the sector if the radius of the circle is 70.
30. A sector of a circle has a central angle of 11° 15′. What is its area if the diameter of the circle is 50 centimeters?
31. A sector of a circle has a central angle of 3° 45′. Its area is 2 sq. in. What is the area of the circle?
32. A segment of a circle has an arc of 60° and a chord of 2 feet. Find its area.
33. A segment of a circle has an arc of 90° and a chord of 1 inch. Find its area.
34. A segment of a circle has an arc of 120° in a circle the diameter of which is 4 inches. Find the area of the segment.
35. The piston of a steam engine has a diameter of 15 inches. What total pressure does it exert if the steam pressure is 80 pounds per square inch?
36. In a certain type of hot air furnace, the sum of the areas of the hot air pipes should equal the area of the cold air pipe. If there are 7 hot air pipes each with a diameter of 8 inches, what should be the diameter of the cold air pipe if only one is used?

37. Which will carry more hot air to a room, two 6 inch pipes or one 9 inch pipe?

38. How many 1 inch gas pipes can be supplied from a six-inch main?

39. Two concentric circles have radii of 1 inch and 2 inches respectively. What is the area of the ring between the circles?

40. Two circles have radii of 1 inch and 2 inches respectively and are internally tangent. What is the area between the circles?

41. A circle is inscribed in a square the sides of which are each 5 inches. What is the area between the circle and the square?

42. A circle is inscribed in a regular hexagon each side of which is 8 inches. What is the area between the circle and the hexagon?

43. Four circular washers $\frac{3}{4}$ inch outside diameter and $\frac{1}{4}$ inch inside diameter are punched from a sheet of metal one and one half inches square. What fractional part of the material is wasted? What fractional part of the material is wasted when washers like these are cut from a sheet of metal 2 feet by 3 feet?

44. A boy stopped the flow of water from a rubber hose $\frac{3}{4}$ inch in diameter by holding his palm against the opening. If water pressure was 52 pounds per square inch, what force did he apply?

45. This figure illustrates a method often used for cutting a square so as to get a regular octagon. Study the figure, write a description of the method, and prove *EFGHJKLM* is a regular octagon.

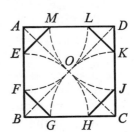

46. A nautical mile is the length of 1' of arc on the earth's circumference. How many feet does it contain? (See Ex. 8 above. 1' is $\frac{1}{60}$ of 1°.)

OUTLINE OF CHAPTER 18

This chapter introduces the following terms:

regular polygon
inscribed polygon
circumscribed polygon
center of a regular polygon
radius of a regular polygon

apothem of a regular polygon
central angle of a regular polygon
dodecagon
sector
segment of a circle

This chapter presents information concerning

1. The method of inscribing each of the following in a circle:

   (*a*) A regular hexagon   (*b*) A square

   (*c*) A regular decagon

2. Regular polygons of $x \cdot 2^n$ sides where x is 3, 4, or 5 and n is zero or any positive integer. Pages 470, 476, 477, 478

3. The method of circumscribing regular polygons about a circle. Page 473

4. The method of inscribing a circle in or circumscribing a circle about any regular polygon. Page 474

5. The relation between perimeters and apothems of similar regular polygons. Page 480

6. The relation between the circumferences of two circles and their radii or diameters. Page 481

7. The relation between the circumference of a circle and its diameter. Page 481

8. The formula for the circumference of a circle. Page 481

9. The formula for the area of a circle. Pages 483, 484

10. The method of finding the side of a regular inscribed polygon when the radius of the circle and a side of a regular inscribed polygon of half the number of sides are given. Page 485

11. The method of finding the area of a sector. Page 485

12. The method of finding the area of a segment of a circle. Page 485

REVIEW

1. Draw a circle and inscribe a regular hexagon in it. Prove your construction.

2. Draw a circle and inscribe a square. Prove the figure is a square.

3. How many degrees are there in each angle of a regular pentagon? Show how you arrive at your answer.

4. How many degrees are there in each central angle of a regular octagon? Show how you arrive at your answer.

5. Polygon P and polygon P' are similar. Side s of polygon P is 1 inch, and side s' of polygon P' is 2 inches. s and s' are corresponding sides. If the area of P is 5 square inches, what is the area of P'?

6. Circle O has a radius of 5 inches, and circle Q has a radius of 3 inches. What is the ratio of the area of O to the area of Q?

7. Find the area of a circle whose radius is $\frac{1}{2}$ inch.

8. The area of a circle is π. How long is its diameter?

9. A circle is inscribed in a square that is 10 inches on a side. Find the area of the circle. (Use $\pi = 3.14$.)

10. Define π.

YES–NO TEST

Approximately 20 minutes

Copy on your paper the numbers of the following questions. If the answer to a question is *yes* under all conditions, place a plus (+) sign after its number. If the answer is *not yes* under all conditions, place a zero (0) after its number.

1. Are the angles of a regular polygon equal?

2. Are the sides of a regular polygon equal?

3. If the angles of a polygon are equal, is it a regular polygon?

4. If the sides of a polygon are equal, is it a regular polygon?

5. Can a circle be circumscribed about a regular polygon?

6. If a circle can be circumscribed about a polygon, is it a regular polygon?

7. Can a circle be inscribed in a regular polygon?

8. If a circle can be inscribed in a polygon, is it a regular polygon?

9. If a regular polygon has 12 sides, does each angle have 150°?

10. If the radius of a circle is 2, is its area 4π?

11. If the diameter of a circle is 2, is its area π?

12. If the area of a circle is 9π, is its diameter 6?

13. If the radius of a circle is doubled, is its area doubled?

14. If the diameter of a circle is doubled, is its area multiplied by 4?

15. If the radius of a circle is 10, is the circumference 20π?

16. If the circumference of a circle is 100, is the diameter 100π?

17. Is π the ratio of the circumference of a circle to its diameter?

18. Is π the same for all circles?

19. Is *ABCDE* a regular polygon?

20. Is *PQRST* necessarily regular?

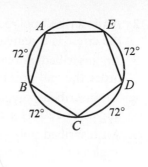

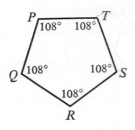

21. Is polygon *K* necessarily regular?

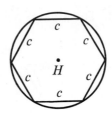

22. Is polygon *H* necessarily regular?

23. Is *ABCDE* necessarily regular?

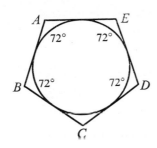

COMPLETION TEST

Approximately 25 minutes

Copy on your paper the numbers of the following statements. After each number write a word, or letters, or a number, or an expression which, if written in the blank, would complete the statement and make it true.

1. A polygon that has all its sides equal and all its angles equal is called a _____ polygon.

Statement: A polygon of 3 sides is a triangle; of 4 sides is a quadrilateral; of 5 sides is a pentagon; of 6 sides is a hexagon; of 8 sides is an octagon; of 10 sides is a decagon.

2. An inscribed polygon the sides of which are chords equal to radii of the circle is a regular _____.

3. An inscribed polygon the sides of which are chords connecting in order the end points of two perpendicular diameters is a _____.

4. An inscribed polygon the sides of which are chords that have central angles of 120° is a regular _____.

5. An inscribed polygon the sides of which are chords that have central angles of 45° is a regular _____.

6. The ratio of the perimeter of $ABCDE$ to the perimeter of $A'B'C'D'E'$ is _____.

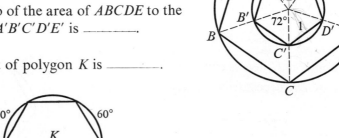

7. The ratio of the area of $ABCDE$ to the area of $A'B'C'D'E'$ is _____.

8. The area of polygon K is _____.

9. The symbol for the ratio of the circumference of a circle to its diameter is _____.

10. The circumference of the smaller circle is 31.4. The circumference of the larger circle is _____.

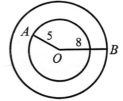

11. The circumference of the larger circle is 37.7. The circumference of the smaller circle is 25.1. $DC = 8$.
$AB =$ _____.

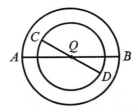

492   GEOMETRY

12. The radius of circle O is

_____.

13. The circumference of circle O
is _____.

14. The area of circle O is _____.

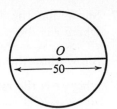

15. The diameter of circle Q is

_____.

16. The circumference of circle Q
is _____.

17. The area of circle C is _____.

18. The circumference of circle C
is _____.

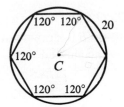

SUPPLEMENTARY EXERCISES

C.

1. Construct a regular hexagon having each side $\frac{3}{4}$ inch.

2. Construct a square in a circle having a radius of $1\frac{1}{4}$ inches.

3. Find the perimeter of a regular hexagon inscribed in a circle having a radius of .06 inch.

4. Find the side of a square inscribed in a circle having a $\frac{1}{4}$ inch diameter.

B.

5. A regular octagon is inscribed in a circle having a 20 inch radius. Find its perimeter.

6. If r is the radius of a circle, show that $\frac{2r}{3}\sqrt{3}$ is the side of a regular circumscribed hexagon.

REGULAR POLYGONS AND CIRCLES **493**

7. Show that the area of a circumscribed equilateral triangle is $3r^2\sqrt{3}$ where r is the radius of the circle.

8. Show that the area of an inscribed equilateral triangle is $\dfrac{3r^2}{4}\sqrt{3}$ where r is the radius of the circle.

9. Show that the area of a regular inscribed hexagon is $\dfrac{3r^2}{2}\sqrt{3}$ where r is the radius of the circle.

10. Tell how an angle of $2\frac{1}{4}°$ can be constructed.

11. How can an angle of 54° be constructed?

12. How many sides would a regular polygon have if central angles of $2\frac{1}{4}°$ were used? 3°? $\frac{1}{10}$ right angle? 24°?

13. OA and OC are perpendicular radii of $\odot O$. $\overset{\frown}{AXB}$ is drawn with C as center. Prove that the shaded area $= r^2$.

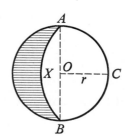

14. Semicircles are constructed on the three sides of a right triangle as shown. Prove that the sum of the shaded crescents equals the area of $\triangle DEF$.

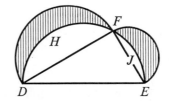

15. The radius of a circle is 100. Find its area.

16. The diameter of a circle is 6 mm. Find its area.

17. The circumference of a circle is $314\frac{1}{6}$. Find its area.

18. The circumference of a circle is 1885. Find its diameter.

19. The area of a circle is 1464. Find its circumference.

20. How many revolutions will a 28 inch bicycle wheel make in going a mile?

21. A steam boiler has 120 draft tubes each 2 inches in diameter. What must be the diameter of a circular smokestack to carry the smoke if the area of its base equals the sum of the areas of the ends of the pipes?

22. A water main is to serve 42 homes each of which gets its water supply through a 1 inch pipe. What should be the diameter of the main if the area of its cross section must be at least equal to the combined areas of the cross sections of the smaller pipes?

A.

23. Prove: If squares are constructed on the sides of a regular hexagon outside the hexagon, the exterior vertices of the squares are the vertices of a regular dodecagon.

24. Prove: The area of a square inscribed in a semicircle is two fifths the area of a square inscribed in the circle. A square is inscribed in a semicircle when two vertices are on the diameter and the other vertices on the arc.

25. Each of three equal circles is tangent externally to the other two. If the radius of each is 1 inch, what is the area lying between the circles?

REVIEW TESTS

CHAPTERS 12 TO 18

YES–NO TEST

Approximately 40 minutes

Copy on your paper the numbers of the following questions. If the answer to a question is *yes* under all conditions, place a plus sign (|) after its number. If the answer is *not yes* under all conditions, place a zero (0) after its number.

1. Is the point of tangency the point on the tangent to a circle nearest the center?

2. If an inscribed angle has 15°, does its intercepted arc have 30°?

3. If an arc has 40°, does the inscribed angle that intercepts it have 80°?

4. If two chords intersect in a circle and intercept nonadjacent arcs of 30° and 50°, is the angle between the chords 40°?

5. If two secants are drawn to a circle from the same point and intercept arcs of 72° and 38°, do the secants meet at an angle of 17°?

6. If a tangent and a chord drawn to the point of contact form an angle of 52°, is the major arc of the circle 308°?

7. If two tangents to a circle from the same point form an angle of 62°, do they intercept arcs of 118° and 242° on the circle?

8. Is the locus of points equally distant from the sides of an angle the bisector of the angle?

9. Is the locus of points equally distant from two points the perpendicular bisector of the line segment that joins them?

10. Is the locus of points equally distant from two parallel lines a line that is perpendicular to each of the parallel lines?

11. Is $\dfrac{x}{y}$ a proportion?

12. Is r a term of the ratio $\dfrac{s-1}{r+1}$?

13. Do the ratios $\dfrac{2a}{3b}$ and $\dfrac{6a}{9b}$ form a proportion?

14. Do the ratios $\frac{2}{3}$ and $\frac{3}{2}$ form a proportion?

15. If $\dfrac{a}{b} = \dfrac{c}{d}$ does $ab = cd$?

16. If $\dfrac{r}{s} = \dfrac{t}{v}$ does $\dfrac{s}{r} = \dfrac{v}{t}$?

17. If $\dfrac{h}{k} = \dfrac{k}{l}$ is k the mean proportional between h and l?

18. If a line divides two sides of a triangle proportionally, is it parallel to the third side?

19. If a line cuts off segments 2 inches and 3 inches on one side of a triangle and corresponding segments 3 inches and 4.5 inches on another side, is it parallel to the third side?

20. If a line cuts off segments 8 inches and 12 inches on one side of a triangle and corresponding segments 12 inches and 8 inches on another side, is it parallel to the third side?

21. Do similar polygons have the same shape?

22. Are congruent polygons similar?

23. If the angles of one triangle are 40°, 50°, and 90° and the angles of another are 50°, 90°, and 40°, are the triangles similar?

24. If two angles of one triangle are 20° and 80° and two angles of another are each 80°, are the triangles similar?

25. If the sides of one triangle are 16, 18, and 20 and the sides of another are 27, 30, and 24, are the triangles similar?

26. If an acute angle of one right triangle is 32° and an acute angle of another right triangle is 58°, are the triangles similar?

27. If two sides of one triangle are 54 and 63 and the angle included by them is 37°, and if two sides of another triangle are 49 and 42 and the exterior angle at the vertex where these sides meet is 143°, are the triangles similar?

28. If the sides of a rectangle are 7 and 9, is its area 16?

29. If the area of a rectangle is 60 and one side is 10, is the other side 6?

30. If two sides of a parallelogram are 5 and 7, is its area 35?

31. If the base and altitude of a triangle are 8 and 12, is its area 96?

32. If the bases of a trapezoid are 13 centimeters and 17 centimeters and the altitude is 10 centimeters, is the area 300 square centimeters?

33. If the sides of a triangle are 6, 8, and 10, is it a right triangle?

34. If the sides of a triangle are 8 inches, 15 inches, and 17 inches, is it a right triangle?

35. If the hypotenuse of an isosceles right triangle is 10 inches, are the arms each 5 inches?

36. Are the angles of a regular polygon equal?

37. Are the angles of a regular octagon $\frac{1}{8}$ of a straight angle?

38. If a regular hexagon is inscribed in a circle of diameter 1 inch, is each side 1 inch long?

39. Is an equilateral triangle a regular polygon?

40. Is a square a regular polygon?

41. Is π the ratio of the area of a circle to its diameter?

42. If the radius of a circle is r, is its circumference πr?

43. If the radius of a circle is r, is the area πr^2?

44. If the diameter of a circle is d, is its area $\frac{1}{4}\pi d^2$?

45. If one circle has a diameter twice that of a second circle, is its circumference twice as great?

46. If the side of a regular hexagon inscribed in a circle is 10, is the circumference of the circle 20π?

47. If the perimeter of a regular hexagon inscribed in a circle is 60, is the area of the circle 36π?

48. Is $3\frac{1}{7}$ the exact value of π? Is 3.1416 the exact value of π?

49. If a square is circumscribed about a circle the radius of which is 10, is the area of the square 100?

Approximately 40 minutes

Copy on your paper the numbers of the following statements. After each number write a word, or number, or expression which, if written in the blank, would complete the statement and make it true. Where two blanks occur, give expressions to fill both.

Problem To construct tangents to a circle O from a point P outside the circle.

Given $\odot O$ and point P outside.

1. Draw _____.
2. _____ OP at A.
3. Draw a circle with center A and radius _____ intersecting circle O at B and C.
4. Draw _____ and _____.
5. _____ and _____ are tangent to circle O.
   Proof. Draw OB and OC.
6. $\angle OBP$ is a _____ angle, and $\angle OCP$ is a _____ angle. (Because each is inscribed in a semicircle.)
7. PB and PC are _____ to circle O because each is _____ to a radius at its end on the circle.

Problem To construct the mean proportional to two given segments x and y.

8. Draw a line AB and on it mark off $AC =$ _____ and CD = _____.
9. Draw a semicircle on _____ as diameter.
10. Construct _____ $\perp AB$ intersecting the semicircle at _____.
11. Then _____ is the mean proportional to x and y.
    Proof. Draw AE and DE.
12. _____ is a right angle because it is inscribed in a semicircle.

13. $\dfrac{x}{?} = \dfrac{?}{y}$ because _____ is the perpendicular from the vertex of the right angle of a right triangle to the hypotenuse.

14. _____ is tangent to $\odot O$.

15. $DF + HK =$ _____

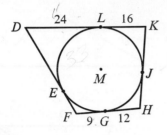

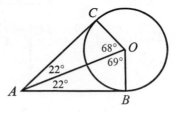

16. $\overparen{PR} =$ _____ °

17. $\angle PSR =$ _____ °

18. $\angle PTR =$ _____ °

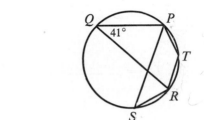

19. $\overparen{AD} =$ _____ °

20. $\angle CBD =$ _____ °

21. $\angle ABC =$ _____ °

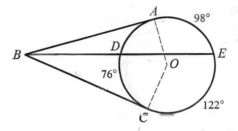

22. $\overparen{JH} =$ _____ °

23. $\overparen{FJ} =$ _____ °

24. $\angle FGJ =$ _____ °

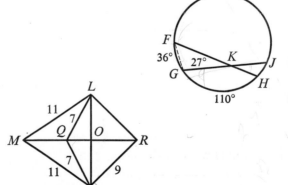

25. $LR =$ _____

26. $\angle LOR =$ _____ °

27. If $\dfrac{x}{14} = \dfrac{12}{70}$, $x =$ _____

28. If $\dfrac{4}{y} = \dfrac{y}{49}$, $y =$ _____

29. If $\dfrac{z - 189}{189} = \dfrac{21 - z}{z}$, $z =$ _____

30. $EC =$ _____

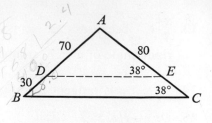

31. $\angle FJK =$ _____ °

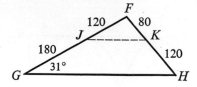

32. $LP =$ _____

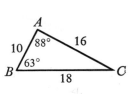

33. $A'C' =$ _____
34. $BC =$ _____

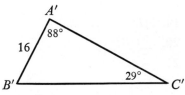

35. $GF =$ _____

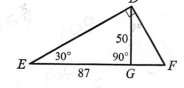

36. HJ is a tangent.
   $HL =$ _____
37. $\overarc{KL} =$ _____ °

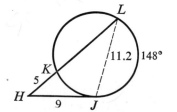

500   GEOMETRY

38. *ABCD* is a □.
Area *ABCD* = _____

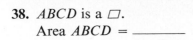
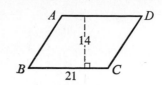

39. Area *EFGH* = _____

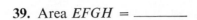
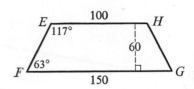

40. *KL* = _____

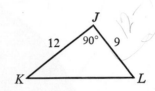

41. Area △*PQR* = _____

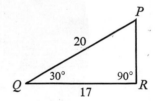

42. *TV* = _____

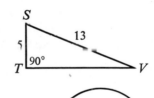

43. Circumference of ⊙*O* = _____
44. Area ⊙*O* = _____

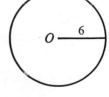

45. $\dfrac{\text{Area } \odot Q}{\text{Area } \odot R} = \dfrac{?}{?}$

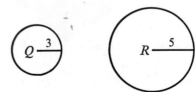

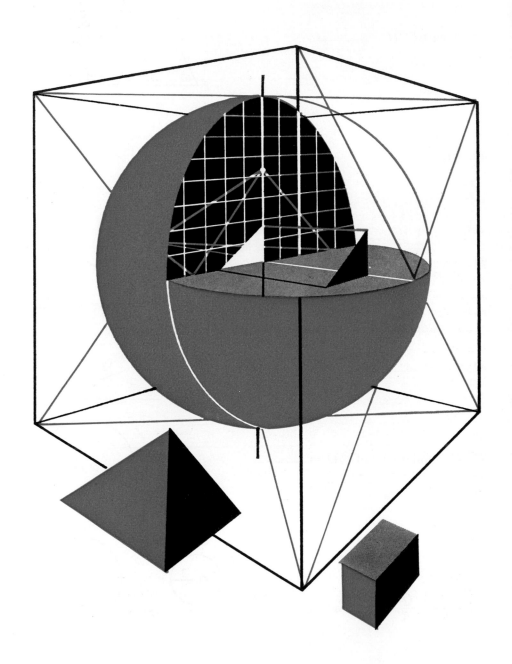

CHAPTER 19

POLYHEDRONS AND THE SPHERE

19–1 Half-line. Half-plane. Half-space
A point P on a line divides the line into three sets of points, namely (a) the point P itself, (b) the set of points A_i on one side of the point P, and (c) the set of points B_i on the other side of the point P. Sets (b) and (c) are called half-lines, where the word *half* is not to be used in the arithmetic sense but merely indicates that this part of the line (which is infinitely long) contains all the points of the line except P and the points on the other side of P. The point P belongs to neither half-line but is the boundary of both half-lines.

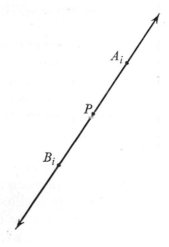

The union of the set of points (a) and (b) or (a) and (c) is called a ray. Thus a ray has an initial point and a half-line as its set of points. By the term union of two sets of points we shall mean all the points that belong to either one or the other (or both) of two sets. A line segment consists of two points and all the points of the line between them. The line segment is said to be *determined* by its two end points.

Line *l* in a plane divides it into three sets of points, (*a*) the set of points on line *l*, (*b*) the set of points P_i in the plane on one side of *l* and (*c*) the set

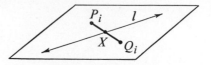

of points Q_i in the plane on the other side of *l*. Sets (*b*) and (*c*) are called half-planes. The line *l* belongs to neither half-plane but is the boundary of both half-planes.

In three dimensions a plane divides space into three sets of points, namely (*a*) the set of points in the plane, (*b*) the set of points P_i in space on one side of the plane, and (*c*) the set of points Q_i in space on the other side of the plane. Each set of points (*b*) and (*c*) is called a half-space. The plane belongs to neither half-space but is the boundary of both.*

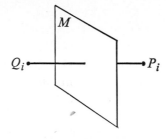

POSTULATE 39 **If a point in a half-line, half-plane, or half-space respectively is connected by a line segment to a point in the other half-line, half-plane or half-space, it intersects the boundary in a point.**

19–2 Convex Sets of Points. Any set or collection of points in one, two, or three dimensions is called a geometric figure. Even three isolated points in a plane make up a geometric figure. We now define a convex set.

A set of points is convex if and only if for any two points belonging to the set, every point on the line segment determined by these points belongs to the set also.

If a set is not convex, then it contains two points for which the determined line segment is not entirely in the given set.

Thus a line, a ray, or a half-line is always a convex set of points. Illustrate this by drawing figures. A given half-space is always a convex set. However, a triangle is not a convex set. The triangle *ABC* consists of the union of the three segments *AB*, *BC*, and *AC*.

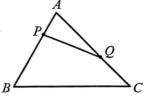

Let *P* and *Q* be points of these segments other than the vertices of the triangle. Then the segment *PQ* has all its points except *P* and *Q* not in

---

* Note: There is no need for a name for the union of a half-plane and its boundary line, or a half-space and its boundary plane. However, the word *ray* for the union of a half-line and its boundary point is useful in plane geometry.

the set of points that make up the triangle. By the definition of convex set, the triangle is not a convex set. Do you believe the set of all points in the interior of the triangle form a convex set? Can you define the interior of a triangle?

19–3 Angle A plane angle AVB has already been defined as the set of points consisting of two rays, VA and VB, having the same boundary, or initial point, V. Every angle AVB thus divides the entire plane into three sets of points, (*a*) the angle itself, (*b*) a region which is a convex set of points, and

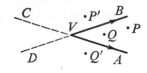

(*c*) the remaining points in the plane, which are a nonconvex set of points. To obtain the convex set we proceed as follows:

(1) Find the set of points constituting the half-plane bounded by the line on which VA is a ray and also containing the point B.

(2) Find the set of points constituting the half-plane bounded by the line on which VB is a ray and also containing point A.

(3) Take the <u>intersection</u> of these two half-planes, that is, the set of points common to both these half-planes. This is a convex set. This is illustrated by the double-hatched area in the figure. Test this region by using the definition of convex set given above.

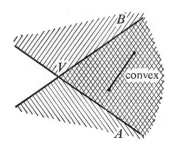

For the rest of this chapter and in subsequent study of mathematics it will be necessary to distinguish convex sets of points. Usually a nonconvex set of points can be subdivided so that each of the subsets is a convex set. In the figure the union of A and B is not convex, but each separate region A and B is convex.

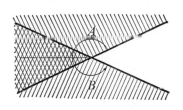

A <u>dihedral angle</u> is the set of points formed by two half-planes and their common boundary. This angle divides all space into three sets of points, one of which is convex. The convex set is defined by the intersection of two half-spaces in a way analogous to that for the convex set of a plane angle. See Sec. 10–20.

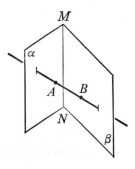

EXERCISES

C.

1. Define the union of two sets of points.
2. Define the intersection of two sets of points.
3. What is the intersection of two lines? Two circles? Illustrate.
4. What is the union of two lines? Two circles? Illustrate.
5. Show by a drawing the nonconvex set of a plane angle *AOB*.

6. Show that all the interior angles of a given triangle *ABC* bound a convex set of points.

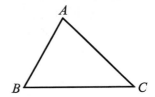

7. Define the interior of a triangle in terms of the intersection of the convex sets of its interior angles. Illustrate your definition by a triple-hatched part of the plane.
8. Define a convex polygon as a boundary of the intersection of convex sets.

A.

9. Prove that there are two points in the nonconvex region of a plane angle formed by two intersecting lines (noncoincident) for which the line segment determined by the two points has points in the convex region.
10. Prove: The measure of a plane angle formed by two intersecting lines and for which the interior is a convex set is less than 180°.
11. Prove: The plane angle of a dihedral angle formed by two intersecting planes for which the interior is a convex set is less than a straight angle.

19–4 Trihedral Angle If two planes intersect they divide space into four convex sets and the planes themselves form four convex dihedral angles.

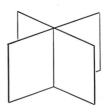

If a third plane intersects these two planes through their line of intersection and not coincident with it, space is then divided into eight convex sets.

The union of the set of points formed by (a) the common point of intersection of the three planes, (b) three half-lines, one from each of the lines
of intersection of the planes, and (c) the convex sets formed by these three
half-lines taken in pairs is called a trihedral angle.

There are eight trihedral angles formed by three planes whose common
intersection is a point. To study one of these space angles, we usually
isolate it from the drawing of Fig. (a) and draw a diagram as shown in
Fig. (b). In drawing these diagrams we either omit segments obscured by
the planes or else make such lines dotted.

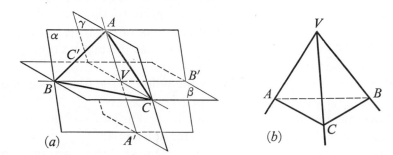

(a)   (b)

The common point of intersection of the planes is called the vertex of
the angle. (V in Fig. (a) or (b))

The selected half-lines are called the edges of the angles. (VA, VB, and
VC in the figures)

The plane angles formed at the vertex are called the face angles. (∠AVB,
∠AVC, and ∠BVC in the figure)

The convex sets of points constituting the interior of these angles are
called the faces of the angles. The angle is named V-ABC.

EXERCISES

C.

1. Name all eight trihedral angles in Fig. (a). We name a trihedral
   angle by giving its vertex, then three other points, one on each edge.
2. Make a drawing of a dihedral angle with a vertical edge.
3. Make a drawing of a dihedral angle with a horizontal edge.
4. Make a drawing of a dihedral angle with an oblique edge.
5. Make a drawing of two intersecting planes with a vertical intersection.
6. Make a drawing of two intersecting planes with a horizontal intersection.

7. Make a drawing of two intersecting planes with an oblique intersection.
8. Make a drawing of a trihedral angle with the vertex at the right of the angle; at the left of the angle; below the angle.
9. Make a drawing of three intersecting planes showing all eight trihedral angles when (*a*) the planes are perpendicular to each other, (*b*) two planes are perpendicular, but the third is not perpendicular to the others, (*c*) none of the planes are perpendicular.

B.

10. Explain: A trihedral angle contains parts of three dihedral angles. (These parts are called the dihedral angles of the trihedral angle.)
11. Define the interior of the trihedral angle as the intersection of convex sets bounded by its dihedral angles.
12. What part of space is covered by the union of the four dihedral angles of two intersecting planes and their convex sets?
13. Show that the union of the eight trihedral angles and the convex sets they form completely fill three-dimensional space.
14. If three planes are perpendicular to each other, how are the trihedral angles formed related? What part of the entire space about the vertex does the interior of each trihedral angle cover? Explain your answer.
15. Discuss how we could set up a procedure for measuring a trihedral angle.

19–5 THEOREM The sum of two face angles of a trihedral angle is greater than the third face angle.

Hypothesis Trihedral angle V–ABC with AVB the greatest face angle.

Conclusion $\angle AVC + \angle CVB > \angle AVB$

Proof In face AVB, construct VE so that $\angle AVE = \angle AVC$, and $VE = VC$; through E and C pass a plane meeting edges VA and VB at F and G. Then $\triangle VFE \cong \triangle FVC$ (s a s). Thus $FE = FC$. In $\triangle FCG$, $FC + CG > FG$. By subtraction we obtain $CG > EG$. Now in $\triangle CGV$ and $\triangle EVG$, VG is common, $VE = VC$, and $CG > EG$, hence $\angle CVG > \angle EVG$. Adding this inequality to the equality of angles AVC and AVE, we have $\angle AVC + \angle CVB > AVB$.

19–6 Polyhedral Angle. Solid Angle

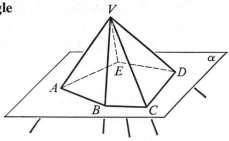

If more than three planes meet at a point, they form a polyhedral angle (*poly* means *many*, *hedral* means *faced*). A polyhedral angle can also be defined as follows: Consider a convex polygon in a plane α and a point V outside the plane. The polyhedral angle is the union of (*a*) the point outside the plane, (*b*) the half-lines determined by V and the vertices of the polygon, and (*c*) the interiors of the plane angles formed by adjacent rays with vertex V. The vertex, edge, face, face angle, dihedral angle, and interior are defined in exactly the same way as for the trihedral angle. A polyhedral angle is also named according to the number of faces (or edges) that it contains — tetrahedral for four, pentahedral for five, hexahedral for six, and so on.

Polyhedral angles are special cases of a more general class called solid angles. A solid angle is the set of all points consisting of the union of a point V outside a plane α and all the half-lines determined by V and the points of a closed convex figure C in the plane α. The half-lines are called elements and the point is the vertex of the solid angle.

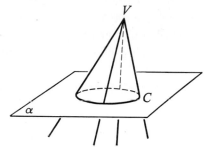

THEOREM The sum of the face angles of a polyhedral angle is less than two straight angles.

Hypothesis Polyhedral angle V–ABCD · · ·

Conclusion Σ face angles at V < 360°.

(The symbol Σ is read "Sum of.")

Proof Pass a plane cutting all the edges of the polyhedral angle in the polygon ABCD · · ·. At each vertex of this polygon a trihedral angle is formed. (Explain.) Let O

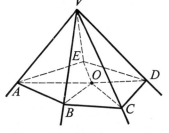

be any point interior to the polygon and draw segments from O to the vertices. Call the triangles with vertex O the O-triangles; those with vertex V, the face triangles. There are the same number of O-triangles as there are face triangles (common base).

By 19–5 we have $\angle VBA + \angle VBC > \angle ABC$; and similarly for the trihedral angles at $C, D, \cdots$. Adding all the inequalities thus obtained we have

(*a*) Σ base $\angle$s of the face triangles $> \Sigma$ base $\angle$s of the O-triangles.
(*b*) But Σ all $\angle$s of the face triangles $= \Sigma$ all $\angle$s of the O-triangles.

Subtracting (*a*) from (*b*), we obtain Σ vertex $\angle$s of the face triangles $< \Sigma$ angles at point O. Since the sum of the angles at O is 360°, the theorem is proved.

EXERCISES

C.

1. Two face angles of a trihedral angle are 70° and 110°. What are the limits of the third angle?
2. The face angles of a pentahedral angle are equal. What is the largest whole number of degrees each angle can have?
3. By passing planes through one edge and all other nonadjacent edges, a polyhedral angle can be transformed into a series of trihedral angles. How many trihedral angles are thus formed?

B.

4. Show that a face angle of a polyhedral angle cannot be 180°.
5. Show that any point on a plane bisecting a dihedral angle is equidistant from each face of the angle.

A.

6. Prove: If two face angles of a trihedral angle are equal, the opposite dihedral angles are equal. *Hint.* In the figure $\angle 1$ = $\angle 2$. Take $VA = VB = VC$; $VD = VE$; make $\angle FDG$ and $\angle HEK$ plane angles of the dihedral angles. Now use triangles VAB, ADF, ADG, AFG and triangles congruent to them in the order given.

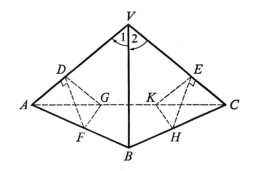

7. Prove: If two trihedral angles have the three face angles of one equal respectively to the three face angles of the other, the corresponding dihedral angles are equal.

8. Desargues's Theorem. If lines joining the corresponding vertices of two triangles, with corresponding sides nonparallel, are concurrent, then the points of intersection of corresponding sides are collinear.

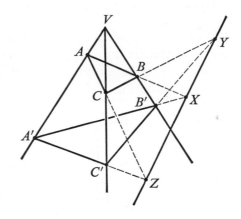

Hint. Let *V*, the vertex of a trihedral angle, be the point of concurrency of the lines *A'A*, *B'B*, and *C'C*. Consider the intersection of the planes *ABC* and *A'B'C'*.

19–7 Polyhedron If a trihedral angle is cut by a plane meeting all the edges but not passing through the vertex, three new trihedral angles are formed. Identify the vertices of all the trihedral angles in the accompanying figure. The set of points consisting of these four vertices, the segments joining the vertices, and the interior regions of all the triangles formed is called a tetrahedron. The tetrahedron divides space into three sets of points,

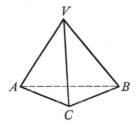

namely (*a*) the tetrahedron itself, (*b*) a convex set of points bounded by the tetrahedron, and (*c*) all other points of space forming a nonconvex set. The interior of the tetrahedron can also be defined as the intersection of (that is, points that belong to all) the interiors of all the trihedral angles formed.

The tetrahedron is thus a continuous surface of triangles and their interiors that separates a convex portion of space from the rest of space.

In general, let there be a continuous surface in space consisting of polygons and their interiors so that each vertex of a polygon is also the vertex of a convex polyhedral angle. This surface is called a polyhedron, and the set of points belonging to the interior of all the polyhedral angles thus formed is a convex set called the interior of the polyhedron.

The set of points consisting of the polyhedron and
its interior is sometimes called a polyhedral solid.
We shall study the commonly used polyhedrons.
An interesting set of polyhedrons is one called regular
polyhedrons. A polyhedron is regular if and only if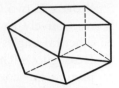
its faces are regular polygons of the same number of sides and its poly-
hedral angles are the same, that is, have the same number of faces at each
vertex. There are only five regular polyhedrons, as shown in the figure
below.

| Tetra-
hedron
4 faces | Hexa-
hedron
6 faces | Octa-
hedron
8 faces | Dodeca-
hedron
12 faces | Icosa-
hedron
20 faces |

Show that in each of these figures $V + F = E + 2$ where V is the number
of vertices, F is the number of faces, and E is the number of edges. This
formula is called Euler's Formula and holds for all convex polyhedrons,
regular or irregular.

19–8 Prisms Frequently we shall refer to a polygon and its interior.
We shall refer to the union of a polygon and its interior as a plane polygon.
A plane polygon is a convex set of points.

A prism is a polyhedron in which two faces are congruent plane polygons in parallel planes, and all the other faces are plane parallelograms
whose vertices are also vertices of the parallel polygons. A solid prism is
the union of the prism and its interior points.

The two parallel congruent faces are called the bases of the prism; the
other faces are termed lateral faces. A side of the lateral face is called a
lateral edge. The perpendicular segment between the bases is the altitude.

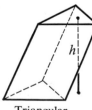 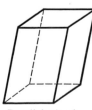  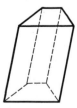

| Triangular | Parallelepiped | Pentagonal | Quadrantal |

Prisms can be named according to the shapes of their bases. If the base is also a parallelogram, the figure is called a parallelepiped. If the lateral edge is perpendicular to the base, the prism is called a right prism. A right prism for which the bases are regular plane polyhedra is called a regular prism. A right parallelepiped with rectangular bases is called a rectangular prism.

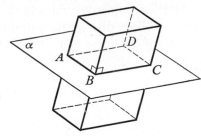

The section of a prism made by a plane perpendicular to an edge is called a right section. The right section of a prism is a polygon; the right section of a solid prism is a plane polygon.

19–9 Properties of Prisms The following properties of a prism are easy to prove as theorems.

(1) The lateral edges of a prism are parallel line segments.
(2) All right sections of the same prism are congruent polygons.
(3) The opposite lateral faces of a parallelepiped are congruent parallelograms.
(4) A right section of a parallelepiped is a parallelogram.
(5) Any section of a prism made by a plane parallel to the bases is a polygon congruent to the bases.
(6) The lateral area of a prism is equal to the product of the lateral edge and the perimeter of a right section.

EXERCISES

1–6. Prove each of the above six properties of a prism.

19–10 Cylindrical Surface and Cylinders
In a plane α, let C be given as a closed curve bounding a convex region. Through any point A of the curve construct a line l not lying in the plane α. The union of all the lines through every point of curve C and parallel to line l is a closed cylindrical surface. The line l is called the generating element, and any parallel line is called an element. Physically,

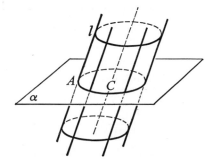

one can imagine a line moving so as to remain parallel to *l* and always contain a point of the curve *C*. This moving line traces a cylindrical surface.

One can talk of a line triangle *ABC*, a one-dimensional figure, as the union of the three segments *AB, BC, CA*. We also called a two-dimensional, or plane triangle the union of a one-dimensional triangle and all its interior points. Similarly, a one-dimensional closed curve is a line figure, while a disc is the union of the closed curved line and its interior points. If the curve is a circle, we call the circle and its interior a circular disc.

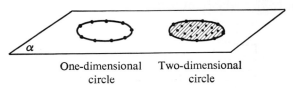

One-dimensional   Two-dimensional
circle   circle

Let all elements of a cylindrical surface be cut by two parallel planes. The union of the part of the surface contained between the two parallel planes and discs of intersection is a cylinder. The cylinder divides all space into three sets of points: (*a*) the cylinder itself, (*b*) the convex set of points bounded by the cylinder, called its interior, and (*c*) all other points

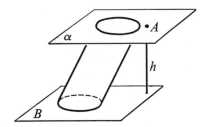

of space, called the exterior of the cylinder. The union of the cylinder and its interior points is called a cylindrical solid. Note the similarity of curve and disc to cylinder and cylindrical solid. One is a boundary, the other the union of the boundary and the interior.

The discs are called the bases of the cylinder. The segment of the generating element included between the parallel bases is called an element of the cylinder. The perpendicular segment between the bases is the altitude. If the base of a cylinder is a circle, the cylinder is called a circular cylinder and the radius of the base is taken as the radius of the cylinder. If the base is an ellipse, it is called an elliptical cylinder. If the element is perpendicular to the base, the cylinder is a right cylinder; otherwise it is an oblique cylinder.

19–11 Properties of a Cylinder

(1) The bases of a cylinder are congruent *discs*.

We shall not prove this, but it is intuitively grasped if we think of the cylinder as having the base as a physical generating element and moving it parallel to its plane with two fixed points always on two fixed parallel elements.

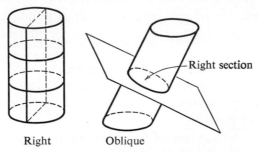

Right   Oblique

(2) All right sections of a cylinder are congruent curves.
(3) The lateral area of a right circular cylinder of radius r and altitude h is $2\pi rh$.
(4) A right section of an oblique circular cylinder or an oblique section of a right circular cylinder is an ellipse.

In this book we shall accept this without proof.

19–12 Pyramids and Cones

Let a plane intersect all the edges of a given polyhedral angle. The polyhedron formed by the union of the portion of the polyhedral angle included between the vertex and the intersecting plane and the plane polygon of intersection is a pyramid. The plane polygon is called the base of the pyramid. The perpendicular segment from the vertex to the intersecting plane is the altitude of the pyramid. The triangles having the vertex V are called the lateral faces. The sides of these triangles having end point V are called lateral edges. A regular pyramid is one for which the base is a regular polygon and the altitude meets the base at its center.

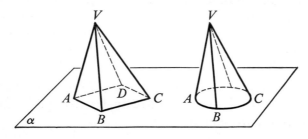

Let a solid angle be cut by a plane intersecting all the elements. The surface consisting of the portion of the solid angle included between the vertex and the cutting plane and the disc of intersection is a cone. The segments of the elements of the solid angle are elements of the cone. The altitude of the cone is the perpendicular segment drawn from the vertex to the intersecting plane.

Both the pyramid and the cone divide all space into three sets of points: (a) the figure itself, (b) an interior convex set of points, and (c) all other points of space. The union of the figure and its interior is a pyramidal solid or conical solid.

If the disc of the cone is circular, the cone is called a circular cone. If the altitude falls in the center of the base, it is called a right circular cone. A line from the vertex to the center of the base of a circular cone is called the axis of the cone.

The altitude of a lateral face of a regular pyramid (and the element of a right circular cone) is called the slant height of the pyramid (or cone).

19–13   Properties of Pyramids and Cones

(1) The lateral faces of a regular pyramid are congruent isosceles triangles. Prove this by drawing the altitude and connecting the foot of the altitude to each vertex of the base.

(2) The elements of a right circular cone are equal. As in (1), draw the altitude of the cone and two radii. Draw the corresponding elements and prove the triangles are congruent.

(3) A section of a pyramid or cone made by a plane parallel to the base is a figure similar to the base.

Proof.

(a) In the figure shown, plane α is parallel to the plane of the base. Then $A'B' \parallel AB$; $\triangle VA'B' \sim \triangle VAB$, and similarly for the other lateral faces. Then

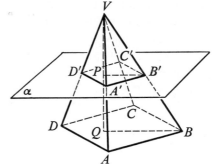

$$\frac{A'B'}{AB} = \frac{VB'}{VB} = \frac{B'C'}{BC}, \text{ etc.}$$

Also, since the sides of polygon $A'B'C'D'$ are parallel respectively to those of $ABCD$, the respective angles are equal. By definition, the polygons are similar.

(b) On the figure shown, the base is a circle C with center P. VA and VB are any two elements meeting α at A' and B'. Axis VP meets α at Q. Show that $QA' = QB'$ and hence C' is a circle. All circles are similar.

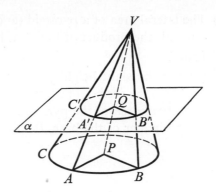

(c) In the figure shown, the base is any convex disc (circular or otherwise). VA and VB are two selected fixed elements. Let VX be any other element of the cone meeting α at X'. Show that $\triangle ABX \sim \triangle A'B'X'$. Thus, since X is any point, disc D is mapped into D' so that corresponding distances in

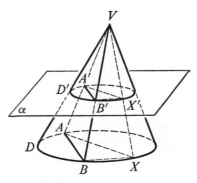

D are proportional to those in D'. Thus the sections are similar.

(4) The area of a section of a pyramid or a circular cone made by a plane parallel to the base varies directly as the square of its distance from the vertex.

Proof.

In the figure for 3 (a), let VQ be $\perp$ the base and meet the parallel section at P. Pass a plane through VQ and VB.

Now $\triangle VPB' \sim \triangle VQB$ and $\dfrac{VP}{VQ} = \dfrac{VB'}{VB}$.

But in theorem 3 (a) above, $\dfrac{VB'}{VB} = \dfrac{A'B'}{AB}$.

Hence $\dfrac{VP}{VQ} = \dfrac{A'B'}{AB}$ and $\left(\dfrac{\overline{VP^2}}{\overline{VQ^2}} = \dfrac{\overline{A'B'^2}}{\overline{AB^2}}\right)$.

But polygon $A'B'C'D' \sim ABCD$ and

$$\text{area } \frac{A'B'C'D'}{ABCD} = \frac{\overline{A'B'^2}}{\overline{AB^2}} = \frac{\overline{VP^2}}{\overline{VQ^2}}.$$

A similar proof holds for the circular cone (or any cone).

(5) The lateral area of a pyramid (and of a right circular cone) is equal to one half the product of the slant height and the perimeter of the base.

Proof.

(a) Let the slant height be s units and the side of the base a units. Then the area of one lateral face is $\frac{1}{2}a \cdot s$. If there are n faces, the lateral area of the pyramid is $n \cdot \frac{1}{2}a \cdot s$ or $\frac{1}{2}s \cdot na$. Since na is the perimeter of the base, the theorem is proved.

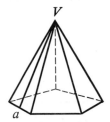 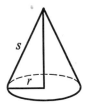 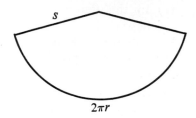

(b) The lateral surface of the cone is a circular sector with radius equal to the slant height s and arc equal to the perimeter of the base of the cone, or $2\pi r$. The ratio of the area of this sector to the area of a whole circular disc of radius s is the same as the ratio of the arc of the sector to the circumference. Then, if L is the lateral area, $\dfrac{L}{\pi s^2} = \dfrac{2\pi r}{2\pi s}$. Solving this equation for L, we get $L = \pi rs$. But πr is one half the perimeter of the base. This proves the theorem.

19–14 Volume Volume is a measure of a solid and is the number of cubic units of space which it occupies. A cubic unit is the amount of space occupied by a cube each edge of which is one linear unit. A cubic unit may take many different forms as illustrated below. Think of the cube as made of putty which may be pressed into various shapes. It will always occupy the same amount of space. The volume of any one of the shapes is still one cubic unit.

 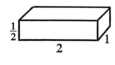 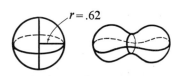

We assume that the volume of any rectangular prism is the product of the area of a face and the altitude to that face. This is plausible since the area of the base is the number of square units in it. For each unit of altitude there are then as many cubic units as square units in the area of the base. Hence the total number of cubic units is the product of the number of square units in the base by the number of linear units in the altitude.

This same reasoning holds for any right prism or right cylinder. We now study a principle which will help us find the volume of oblique prisms and cylinders.

19–15 Cavalieri's Rule It is possible to conceive of a polyhedral solid as made up of sequential sections cut off by planes parallel to one face. If the planes are very close to one another, the small slices of the solid between two adjacent planes can be considered as approximately a cylinder or prism for which the bases are almost equal in area. A stack of cards or a pile of sheets of paper is an illustration in which one card or one sheet of paper is a solid which is a small part of the solid formed by the stack.

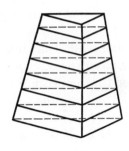

In the figure below, two solids are shown, both bounded by parallel planes α and β. Let γ be any plane parallel to the bounding planes and intersecting both the solids. (When the word *any* is used in this way, it implies that whatever is true for this one plane will be true for all such planes.) Cavalieri's Rule states that **if the sections of the solids made by any plane γ parallel to the boundary planes are equal in area, then the solids are equal in volume.**

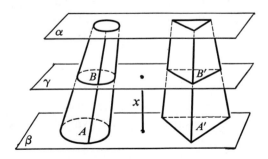

19–16   Volume of Prisms, Cylinders, Pyramids, and Cones

THEOREM 1   **The volume of any cylinder or prism is the product of the area of the base and the length of the altitude.**

Proof   Given oblique prism R' with its bases in parallel planes α and β; construct the right prism R having the same base as prism R', and pass a parallel plane γ between α and β meeting the prisms in sections B and B'.   By (5) of Sec. 19–9, both B and B' are equal to A and therefore to each other.

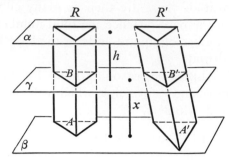

By Cavalieri's Rule, the two prisms are equal in volume.   But by Sec. 19–14 the volume of the right prism is $A \cdot h$.   Hence the volume of any prism is $A \cdot h$.

Note that while triangular prisms were used in the proofs the proof is valid for any prisms.   The proof for the cylinder is exactly the same as that given for the prism.   If the cylinder is circular of radius r, the area of the base is πr^2 and the volume is given by $V = \pi r^2 h$.

THEOREM 2   **If pyramids or cones have equal bases and equal altitudes, their volumes are equal.**

Proof   Let the bases of the two solids be in the same plane (α) and the vertices in the same plane parallel to the bases.   Pass a plane β, a distance x from the vertex, parallel to the plane of the bases and cutting the solids in sections C and D.   Then by (4) of Sec. 19–13, the areas of these sections vary directly as the square of the distance from the vertex, i.e.

$$\frac{\text{area } C}{\text{area } A} = \frac{x^2}{h^2} \quad \text{and} \quad \frac{\text{area } D}{\text{area } B} = \frac{x^2}{h^2}$$

But A is given equal to B, and since three terms of the proportions are respectively equal, area C = area D.   By Cavalieri's Rule, the two solids are equal in volume.

THEOREM 3 The volume of a triangular pyramid is equal to one third the volume of a prism having the same base and altitude.

Proof Given pyramid V–ABC having base ABC and vertex V, construct a prism with the same base and VC a lateral edge as shown in the figure. In this prism pass planes VYA and VAB dividing the prism into three pyramids, namely the original one V–ABC, A–XVY, and V–YAB.

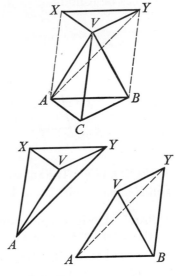

(a) V–ABC and A–XVY are equal in volume, having the same altitude and equal bases.

(b) Pyramid A–XVY may be looked upon as having the vertex V and base XYA; the remaining part of the prism is pyramid V–YAB.

(c) The pyramids V–YAB and V–XYA are equal in volume, since they have the same altitude (from V to the plane $XYBA$) and equal bases XYA and BYA (formed by the diagonal of parallelogram $XYBA$).

(d) Thus all three pyramids have the same volume and each is one third of the prism. Since for the prism $V = A \cdot h$, for the triangular pyramid $V = \frac{1}{3}A \cdot h$.

THEOREM 4 The volume of any pyramid or cone is equal to one third the product of the area of the base and the length of the altitude.

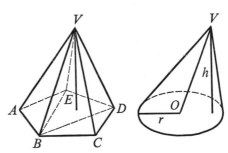

This follows at once, since any pyramid can be separated into triangular pyramids, all having the same altitude, and the sum of the areas of the bases will equal the area of the base of the given pyramid. For a cone, we shall assume that there exists some polygon with an area equal to that of the base of the cone. Then the pyramid and cone with these bases and the same altitude will be equal in volume by Theorem 2 above.

If the cone has a circular base with radius r its volume is given by

$$V = \frac{1}{3}\pi r^2 h.$$

A frustum of a cone or pyramid is the solid bounded by the base, a plane parallel to the base and cutting all the lateral elements, and the lateral surface between the base and parallel plane. The section formed by the intersecting plane is called the upper base. The line segment perpendicular to the bases and included between them is the altitude. What part of a cone or pyramid is not included in the frustum? How can their volumes be found?

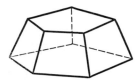 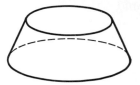

THEOREM 5 **The volume of a frustum with altitude h units and bases A and B square units is $\frac{1}{3}h(A + \sqrt{AB} + B)$.**

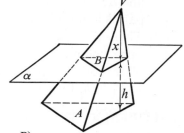

Proof Designate by x the altitude of the part of the cone or pyramid not included in the frustum. The volume of the whole solid is $\frac{1}{3}A(h + x)$; of the missing section it is $\frac{1}{3}Bx$. Hence, for the frustum,

$$V = \tfrac{1}{3}Ah + \tfrac{1}{3}Ax - \tfrac{1}{3}Bx, \text{ or } \tfrac{1}{3}Ah + \tfrac{1}{3}x(A - B).$$

By (4) of Sec. 19–13: $\dfrac{B}{A} = \dfrac{x^2}{(x + h)^2}$, or $\dfrac{x}{x + h} = \dfrac{\sqrt{B}}{\sqrt{A}}$.

Solving for x, we find $x = \dfrac{h\sqrt{B}}{\sqrt{A} - \sqrt{B}}$.

Substituting for x, $V = \dfrac{1}{3}Ah + \dfrac{1}{3}\dfrac{h\sqrt{B}(A - B)}{(\sqrt{A} - \sqrt{B})}$.

Since $(\sqrt{A} + \sqrt{B})(\sqrt{A} - \sqrt{B}) = A - B$,
$(A - B) \div (\sqrt{A} - \sqrt{B}) = \sqrt{A} + \sqrt{B}$.

$$V = \tfrac{1}{3}Ah + \tfrac{1}{3}h\sqrt{B}(\sqrt{A} + \sqrt{B}) = \tfrac{1}{3}Ah + \tfrac{1}{3}h\sqrt{B}\sqrt{A} + \tfrac{1}{3}h\sqrt{B}\sqrt{B}$$

or
$$V = \tfrac{1}{3}h(A + \sqrt{AB} + B)$$

SUMMARY OF AREA AND VOLUME FORMULAS

Figure	Lateral Area (sq. units)	Volume (cubic units)
Prism	Add areas of polygons	$B \cdot h$
Circular Cylinder	(Right) $2\pi rh$	$\pi r^2 h$
Pyramid	(Regular) $\frac{1}{2}$ per. $\times$ slant height	$\frac{1}{3}B \cdot h$
Circular Cone	(Right) πrs	$\frac{1}{3}\pi r^2 \cdot h$
Pyramid	(Regular) $\frac{1}{2}$ sum of per-	$\frac{1}{3}h(A + \sqrt{AB} + B)$
Frustum	imeters $\times s$	
Cone	(Right) $\pi s(R + r)$	$\frac{1}{3}\pi h(R^2 + Rr + r^2)$

EXERCISES ON POLYHEDRONS

C.

Find the total area and volume of

1. Rectangular prism with dimensions 3", 5", and 8".
2. Right circular cylinder with altitude 8", radius 5".
3. Right circular cone with slant height 17", radius 8".
4. Regular square pyramid with altitude 4", side of base 6".
5. Hexagonal right prism, every edge 8 units.

B.

6. Prove: Sections of a prism made by two parallel planes are congruent polygons.
7. Prove: The lateral area of an oblique prism is the product of the lateral edge by the perimeter of a right section.
8. Prove: A plane passed through two parallel diagonally opposite edges of a parallelepiped bisects the volume.

A.

9. Prove: The four diagonals of a cube are concurrent.
10. Prove: The four diagonals of any parallelepiped are concurrent.
11. Show that for a cube the edge, the diagonal of a face, and the diagonal of the cube are in the ratio $1 : \sqrt{2} : \sqrt{3}$.
12. Prove: Any section of a cylinder made by a plane parallel to an element is a parallelogram.
13. In each of two right circular cylinders, the altitude of one is the radius of the other. Compare their lateral areas, total areas, and volumes.

MISCELLANEOUS EXERCISES

1. The number of square units in the lateral area of a circular cylinder is the same as the number of cubic units in the volume. Find the radius and the altitude.

2. A gallon is 231 cu. in. How tall is a cylindrical can of radius 4 inches that holds one gallon?

3. A pyramidal coal container with square base holds 640 cubic feet. The side of the base is 8 ft. Find the altitude of the pyramid.

4. The diagonal of a cube is $8\sqrt{3}$ units; find the area and volume of the cube.

5. A right circular conical funnel is made from a circular sector of tin of radius 13 inches. The arc is 10π units. Find the radius, depth, lateral area, and cubical content of the funnel.

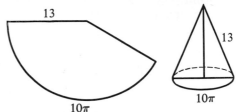

6. A regular tetrahedron has each edge 8″. Find (*a*) the slant height, (*b*) the altitude if *F* is two thirds the distance from *D* to *E* in the figure, (*c*) the total area, (*d*) the volume.

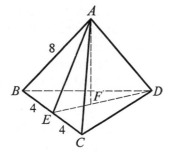

19–17 The Sphere A sphere is the surface consisting of the set of all points whose distances from a fixed point are constant. This surface divides space into three regions: (*a*) the sphere itself, (*b*) a set of convex points called the interior of the sphere for which the distance of any point from the fixed point is less than the distance for the sphere; and (*c*) a nonconvex region of all the other points in space.

The union of the sphere and its interior is a spherical solid.

The fixed point is called the center of the sphere. It is not a part of the sphere. The line segment from one point of the sphere to another and containing the center of the sphere is a diameter.

The sphere with which we are most intimately acquainted is the earth. While it is not an exact sphere, it is very nearly so. The sun, moon, and planets also are nearly spheres.

If a plane intersects a sphere, the intersection is a circle. Prove this. The diameter perpendicular to the plane of this circle is called the axis of the circle. The ends of the axis are called the poles of the circle. At the right, the plane α intersects the sphere. The axis of the small circle formed by the intersection is PP'.

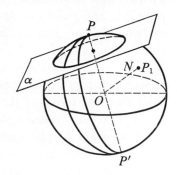

If the intersecting plane passes through the center of the sphere, the radius of the circle of intersection is the same as the radius of the sphere. All circles of this type are called great circles. All the other circles, formed by planes not containing the center, have different radii and are called small circles because their radii are less than the radius of the sphere. Prove this. On a globe representing the earth as a sphere, the meridians and the equator are great circles. The parallels are small circles. The geographical poles are poles of the equator and of all small circles parallel to it. What can you say about the axis of the earth and these same circles?

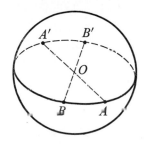

Two points in a sphere, not the ends of a diameter, and the center of the sphere determine a plane which intersects the sphere in a great circle. To measure distances between two points on a sphere we use the minor arc of this great circle. If the two points are the ends of a diameter, their distance is a great semicircle, or πr linear units. It is also 180 degrees of arc. One fourth of a great circle is called a quadrant. Every point on a great circle is a quadrant's distance from either of its poles. Since, in the figure at the right, $PO \perp OC, POC$ is a right angle, and arc PC is a quadrant. It is also easy to prove

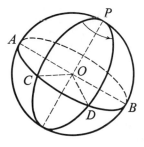

that if $\overparen{PC}$ and $\overparen{PD}$ are each 90°, then PO is perpendicular to plane $ACDB$. Hence, P is the pole of the circle.

19–18   Spherical Angle   In the lower figure on the preceding page, suppose P is any point on the sphere.   From P, let PC and PD be minor arcs of two different great circles.   The figure formed by these two arcs is a spherical angle. P is the vertex and the arcs are the sides of the angle. If from the vertex P, used as pole, a great circle is described, it will intersect the sides of the spherical angle in points C and D.   We shall consider as the interior of the spherical angle the part of the sphere between the sides which contains the minor arc CD.

To measure a spherical angle we use the arc CD.   Thus a spherical angle in this book is always less than 180°; it is also greater than 0° because arcs of two different great circles are needed for an angle.

THEOREM   A spherical angle is measured by the dihedral angle formed by the planes containing its sides.

Proof   In the lower figure on the preceding page, since P is the pole of great circle $ACDB$, $PO \perp$ plane $ACDB$.   Hence $PO \perp CO$ and $PO \perp OD$. Thus $\angle COD$ is the plane angle of dihedral angle C–PO–D.   But $\angle COD$ is measured by arc CD, which is the measure of spherical angle CPD. Hence, $\angle CPD$ is measured by the dihedral angle C–PO–D.

19–19   Spherical Triangles   Through the center of the sphere pass three distinct planes meeting the sphere in the three great circles AA', BB', and CC'.   The surface of the sphere is thus divided into eight distinct parts.   The arcs bounding any one of these parts form a spherical triangle.   Name all eight spherical triangles in the figure.

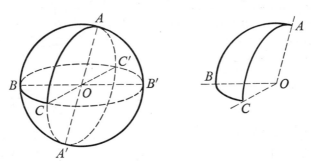

At the center of the sphere the planes form eight trihedral angles, one for each triangle, the edges of which are the extensions of radii through the vertices of the spherical triangle.   From the right figure, which is the special case for spherical $\triangle ABC$ and its trihedral central angle it is evident that:

(1) The <u>sides</u> of a spherical triangle are measured by the face angles of its *trihedral angle*. Thus the sides of a spherical triangle may be measured in degrees, as well as in linear units.

(2) The sum of the sides of a spherical triangle is less than 360 degrees, and the sum of any two sides is greater than the third. This follows from Sec. 19–6 and 19–5 respectively.

(3) The sum of the spherical angles of a spherical triangle is less than 540°. This follows, since no angle can be greater than 180°.

From the left figure we also see that to any given spherical triangle ABC, there is a symmetrical spherical triangle $A'B'C'$ for which the vertices are the other ends of diameters from A, B, and C. We say $A'B'C'$ is obtained from ABC by reflection through the center O. For any point on (or inside) triangle ABC, there is one and only one point on (or inside) $\triangle A'B'C'$. The sides of ABC are equal respectively to those of $A'B'C'$ (because of equal vertical angles at O). The angles of triangle ABC are equal respectively to those of $A'B'C'$ (because of vertical dihedral angles with the diameters as edges). The triangles are equal in all their parts, but because these parts are arranged in inverse order (i.e., AC and $A'C'$ are in opposite directions around the circle of the sphere, and similarly for the other sides and angles), we say the triangles are <u>symmetric</u>. Name the four pairs of symmetric spherical triangles in the figure. We shall make the assumption that symmetric spherical triangles have the same surface area.

19–20 Spherical Degree. Lune Spherical triangles may have one, two, or all three angles right angles as illustrated in the figures below. We now show how a sphere can be divided into 720 equal birectangular spherical triangles (two right angles in each triangle). In the upper figure

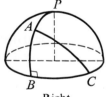 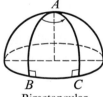 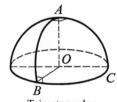

| Right | Birectangular | Trirectangular |

(on the next page), let P be the pole of the great circle ACB. Then the surface bounded by this circle and containing P is half the sphere. At P we construct a birectangular spherical triangle with P as a vertex and arc XY equal to one degree of arc. The *surface* bounded by this triangle is one spherical degree. Since arc ACB can be divided into 360 equal arcs, each one degree, there are 360 spherical degrees in a hemisphere, or 720 spherical degrees in the surface of a sphere. Just as a degree of arc has a variable length depending on the length of the radius of the circle, a spherical degree has a variable area depending on the radius of the sphere.

If two planes intersect a sphere and contain the center of the sphere, they divide the surface of the sphere into four nonoverlapping regions. Each of these regions is bounded by two semicircles. The surface thus formed and its bounding semicircles is called a lune. The angle at either intersection of the semicircles (they are equal) is called the angle of the lune.

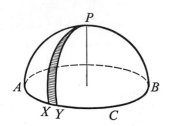

THEOREM **The area of a lune measured in spherical degrees is twice the number of degrees in the angle of the lune.**

Proof Let CD be the arc of the great circle with A and B as poles. Then angle A is measured by arc CD. Triangle ACD has as many spherical degrees as angle A has degrees. The same is true for $\triangle BDC$. Since these two triangles make the lune, the area of the lune in spherical degrees is twice the number of degrees in the angle of the lune.

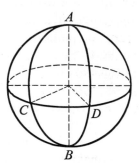

19–21 Area of a Spherical Triangle

THEOREM **The area of a spherical triangle measured in spherical degrees is equal to the sum of the degree measures of the three angles minus 180, or $(A + B + C - 180)$ spherical degrees.**

Proof In the figure of Sec. 19–19, consider $\triangle ABC$. Each angle of this triangle is an angle of a lune consisting of the triangle and another adjacent triangle on the sphere. Note that $\triangle BC'A'$ is symmetrical to $\triangle B'CA$ and hence the one can replace the other in area. We then have

Lune $BAB'CB = \triangle ABC + \triangle AB'C = \triangle ABC + \triangle A'BC'$

I Area lune $BAB'CB = \triangle ABC + \triangle A'BC' = 2B$ sph. deg.
II Area lune $ABA'CA = \triangle ABC + \triangle BA'C = 2A$ sph. deg.
III Area lune $CBC'AC = \triangle ABC + \triangle ABC' = 2C$ sph. deg.

Now $\triangle ABC + \triangle A'B'C' + \triangle BA'C + \triangle ABC'$ form half the 4 equal pairs of triangles on the sphere and are therefore half the sphere, or 360 sph. degrees.

Adding I, II, and III we obtain

$$2\triangle ABC + 360 \text{ sph. degrees} = 2(A + B + C) \text{ sph. deg. or}$$
$$\triangle ABC = (A + B + C - 180°) \text{ sph. deg.}$$

Corollary The sum of the angles of a spherical triangle is greater than 180° and less than 540°.

This follows from the area formula, for if $A + B + C \leq 180°$, the area would be negative or nonexistent. Also by (3) of Sec. 19–19, the sum of the angles is less than three straight angles or 540°.

19–22 Area in Square Units The sphere can be conceived as being generated by a semicircle AMB by rotating it about the diameter AB through 360°. Any point x on the semicircle thus generates a circle of the sphere. Any arc xy generates a part of the surface of a sphere called a zone.

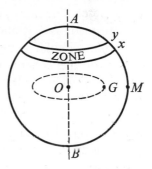

To determine the area of the sphere thus generated is a difficult problem, since each point x of the quarter circle AM rotates through a circle of different length. In higher mathematics it can be proved that the arithmetic mean of the lengths of all the circles on the sphere is that of a circle with radius OG equal to $\dfrac{2r}{\pi}$ where r is the radius of the great circle AMB. (This means OG is about .637r.) The area generated is the length of the semicircle multiplied by the arithmetic mean distance. The length of the semicircle is πr. The distance of rotation is the length of the circle with radius OG or $2\pi\left(\dfrac{2r}{\pi}\right) = 4r$. Thus the area of the sphere is $\pi r \cdot 4r$ or $4\pi r^2$ square units.

We can now translate a spherical degree into square units.

(1) Since 720 sph. deg. cover the sphere, we have

720 sph. deg. are equivalent to $4\pi r^2$ sq. units, or

1 sph. deg. is equivalent to $\dfrac{\pi r^2}{180}$ sq. units.

(2) The area of a lune is $2A$ sph. degrees where A is the number of degrees in the angle of the lune. Hence the area of a lune $= 2A \cdot \dfrac{\pi r^2}{180}$ or $\dfrac{\pi r^2 A}{90}$ square units.

(3) The area of a spherical triangle is $(A + B + C - 180)\dfrac{\pi r^2}{180}$ sq. units, where A, B, and C are measured in degrees.

19–23 Volume of a Sphere

THEOREM **The volume of a sphere is $\frac{4}{3}\pi r^3$, where r is the number of linear units in the radius.**

Proof Circumscribe a right cylinder about the sphere. The radius of the cylinder is r and its altitude is $2r$. Remove from this cylinder two right circular cones with vertices at the center of the sphere and with bases those of the cylinder. Call the remaining solid Q.

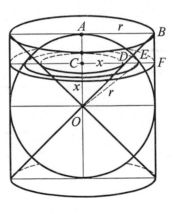

(1) The volume of the cylinder is $\pi r^2 \cdot 2r$
$= 2\pi r^3$.

(2) The volume of the two cones is $2 \cdot \frac{1}{3}\pi r^2 \cdot r$
$= \frac{2}{3}\pi r^3$.

(3) The volume of Q is $2\pi r^3 - \frac{2}{3}\pi r^3 = \frac{4}{3}\pi r^3$.

Now pass a plane parallel to the bases of the cylinder, any distance x from the center O. This plane meets the cylinder in a circle of radius r, and the cone in a circle of radius x. The area of the circular ring of solid Q is $\pi r^2 - \pi x^2$ or $\pi(r^2 - x^2)$. The area of the circle of the solid sphere is πd^2. But $d^2 = r^2 - x^2$. Hence the area of the section of the solid is $\pi(r^2 - x^2)$.

For any x, we thus have: The area of the section of solid Q is equal to the area of the section of the sphere. By Cavalieri's Rule the solids are then equal in volume. Thus the volume V of the sphere is

$$V = \tfrac{4}{3}\pi r^3.$$

19–24 Other Figures (Optional)

A spherical polygon is a closed curve formed by the intersection of a sphere and a polyhedral angle with its vertex at the center of the sphere.

A spherical zone is the *surface* of a sphere bounded by two parallel planes intersecting the sphere. The perpendicular line segment between the planes is the altitude of the zone (*ACDB*). If one of the planes is tangent, the zone has only one base and is called a spherical cap.

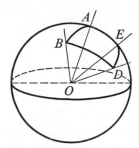
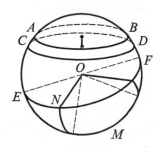

A spherical segment is the *solid* convex set of points bounded by a zone and the parallel planes.

A spherical wedge is the *solid* convex set of points bounded by a lune and the two planes through the diameter of the lune (*ENFME*).

A spherical cone is the *solid* convex set bounded by a spherical cap and a conical surface having the same base as the cap and the vertex at the center of the sphere.

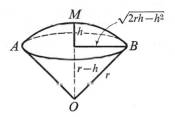

A spherical sector is the solid *nonconvex set* bounded by a zone of two bases and the two conical surfaces with vertex at the center of the sphere and with the same bases as the zone.

What is the torrid zone of the earth? The north temperate zone? The north polar cap? Is the south polar cap a zone? (See the definition of zone above.) Does the planet Mars have zones? (See an encyclopedia.)

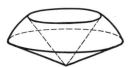

Without proof, we give the following formulas for spherical figures.

Figure	Area (sq. units)	Volume (cubic units)
Sphere	$4\pi r^2$	$\frac{4}{3}\pi r^3$
Lune	$A \cdot \dfrac{\pi r^2}{90}$	
Spherical triangle	$(A + B + C - 180°)\dfrac{\pi r^2}{180}$	
Zone	$2\pi rh$	
Segment of one base		$\dfrac{\pi h}{6}(3r_1{}^2 + h^2)$
Wedge		$A \cdot \dfrac{\pi r^3}{270}$
Spherical sector		$\frac{2}{3}\pi r^2 h$

In the formulas for lune and wedge, A is the area of the surface of the sphere. In the formula for the triangle, A, B, and C are the angles measured in degrees. r_1 is the radius of the section.

19–25 Polar Spherical Triangles

Let ABC be a given spherical triangle. Use A as a pole, and a quadrant as AD, and describe the great circle $DC'B'$ around the sphere. The distance from A to any point on this great circle is $90°$. Now do the same construction with B and C as poles.

The three great circles thus described divide the sphere into 8 separate regions each bounded by a spherical triangle. One of these triangles is shown in the figure and is labeled $A'B'C'$. Let us see how we selected this triangle. The great circles $A'B'$ and $A'C'$ meet in opposite ends of a diameter $A'A''$. If we think of arc CB, its circle bisects the sphere. Then A and A' are on the same hemisphere, while A and A'' are on opposite hemispheres. We selected A' because it was on the same hemisphere as A.

Similarly we select C' on the same hemisphere as C with respect to arc AB, and B' on the same hemisphere as B with respect to CA. The triangle $A'B'C'$ is called the polar triangle of ABC. Recall A, B, and C were used as poles to get its polar triangle $A'B'C'$.

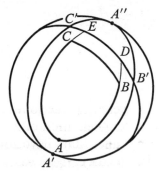

THEOREM A If $A'B'C'$ is the polar triangle of ABC, then ABC is the polar triangle of $A'B'C'$.

Proof It is only necessary to show that A' is the pole of arc BC. Now $CA' = 90°$ (since C is the pole of arc $A'B'$), and $BA' = 90°$ (since B is the pole of arc $A'C'$). Thus A' is $90°$ from two points of great arc BC and is therefore the pole of this arc. Similarly B' and C' are poles of arcs AC and AB respectively.

THEOREM B In two polar triangles an angle of one and the side opposite this angle in the other are supplementary.

Proof In the figure we prove $\angle A + \overset{\frown}{B'C'} = 180°$. First $\overset{\frown}{C'D} = 90°$ (C' is the pole of $\overset{\frown}{AD}$) and $\overset{\frown}{B'E} = 90°$ (B' is the pole of $\overset{\frown}{AE}$).

$$\overset{\frown}{C'D} + \overset{\frown}{B'E} = (\overset{\frown}{C'E} + \overset{\frown}{ED}) + (\overset{\frown}{ED} + \overset{\frown}{DB'}) = \overset{\frown}{B'C'} + \overset{\frown}{ED} = 180°.$$

But $\angle A$ is measured by $\overset{\frown}{ED}$ (A is the pole of $\overset{\frown}{B'C'}$). Hence $\overset{\frown}{B'C'} + \angle A = 180°$.

To prove $A' + \overset{\frown}{BC} = 180°$ extend $\overset{\frown}{BC}$ to meet $\overset{\frown}{A'C'}$ at E' and $\overset{\frown}{A'B'}$ at D' and follow the proof above.

THEOREM C The sum of the angles of a spherical triangle is greater than $180°$ and less than $540°$.

Proof Given $\triangle ABC$, construct its polar triangle with sides a', b', and c'. By Theorem B,

$$\angle A + a' = \angle B + b' = \angle C + c' = 180°$$
$$\angle A + \angle B + \angle C + a' + b' + c' = 540°$$

By (2) of Sec. 19–19, $$0 < a' + b' + c' < 360°$$
Subtracting, $$540° > \angle A + \angle B + \angle C > 180°$$

The amount by which the sum of the angles of a spherical polygon exceeds those of a plane polygon of the same number of sides is called its spherical excess. For a triangle, the spherical excess $E = \angle A + \angle B + \angle C - 180°$.

EXERCISES ON THE SPHERE

C.

1. Find the radius of a circle of a sphere of radius 6″ made by a plane 3″ from the center.
2. When will a plane be tangent to a sphere?
3. If two spheres intersect, what figure does the intersection form?

4. The radii of two spheres are R and r. The distance between the centers of the spheres is l. Tell the relation of the spheres in each of the following cases: $(a)\ l > R + r$, $(b)\ l = R + r$, $(c)\ l < R + r$ but $l > R - r$, $(d)\ l = R - r$, $(e)\ l < R - r$, $(f)\ l = 0$. Draw figures for each case.

5. Find the area and volume of a sphere of radius 7″.

B.

6. Find the number of square units in one sph. deg. on a sphere of radius 10 inches.

7. Find the area of a spherical triangle on the sphere of Ex. 6, if the angles are 80°, 100°, and 140°. Give the answer in square units.

8. Prove that the distance from the pole to any point on a circle of the pole is constant.

9. If the angles of a spherical triangle are those of Ex. 7, find the sides of its polar triangle.

10. Could the angles of a spherical triangle be 80°, 120°, and 150°? *Hint.* Consider the sides of its polar triangle.

A.

11. Prove that any point in a plane perpendicular to a line segment at its mid-point is equidistant from the end points of the segment.

12. State and prove the converse of Ex. 11.

13. Prove: Four noncoplanar points determine one and only one sphere.

14. On a sphere two triangles are congruent (or symmetrical) if three sides of one equal the three sides of the other. Using this fact, prove two spherical triangles are equal or congruent if three angles of one are equal to the three angles of the other. *Hint.* Construct the polar triangles.

NOTE: *Constructions in three-space.* If we are restricted to only straightedge and compasses, as in plane geometry, then evidently it is not possible to construct three-dimensional figures. However, it is possible to construct certain points, lines, and figures discussed in this geometry, confining constructions to figures drawn in a plane.

Of the three famous geometry problems of ancient times, one was a three-space problem. It is known as the duplication of the cube and can be stated thus: To construct the edge of a cube whose volume is twice that of a given cube, or given x to construct y so that $y^3 = 2x^3$. Like the squaring of the circle and trisection of an angle it has been proved to be impossible, using only the two accepted instruments.

15. Using only a pair of compasses, a straightedge, and a sheet of paper, we can construct the radius of a *material* sphere, such as a spherical blackboard or a baseball. Using the figures shown, reconstruct how this was done and prove $P'R'$ is the diameter of the sphere.

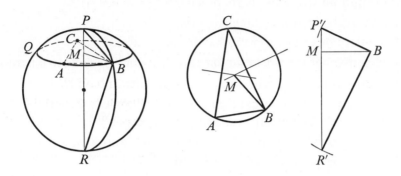

OUTLINE OF CHAPTER 19

This chapter introduces the following terms:

union	generating element
intersection	pyramid
convex set	cone
polyhedral angle	sphere
solid angle	frustum
polyhedron	spherical figures
prism	pole
cylinder	great circle
half-space	Cavalieri's Rule
parallelepiped	volume
circular disc	axis

This chapter extends the study of geometry in three dimensions by:
   1. Developing the meaning of dihedral and polyhedral angles.
   2. Extending the meaning of convex sets of points.
   3. Treating the figures in space — polyhedrons and solids.
   4. Studying the properties of prisms, pyramids, cylinders, and cones.
   5. Making a study of the sphere and figures on a sphere.
   6. Finding the area of surfaces and volumes of solids in space.

REVIEW

1. Describe the set of points that form (*a*) a plane angle, (*b*) a dihedral angle, (*c*) a trihedral angle, (*d*) a polyhedral angle.

2. Give physical illustrations of each of the angles in Ex. 1.

3. Name and illustrate the parts of each angle in Ex. 1.

4. Is a parallelepiped a rectangular prism?

5. How many faces can a prism have? A pyramid?

6. In what manner is a prism similar to a cylinder? A cone to a pyramid?

7. How does a polyhedron differ from a polyhedral solid?

8. Can a plane intersect a cube and form a triangle? A parallelogram? A pentagon? A regular hexagon? An octagon?

9. Describe a regular pyramid, a regular prism, and a right cone.

10. Name the parts of the polyhedrons of Ex. 9.

11. Define a sphere (1) as a surface, (2) as a solid.

12. How are distances between points on a sphere measured?

13. Describe a spherical angle, a lune, a spherical triangle, a spherical polygon, a zone, a segment, and a spherical wedge.

14. Describe and illustrate symmetrical spherical triangles.

15. Within what limits is the sum of the angles of a spherical triangle?

16. Describe and illustrate polar spherical triangles.

17. Find the area and volume of a cube with edge 6 inches.

18. Find the total area and volume of a rectangular prism with dimensions 9 in., 11 in., and 15 in.

19. Find the total area and volume of a regular hexagonal prism with the lateral edge 10 units and the side of the base 6 units.

20. The volume of a square pyramid is 108 cu. units. The altitude is 12 units. Find the side of the base.

21. The area of the base of a pyramid is 60 sq. in. What is the area of a section made by a plane parallel to the base and bisecting the altitude?

22. In Ex. 21, where must the plane be passed to give a section area of 30 sq. in.?

23. Find the total area and volume of a right circular cone with radius 5 inches and altitude 12 inches.

24. Find the area and volume of a sphere of radius 4 units.

25. Find the area of a zone with altitude 1 unit on the sphere in Ex. 24.

26. Two face angles of a trihedral triangle are 80° and 120°. Between what limits will the third face angle be?

27. Find the volume of a frustum of a cone if the altitude is 4 inches and the radii of the bases are 2 inches and 3 inches.

28. Describe the conditions that would be required for two polyhedrons to be *similar*.

29. Two cones are similar. Their altitudes are 4″ and 3″. What is the ratio of their total areas? Their volumes?

TEST

1. Illustrate and discuss the two following statements.
    (*a*) Three noncollinear points in a plane determine a convex region in the plane.
    (*b*) Four noncoplanar points determine a convex region in space.

2. A cube has each edge 4 in.
    (*a*) Find the total area.
    (*b*) Find the volume.
    (*c*) Find the length of a diagonal of the cube.
    (*d*) Find the volume of a sphere containing all the vertices.

3. A triangle on a sphere has two sides 60° and 80°.
    (*a*) Between what limits does the third side lie?
    (*b*) Between what limits does the angle opposite the third side in the polar triangle lie?

4. Prove: An exterior angle of a spherical triangle is less than the sum of the two opposite interior angles of the triangle.

5. On a sphere of radius 1 unit, a lune has an angle of 30°.
    (*a*) Find the area of the lune in spherical degrees.
    (*b*) Find the area of the lune in square units.
    (*c*) Find the area of the sphere in square units.

6. In a regular tetrahedron, a median is a line segment drawn from a vertex to the center of gravity of the opposite face. Prove these medians meet in a point *G*, three fourths the distance from each vertex to the opposite face.

    Hint. Use △*HGF* and △*AGD*. Compare *AH* and *AM*, etc.

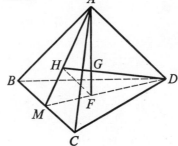

CHAPTER | 20

THE NATURE OF MATHEMATICAL REASONING

THIS chapter discusses some of the principles that are employed in all reasoning. Our discussion draws on arithmetic, algebra, and geometry for most of its illustrations, but the principles are not limited to mathematics. They are used to some degree and in some form in every subject in which conclusions are established rationally. The principles have been discussed and used many times in this course in geometry. Our present purpose is to summarize, discuss, and illustrate them so that they shall be of the greatest value to you. In preparation for the study of this chapter you should review the discussions of Chapter 2 and Chapter 4, also Sec. 0–2 and Sec. 0–3.

EXERCISES

1. Show that any selected even number greater than 4 is the sum of two odd prime numbers. (1 is not considered a prime number) e.g. 60 = 7 + 53, etc. If you show this for every even number up to 100, does this prove the theorem for all even numbers?

2. In a plane figure let V = number of vertices (points), E = number of edges (line segments) and F = number of faces (polygons). For which of the figures shown is the relation $E + 1 = V + F$ true? Prove this relation for all convex polygons.

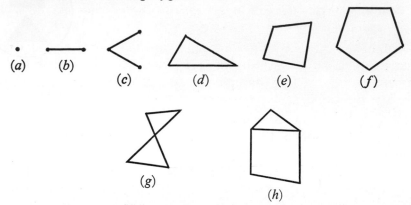

(a)   (b)   (c)   (d)   (e)   (f)   (g)   (h)

3. For every integer 1 to 39, $n^2 + n + 41$ is a prime number. Is it prime for n replaced by 40? What does this prove?

4. Write a short paragraph describing how you prove a theorem.

20–1 Definitions. Undefined Terms. Defined Terms When people reason together, it is essential that they attach the same meaning to each word that is used, *so far as this is possible*. The meaning of a word can come from a stated definition, or it can come from previous experience in using it. Reliance on previous experience for the meaning of a term often leads to difficulty because the experiences of any two persons are never quite the same. Still, there is often less trouble in accepting a meaning from experience than in trying to define a term. For example, there is less trouble if we talk about *straight line* as if all persons concerned understand the term alike than there is if we try to define it. A term that we use without giving it an explicit definition is called an <u>undefined term</u>. It is best to have as few as possible of these but there must be a few.

A <u>defined term</u> is one for which a definition is specifically given. As you know, the same word may have different meanings in different discussions. For example, the word *radical* has one meaning when we are discussing mathematics and a very different meaning when we are talking about political opinions. In a mathematical discussion it is well to define the term specifically so that there can be no doubt as to how the term is to be used. A good definition is one in which the subject and the predicate complement are different expressions for the same mathematical idea.

Thus a definition is reversible, that is, the subject and predicate of the definition can be interchanged.

Example: A prime number is an integer greater than 1 that has no factor except itself and one.

The definition reversed: An integer greater than 1 that has no factors except itself and one is a prime number.

A definition not only is valuable to make sure that everyone understands the meaning of the term used, but it is often also used as a step in the argument or proof. For example, suppose that we wish to show that 101 is a prime number. We might argue as follows:

(1) The square root of 101 is less than 11.
(2) As possible factors of 101, we need to test only primes that are smaller than 11.
(3) The prime numbers smaller than 11 are 2, 3, 5, and 7.
(4) By trial we find that neither 2, 3, 5, nor 7 is a factor of 101.
(5) Then 101 has no factor other than 1 and 101.
(6) Hence 101 is prime by definition.

You have often used a definition as a step in geometric proof. For example, when you bisect an angle, you follow certain steps in construction. Then you prove congruent a pair of triangles and conclude that two angles are equal. Your final step is to assert that the given angle has been bisected and as a reason you refer to the definition of angle bisector. (See Sec. 3–16.)

EXERCISES

1. Make a list of five undefined terms used in this book.
2. Make a list of five defined terms used in this book.
3. (*a*) Give two different statements each of which could be used as a definition for a parallelogram. (*b*) If one of these statements is accepted as the definition, then what is the other statement?
4. Define *intersection* of two geometric figures.
5. (*a*) The *union* of two geometric figures is defined to be all the points that belong to either of the two figures. Reverse this definition. (*b*) Describe union and intersection using triangles as shown. Are there triangles other than $\triangle ABC$ and $\triangle DEF$.

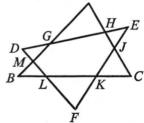

20–2 Postulates A postulate is a statement that is assumed. That is, we make no attempt to prove the statement. We do not argue that it is true. We give no reason for assuming it except that it is useful in the system of reasoning that we are constructing. Usually, but not always, we may somehow show that a postulate is natural or reasonable (whatever *natural* and *reasonable* may mean) but we do not insist that the particular postulate that we state is the only possible one that could be accepted. One of the best examples of the arbitrary nature of a postulate is the Parallel Postulate, our Postulate 18 (see Sec. 5–3). We pointed out that there are at least two other postulates that could be stated in place of our Postulate 18. You should not think of Postulates *A* and *B* as being *unreasonable*. Each is just as reasonable as Postulate 18. A whole system of geometry has been constructed with Postulate *A* as one of its postulates, and likewise Postulate *B* is the base of another system of geometry. The geometry that uses Postulate *A* is sometimes called elliptic geometry. The geometry that uses Postulate *B* is sometimes called hyperbolic geometry. Each of these geometries is just as logical as Euclidean geometry, and there are certain scientific connections in which one or the other of these non-Euclidean geometries must be used in preference to Euclidean geometry.

In building a logical organization of mathematical knowledge a set of postulates is necessary. These postulates are merely accepted theorems about the undefined terms (geometric elements) and definitions. In a given mathematical system it is not possible to prove a postulate. The Parallel Postulate is an example of this type of statement.

The selection of the set of postulates is optional with the person who is constructing the mathematical system. One person, by accepting a certain theorem of another person's system as a postulate, can prove one of that person's postulates as a theorem. To show this, consider the two statements:

I. If two lines intersect, they have only one point in common.

II. Through two points there is only one straight line.

If a person accepts one of these as a postulate, he can prove the other as a theorem.

Let us accept statement I as a postulate. Then we *prove* statement II as follows: Suppose there are at least two distinct straight lines through points *A* and *B*. Then these two intersecting lines have two points in common. But by I above they have only one point in common. Hence a contradiction. Thus there can be only one straight line. So in some other books some of our postulates may appear as theorems, and some of our theorems as their postulates. This should not be disturbing to you now.

Of course, in a first study of geometry and algebra it would be too difficult to use only the postulates that are necessary and prove everything else. So we frequently list as postulates certain statements that could be proved, because the proof is too difficult for the beginner.

In this book we also used certain assumptions without stating them, because the very writing of them would raise questions that are very difficult to answer for a beginner. For example, we tacitly used the idea throughout the book that *there is no part of any line that does not contain a point*. Thus we agreed that a line has no gap or vacancy. In a rigorous development we would have to list it among our postulates. In later work you will study this as a postulate of continuity.

We also tacitly assumed that a *straightedge exists*. The attempt to explain whether or not the existence of a straightedge must be a postulate would not help us to understand better the geometry we studied, so we did not talk about it. Actually, Peaucillier's cell was perhaps the first device to construct a straight line without assuming the existence of a straightedge. You can read about this in a good encyclopedia.

Mathematicians do not regard postulates as *common notions* nor as *obviously true*. They do not believe such tests should be applied to any postulate. All they demand is that the postulates be consistent (do not contradict each other) and are sufficient to prove the theorems that occur in the subject. Some books use the word *axiom* instead of *postulate*. These are merely two names for the same thing. We chose to use *postulate* in this book.

EXERCISES

1. Accept statement II on page 542 as a postulate and prove statement I as a theorem.
2. If a point interior to a circle is connected by a line segment to a point outside the circle, in how many points will the segment meet the circle? Is this a theorem or a postulate? If it is a theorem, prove it.
3. If a line not containing a vertex of a triangle intersects one side of a triangle, it intersects a second side of the triangle. This statement is

known as Pasch's axiom or postulate. Is the statement, "A line not containing a vertex of a triangle can intersect only two sides of a triangle," a postulate or a theorem? If it is a theorem, can you prove it using Pasch's postulate?

4. In the figure, lines are drawn through A to meet line l at C. Consider line l of infinite length and let the point of intersection C move away from B to an *infinite* distance. Which of the following do you accept?

(*a*) Line AC never is parallel to line l.

(*b*) After reaching an infinite distance, there are many lines through A that are parallel to l.

(*c*) Only one line through A is parallel to l.

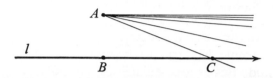

Discuss your answers in light of the above discussion about postulates.

20–3 Mathematical Abstractions In the Hindu-Arabic system of numeration we use the written or printed symbols 1, 2, 3, and so on (called numerals) to *represent* or name numbers. In the Roman system of numeration the written or printed symbols I, V, X, and so on are used to name numbers. There are many other systems that use still other symbols. In each system there is a written or printed symbol that represents *one*. It is evident that the symbol 5 or V is not the number "five" for then "five" would be two different things. In other words, number is abstract. When we discuss numbers, then, we are talking about abstractions and not about the set of symbols by which numbers are represented.

In like manner, the figures that we discuss in geometry are abstractions. For example, we draw a figure which we call a line segment, name it AB, and talk about its properties, but it is not the mark on the paper that we are discussing; it is an abstract line for which the mark on the paper is only an illustration or representation. In like manner, all triangles, circles, polygons, points, and so on, discussed in this book are really abstractions. As an aid to our understanding we draw various pencil lines and make dots, but these lines and dots are symbols that illustrate abstract figures whose properties we study. It would be quite possible to study geometry without drawing any figures. However, most of us would find such a study very difficult.

No matter how careful we are in our physical constructions, the figures that we draw are never perfect. We do not let that bother us because we know that these figures are only illustrations and guides to the study of the geometric abstractions stated in the theorem. Our proof is about a set of points, lines, triangles, circles, and so on, whatever these things may be, and not about the marks (drawings) on our paper.

EXERCISES

Consider · as representing a line, and / as representing a point. Then make illustrations for each of exercises 1 to 4.

1. Only one line lies on two points.
2. Two lines have only one point in common.
3. A triangle is formed by the segments of three points not all on the same line.
4. A convex polygon has as many vertices as it has point segments. A vertex is the line common to two points.
5. Explain the difference between a circle and a drawing of a circle.
6. In the drawings shown, we started with a point, took a point in the next higher dimension, and connected it to all the vertices in the previous dimension. Suppose there is a fourth dimension and a point in it (E). Connect E to all the vertices in the third dimension. Now count the number of vertices, edges, faces, and tetrahedrons. Calling the entire figure a hypersolid show that for all the figures

$$V = 1 + E - F + S - H$$

whore V — number of vertices, E — the number of edges, F = the number of faces, S = the number of solids, and H = the number of hypersolids.

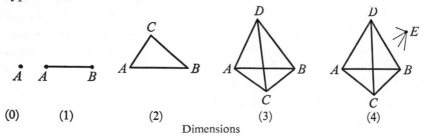

(0) (1) (2) (3) (4)

Dimensions

Note that the figure for the hypersolid is merely an illustration and not a fourth-dimensional abstraction.

7. Use the figure at the right to prove that the base angles of an isosceles triangle are equal. Does the figure make the proof valid? Explain.

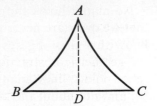

20–4 Consistency One essential of Euclidean geometry, and any other logically constructed body of mathematics, is that all of its statements, whether definitions, postulates, or theorems, must be consistent. That means that no two of its statements may be in conflict. What is proved or postulated in one place cannot be contradicted in another place. At the beginning geometry consists of only a few statements. The subject grows as we find more and more statements that are consistent with those previously made and with each other. In a sense, the accumulation of consistent statements about geometric figures is all there is to the subject.

Since all the theorems can be eventually traced back to the postulates, the consistency of the postulates is the first requirement for building mathematical knowledge.

Exercise. Show that the statement "Through a point there are two lines parallel to a given line" is inconsistent with the theorem "Alternate interior angles of parallel lines are equal."

Mathematicians are not concerned with discovering relations that are practical, as we often understand that word. They are concerned only with discovering consistent statements. Thus, all postulates, definitions, and propositions must constitute a consistent system of statements.

20–5 Proposition. Theorem A proposition is a statement for investigation or consideration. Concerning any statement we ask the question "Is the statement consistent with statements that have been accepted previously?" If the proposition calls for a construction to be done, is it possible to do the construction with the permitted tools, and what are the steps? How can it be proved, using stated definitions, postulates, and previously proved propositions?

Most of the propositions of geometry relate either to constructions to be made or to proofs to be given. In either case there is (*a*) a statement of conditions (hypothesis), and (*b*) a statement of what is required to be done (conclusion). The statement of conditions (*a*) can always be made to follow the word *if* when a proof is to be given; the statement of what is required to be proved can always be made to follow the word *then*.

For this reason we often refer to such a proposition as an "if ... then ..." statement. An "if ... then ..." statement that can be proved is called a *theorem.*

A proposition may or may not be true. If it can be proved (is true), it becomes a theorem. If it cannot be proved (is false, or at least sometimes false), it is rejected from the accepted statements of the subject. Thus, "If two triangles are congruent, they agree in two sides and an angle opposite one of these sides" is true and can be accepted as a theorem. But, "If two triangles agree in two sides and an angle opposite one of these sides, they are congruent" is false and this proposition is rejected. It is not a theorem.

Exercise. In the figure, name two triangles that agree in two sides and an angle opposite one of these sides, and prove that the triangles are not congruent.

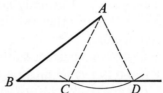

20–6 Converse You have seen that the hypothesis of a theorem can have several parts, and also the conclusion can have several parts. If we interchange one or more parts of the hypothesis with one or more parts of the conclusion, we get a statement that is a converse of the given theorem. We may or may not be able to prove the converse; that is, it may or may not be consistent with previously accepted statements. A converse becomes a theorem only if it can be proved. An example of a converse is the theorem of Sec. 5–10.

20–7 Contradictory Statements. Indirect Proof Consider the following statements.

(a) Point X is on circle O.
(b) Point X is not on circle O.

If statement (a) is true, then statement (b) must be false. If statement (b) is true, then statement (a) must be false. Statements (a) and (b) are contradictory statements. In general, the contradiction of any given statement can be written by making a second statement which begins, "It is not true that . . ." and then repeating the given statement. Of two contradictory statements, one must be true and only one can be true; one must be false and only one can be false; if one is false, then the other must be true.

The above statements regarding contradictory assertions enable us to prove some theorems indirectly by proving the falsity of contradictory statements. In order to prove that statement (*a*) is true, we can make statement (*b*) which contradicts (*a*) and prove that (*b*) is false. Then we immediately accept (*a*) as true. This is indirect proof. Sec. 4–9 is an example of indirect proof by use of contradictory statements.

In using contradictory statements in a proof, we must always be sure that two statements are really contradictory. Consider the following statements.

(*c*) Line segment *Z* is 2 inches long.
(*d*) Line segment *Z* is 2.1 inches long.

If I can prove that *Z* is not 2 inches long, have I proved that it is 2.1 inches long? Certainly not; it may be 3 inches long or it may have any one of many other possible lengths. (*c*) and (*d*) are not contradictory statements.

Or again, consider statements (*e*) and (*f*).

(*e*) Point *Q* is outside circle *M*.
(*f*) Point *Q* is inside circle *M*.

(*e*) and (*f*) are not contradictory statements, and if I can prove (*e*) false, it does not follow that (*f*) is true.

Use of contradictory statements in proof outside the field of geometry often leads to great difficulties because of the possibility of shades of truth and falsity (the "included middle") and should be sparingly used. For example, you might examine statements (*g*) and (*h*).

(*g*) Mr. H has quit beating his wife.
(*h*) Mr. H has not quit beating his wife.

20–8   Contrapositive   Consider the conditional statement:

A. If it is iron, then it is metal.

Now we form another conditional statement by negating both the hypothesis and the conclusion and then writing the converse. Thus we obtain:

B. If it is not metal, then it is not iron.

The last statement is called the contrapositive of the first statement. To form a contrapositive, interchange the hypothesis and conclusion and then write their negatives. Note that if statement *A* is true then *B* is also true, and if *B* is true then *A* is also true.

The contrapositive of "If a triangle has two equal sides, then the angles opposite these sides are equal" is "If two angles of a triangle are unequal, then the sides opposite these angles are unequal." Note again that if either one of these statements is true, the other is also. This fact can be proved in the study of logic, but we shall postulate it as *The Law of the Contrapositive.*

If the contrapositive of a proposition is true, then the proposition is true, and conversely.

We can use this law to prove theorems that are usually otherwise very difficult to prove. The following are only two of many examples.

THEOREM A If a line divides two sides of a triangle into proportional segments, then it is parallel to the third side.

We first write and then prove the contrapositive.

Contrapositive A̅ If a line intersects two sides of a triangle and is not parallel to the third side, then it does not divide the two sides proportionally. (A̅ is read "A bar.")

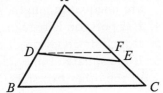

Hypothesis $\triangle ABC$; $DE \not\parallel BC$

Conclusion $\dfrac{AD}{AB} \neq \dfrac{AE}{AC}$

Proof Draw $DF \parallel BC$ meeting AC at F. F and E are not the same point, otherwise DE would be $\parallel$ to BC. Now $\dfrac{AD}{AB} = \dfrac{AF}{AC}$, since DF is parallel to BC. But $\dfrac{AF}{AC} \neq \dfrac{AE}{AC}$ since $AF \neq AE$. Hence $\dfrac{AD}{AB} \neq \dfrac{AE}{AC}$. Since we have proved the contrapositive, by the law of the contrapositive the theorem A is now known to be true.

THEOREM B If the alternate interior angles formed by a transversal of two lines are equal, the lines are parallel.

Contrapositive B̅ If two lines are not parallel, then the alternate interior angles formed by a transversal are not equal.

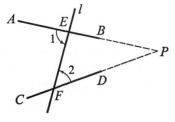

Hypothesis AB is not $\parallel CD$. l is a transversal to AB and CD.

Conclusion $\angle 1 \neq \angle 2$

Extend *AB* and *CD* until they meet, which can be done since they are not parallel. Then a triangle *PEF* is formed. Since angle 1 (or 2) is an exterior angle of this triangle and angle 2 (or 1) is an opposite interior angle of the triangle, $\angle 1 \neq \angle 2$. This proves the contrapositive.

Hence by the law of the contrapositive, the theorem B is also true.

EXERCISES

C.

Write a contrapositive to each of the following statements.

1. If a point is on a perpendicular bisector of a line segment, then it is equally distant from the ends of the segment.
2. Any point equally distant from the sides of an angle is on the bisector of the angle.
3. If two chords are unequally distant from the center of a circle, they are unequal in length.
4. If a polygon is regular, it can be inscribed in a circle.
5. If a commercial product bears brand A, it is good material.
6. If the square of one side of a triangle is equal to the sum of the squares of the other two sides, it is a right triangle.

B.

7. Prove: "If a line is perpendicular to a radius at its outer extremity, it is tangent to the circle" by first proving the contrapositive and then using the law of the contrapositive.

20–9 Meaning of Formal Proof in Geometry In writing a proof of a theorem, we usually use one drawing as an illustration of the geometric figure we are considering. The drawing we select is optional. It is merely one of the set of all possible figures that could be used in *formulating* the proof. A proof, by merely changing the letters and names used in the figure, would be valid for every other figure in the set of all possible figures.

Consider the proof below in which the figure is an illustration of the isosceles triangle under consideration.

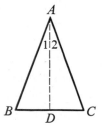

Hypothesis $\triangle ABC$, $AB = AC$

Conclusion $\angle C = \angle B$

Proof Construct *AD* bisecting $\angle A$.

Then $\triangle ADB \cong \triangle ADC$ (s a s), and hence $\angle C = \angle B$.

Suppose we replace figure *ABC* with any of the following figures. Without changing the form of the above proof, but merely replacing *A*, *B*, *C*, *D* respectively with *X* (or *α* or *L* or I), *Y* (or *β* or *K* or II), *Z* (or *γ* or *M* or III), and *W* (or *δ* or *P* or IV) the proof is valid for each of the other figures. (*α* = alpha, *β* = beta, *γ* = gamma, *δ* = delta are Greek letters.)

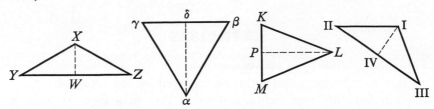

Thus we see that just as in algebra when we prove $(x + y)^2 = x^2 + 2xy + y^2$ this proof holds for every replacement of *x* and *y* by particular numbers, so in geometry a formal proof holds for every figure of the kind under discussion. The above proof, in this sense, holds for every possible isosceles triangle.

Of course when a drawing is made to illustrate a geometric theorem, the drawing should be made as accurately as possible. If we are careless in our drawing and not sufficiently rigorous in our reasoning, we can readily make mistakes. Consider the following *false* proposition.

Every scalene triangle is isosceles.

Hypothesis $\triangle ABC$ with $AB \neq AC$

To prove $AB = AC$

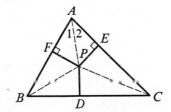

Proof   Draw the bisector of angle *A*, the perpendicular bisector of *BC*, and let them intersect at *P*. Draw $PF \perp AB$, $PE \perp AC$. Then $\triangle APF \cong \triangle APE$ by Sec. 6–11. Then $AF = AE$, and $FP = PE$. Now $\triangle FPB \cong \triangle PEC$ (Sec. 3–25). Hence $FB = EC$, and then $AB = AC$.

Now consider the sequence of steps in the proof. Will it hold for any other selected triangle? If you are careful, you will note that it says that the angle bisector *AP* and perpendicular bisector *PD* meet at *P* but *fails to tell where and why*. This *where* or *why* is a necessary part of the form of proof. A carefully drawn figure would have guided us to a correct formal proof. The point *P* must lie outside the triangle.

Thus even though a figure is only a model for our geometric thinking, it can be a very important guide if it is well drawn, or a very strong block if it is not well drawn.

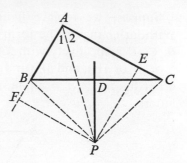

EXERCISES

1. Explain the difference between proving $3 \times 6 = 6 \times 3$ and proving $x \cdot y = y \cdot x$ where x and y can be replaced by any integers.
2. Explain the difference between proving that in a right triangle with sides $3''$ and $4''$ the hypotenuse is $(\sqrt{3^2 + 4^2})''$ and proving for any right triangle the corresponding fact.
3. If a theorem refers to "any" triangle, is it possible to use a right triangle as a drawing for the theorem? Can you use the fact that your drawing is a right triangle in the formal proof?
4. Tell why, in a drawing for a theorem, nothing should be assumed from the figure except that which is given in the hypothesis or is a logical consequence.

20–10 Application of Mathematical Structure to the Arithmetic of Natural Numbers To see how the same structure used in studying geometry can be applied to other areas of mathematical study, we shall give an example using *only* the numbers 1, 2, 3, and so on but not fractions or any other kinds. We shall list some undefined terms, definitions, and postulates and use them to prove theorems. Just as *point* was undefined in geometry, so *number* shall be undefined in our new system. Similarly, just as *line* (as a collection of points) was undefined, we shall take as undefined certain operations on number. We proceed as follows:

Undefined Terms

1. Number, by which we mean anything represented by 1, 2, 3, 4, $\cdots$
2. Addition of two numbers, which we symbolize by $+$
3. Multiplication of two numbers, which we symbolize by $\times$
4. Factor of a number

In the following definitions and postulates, whenever we use letters such as x, y, a, b, etc., we mean that these are symbols that can be replaced by any particular numbers, to give true statements.

Definitions

1. The number 1 is an odd number.
2. The expression *x is an even number* means $x = 2a$ where a can be replaced by any number.
3. The expression *y is an odd number* means $y = 2b + 1$ where b can be replaced by any number.

The definitions and undefined terms are meaningful to you, since you have used them from the first years of your school life. However, we give them further meaning by giving them certain properties which are formulated as postulates.

Postulates

1. For every pair of numbers, a and b, there is a unique number c such that $a + b = c$.
2. For every pair of numbers, a and b, there is a unique number d such that $a \times b = d$.
3. For every pair of numbers, a and b, $a + b = b + a$. This is the commutative law for addition.
4. For every pair of numbers, a and b, $a \times b = b \times a$. This is the commutative law for multiplication.
5. For every triplet of numbers, a, b, and c, $(a + b) + c = a + (b + c)$. This is the associative law for addition.
6. For every triplet of numbers, a, b, and c, $(a \times b) \times c = a \times (b \times c)$. This is the associative law for multiplication.
7. For every triplet of numbers, a, b, and c, $a \times (b + c) = a \times b + a \times c$. This is the distributive law of addition with respect to multiplication.
8. For every number a, $a = a$. This is called the reflexive property.
9. For every a, b, if $a = b$, then $b = a$. This is called the symmetric property.
10. For every a, b, and c, if $a = b$ and $b = c$, then $a = c$. This is called the transitive property.
11. For every quadruplet of numbers, a, b, c, and d, if $a = b$ and $c = d$, then $a + c = b + d$.
12. For every quadruplet of numbers a, b, c, and d, if $a = b$ and $c = d$, then $a \cdot c = b \cdot d$.
13. Every number is either even or odd.

Test these postulates by inserting particular numbers for the letters. We are now ready to prove some theorems.

THEOREM 1 The sum of two even numbers is an even number.

Hypothesis $a = 2x, b = 2y$

Conclusion $a + b = 2z$

Proof

$a + b = 2x + 2y$	Post. 11
$2x + 2y = 2(x + y)$	Post. 8 and 7
$a + b = 2(x + y)$	Post. 10
$x + y = z$, where z is a natural number	Post. 1
$2 = 2$ and $2(x + y) = 2z$	Post. 8 and 12
then $a + b = 2z$	Post. 10
$2z$ is an even number	Def. 2

THEOREM 2 The sum of two odd numbers is an even number.

Hypothesis $a = 2x + 1, b = 2y + 1$

Conclusion $a + b = 2z$

Proof

$$
\begin{aligned}
a + b &= (2x + 1) + (2y + 1) \\
&= 2x + [1 + (2y + 1)] \\
&= 2x + [(1 + 2y) + 1] \\
&= 2x + [(2y + 1) + 1] \\
&= 2x + [2y + (1 + 1)] \\
&= 2x + (2y + 2) \\
&= 2x + 2(y + 1) \\
&= 2[x + (y + 1)]
\end{aligned}
$$

Post. 5 and 3 (for lines 2–5)

Post. 7

Post. 7

Now $(y + 1)$ is a number and $x + (y + 1)$ is a number by postulate 11. Let $x + (y + 1) = z$,

then $a + b = 2z$

You should now be able to prove the following theorems.

EXERCISES

1. **Theorem 3.** The sum of an even number and an odd number is an odd number.

2. **Theorem 4.** The product of two even numbers is an even number.

3. **Theorem 5.** The product of two odd numbers is an odd number.

4. **Theorem 6.   The product of an even number and an odd number is an even number.**

Using the definition that the square of a number is the product of the number by itself, prove:

5. **Theorem 7.   The square of an even number is an even number.** (Use Theorem 4.)

6. **Theorem 8.   The square of an odd number is an odd number.**

Using the definition that a perfect square is a number having two equal factors, each called a square root of the number, prove:

7. **Theorem 9.   If a perfect square is odd, its square root is an odd number.** (Use the indirect method with Theorems 7 and 8.)

8. **Theorem 10.   If a perfect square is even, its square root is an even number.**

9. **Theorem 11.   If a and b have no common factor, it is impossible for $a \cdot a = 2 \cdot b \cdot b$.** (Use the indirect method.)

SQUARES AND SQUARE ROOTS OF NUMBERS 1–150

Number	Square	Square Root	Number	Square	Square Root	Number	Square	Square Root
1	1	1	51	2,601	7.141	101	10,201	10.050
2	4	1.414	52	2,704	7.211	102	10,404	10.100
3	9	1.732	53	2,809	7.280	103	10,609	10.149
4	16	2	54	2,916	7.348	104	10,816	10.198
5	25	2.236	55	3,025	7.416	105	11,025	10.247
6	36	2.449	56	3,136	7.483	106	11,236	10.296
7	49	2.646	57	3,249	7.550	107	11,449	10.344
8	64	2.828	58	3,364	7.616	108	11,664	10.392
9	81	3	59	3,481	7.681	109	11,881	10.440
10	100	3.162	60	3,600	7.746	110	12,100	10.488
11	121	3.317	61	3,721	7.810	111	12,321	10.536
12	144	3.464	62	3,844	7.874	112	12,544	10.583
13	169	3.606	63	3,969	7.937	113	12,769	10.630
14	196	3.742	64	4,096	8	114	12,996	10.677
15	225	3.873	65	4,225	8.062	115	13,225	10.724
16	256	4	66	4,356	8.124	116	13,456	10.770
17	289	4.123	67	4,489	8.185	117	13,689	10.817
18	324	4.243	68	4,624	8.246	118	13,924	10.863
19	361	4.359	69	4,761	8.307	119	14,161	10.909
20	400	4.472	70	4,900	8.367	120	14,400	10.954
21	441	4.583	71	5,041	8.426	121	14,641	11
22	484	4.690	72	5,184	8.485	122	14,884	11.045
23	529	4.796	73	5,329	8.544	123	15,129	11.091
24	576	4.899	74	5,476	8.602	124	15,376	11.136
25	625	5	75	5,625	8.660	125	15,625	11.180
26	676	5.099	76	5,776	8.718	126	15,876	11.225
27	729	5.196	77	5,929	8.775	127	16,129	11.269
28	784	5.292	78	6,084	8.832	128	16,384	11.314
29	841	5.385	79	6,241	8.888	129	16,641	11.358
30	900	5.477	80	6,400	8.944	130	16,900	11.402
31	961	5.568	81	6,561	9	131	17,161	11.446
32	1,024	5.657	82	6,724	9.055	132	17,424	11.489
33	1,089	5.745	83	6,889	9.110	133	17,689	11.533
34	1,156	5.831	84	7,056	9.165	134	17,956	11.576
35	1,225	5.916	85	7,225	9.220	135	18,225	11.619
36	1,296	6	86	7,396	9.274	136	18,496	11.662
37	1,369	6.083	87	7,569	9.327	137	18,769	11.705
38	1,444	6.164	88	7,744	9.381	138	19,044	11.747
39	1,521	6.245	89	7,921	9.434	139	19,321	11.790
40	1,600	6.325	90	8,100	9.487	140	19,600	11.832
41	1,681	6.403	91	8,281	9.539	141	19,881	11.874
42	1,764	6.481	92	8,464	9.592	142	20,164	11.916
43	1,849	6.557	93	8,649	9.644	143	20,449	11.958
44	1,936	6.633	94	8,836	9.695	144	20,736	12
45	2,025	6.708	95	9,025	9.747	145	21,025	12.042
46	2,116	6.782	96	9,216	9.798	146	21,316	12.083
47	2,209	6.856	97	9,409	9.849	147	21,609	12.124
48	2,304	6.928	98	9,604	9.899	148	21,904	12.166
49	2,401	7	99	9,801	9.950	149	22,201	12.207
50	2,500	7.071	100	10,000	10	150	22,500	12.247

INDEX

Abscissa, 418
Absolute value, 416
Acute
  angle, 21
  triangle, 24
Adjacent angles, 20
Alternate angles, 113
Altitude, 444
  of parallelogram, 444
  of polyhedrons, 512, 516, 522
  of trapezoid, 444
  of triangle, 26, 444
Analysis, 71
Angle, 15, 505
  acute, 21
  base, 79
  bisector, 29
  central, 254, 475
  critical, 398
  degree, 17, 43, 301
  dihedral, 242, 505, 507
  exterior, 98, 113
  face of trihedral, 507
  of incidence, 397
  initial side of, 17
  inscribed, 301
  interior, 98, 113
  interior of, 15
  measurement of, 17
  oblique, 20
  obtuse, 21
  of polygon, 135
  polyhedral, 509
  of reflection, 397
  right, 20
  sides of, 13, 17
  solid, 509
  spherical, 525
  straight, 16, 20
  terminal side of, 17
  of a triangle, 24
  trihedral, 507
  trisection of, 142, 308, 309
  unit of, 18
  variable, 211
  vertex, of isosceles triangle, 79
  vertex of, 15
Angles
  adjacent, 20
  alternate, 113
  complementary, 50
  corresponding, 30
  equal, 17
  pairs, 43

supplementary, 50
  vertical, 53
Apothem, 475
Arc, 11
  degree, 258, 301
  intercepted, 254
  major, 254
  minor, 254
  negative, 306
  positive, 306
  unit of, 258, 301
Area, 444
  of a circle, 484
  lateral, 513, 523
  of a parallelogram, 447
  of a rectangle, 445
  of a regular polygon, 483
  of a sphere, 532
  of a trapezoid, 452
  of a triangle, 449
  unit of, 444
Arm, 24
Associative law, 553
Axiom, 45, 543
Axis
  of a circle, 525
  radical, 401
  of symmetry, 199
Base, 444
  angle, 79
  of isosceles triangle, 79
  of polyhedrons, 512
  of rectangle, 444
  of trapezoid, 186, 444
  of triangle, 79
Bisector
  of angle, 29
  perpendicular, 23
Cap, spherical, 531
Cavalieri's rule, 519
Center
  of circle, 11
  of gravity, 231
  of regular polygon, 475
  of sphere, 524
Centers, line of, 291
Central angle, 254, 475
Centroid, 231
Chord, 254
Circle, 11
  arc of, 11
  axis of, 525
  center of, 11
  chord of, 254

Circle (*cont.*)
  circumference of, 257, 479
  circumscribed, 252
  diameter of, 11
  escribed, 310
  exterior of, 253
  great, 525
  inscribed, 252, 309
  interior of, 253
  length of, 257
  radius of, 11
  small, 525
  tangent, 287
Circles
  concentric, 11, 294
  equal, 253
  intersecting, 292
  line of centers of, 291
  tangent, 292
  unequal, 253
Circumcenter, 229
Circumference, 257, 479
Circumscribed
  circle, 252
  polygon, 309
Clockwise, 17
Closed figure, 10
Coincide, 70
Collinear, 24
Common
  point, 9
  tangent, 294
Commutative law, 553
Compasses, 9
Complement, 50
Concentric circles, 11, 294
Conclusion, 44
Concurrent lines, 227
Condition, 44
Conditional statement, 44
Cone, 515
  altitude of, 516
  axis of, 516
  base of, 515
  circular, 516
  element of, 516
  face of, 515
  right, 516
  spherical, 531
  volume of, 521
Congruence, 29, 65, 70
Congruent figures, 29, 65, 70, 159
Consistency, 546
Consistent statements, 101
Construction, 10
Contradiction, 547
  law of, 100
Contrapositive, 548
Contrary statements, 101

Converse theorem, 116, 547
Convex
  polygon, 136
  set, 504
Coordinates, 418
Corollary, 81
Correspondence, 29, 61
  of points, 373
Corresponding parts, 29, 111
Counterclockwise, 17
Critical angle, 398
Cylinder, 514
  oblique, 514
  right, 514
  volume of, 520
Cylindrical surface, 513
Decagon, 136, 478
Deductive reasoning, 46
Definition, 5, 540
Degree
  of angle, 18, 43
  of arc, 258
  spherical, 528
Demonstration, 47
Determination
  of a circle, 253
  of line segment, 503
  of a plane, 235
  of a triangle, 70
Diagonal, 144
Diameter
  of circle, 11
  of sphere, 524
Dihedral angle, 242, 505, 507
  edge of, 242
  face of, 242
Direct reasoning, 46, 97
Disc, 514
Distance
  between parallel lines, 165
  between a point and a line, 26
  between points, 9, 420
  directed, 423
Distributive law, 553
Division
  external, 352
  harmonic, 361
  internal, 352
  of line segment, 352, 421
  proportional, 352
Dodecagon, 136, 479
Edge, 242, 512
Element, 509, 513
Equal
  angles, 17
  segments, 14
Equiangular, 81
Equilateral, 81
Equivalence, 122

Escribed circle, 310
Euler's formula, 512
Excenter, 228
Excess, spherical, 533
Exterior
    angle, 98, 113, 137
    of a polygon, 136
    of a triangle, 67
External division, 352
Extreme and mean ratio, 362
Extremes, 348
Face
    of dihedral angle, 242
    lateral, 512
    of trihedral angle, 507
Figure, closed, 10
Foot of line, 236
Fourth proportional, 348
Frustum, 189, 522
    volume of, 522
Geometry, 4
    coordinate, 415
    instruments of, 9
Golden section, 362, 390
Great circle, 525
Half-line, 15, 503
    vertex of, 15
Half-plane, 7, 242, 291, 504
Half-space, 504
Harmonic division, 361
Height, slant, 516
Hexagon, 136
Hypotenuse, 24
Hypothesis, 44
Identity, 71
If and only if, 120
Incenter, 228
Included parts, 31
Inconsistent statements, 101
Indirect reasoning, 98, 103, 547
Inequalities, 213
Initial
    position, 17
    side, 17
Inscribed
    angle, 301
    circle, 252, 309
    polygon, 252
Instruments of geometry, 9
Integer, Pythagorean, 385
Intercept, 182
Interior
    angle, 113
    of an angle, 15
    of a polygon, 136
    of a polyhedron, 511
    of a triangle, 67
Internal division, 352
Intersect, 7, 9

Intersection
    of half-planes, 505
    of lines, 9
    of loci, 337
    of planes, 236
    of sets of points, 9
Isosceles triangle, 79
    base of, 79
    vertex angle of, 79
Kite, 80
Lateral
    area, 513, 523
    edge, 512
    face, 512
Length of a circle, 254
Level, 85
Line, 6
    broken, 6
    of centers, 291
    curved, 6, 8
    segment, 6, 8, 503
    slope of, 423
    straight, 6, 429
    of symmetry, 199
    through two points, 433
Lines
    concurrent, 227
    parallel, 111, 433
    perpendicular, 20, 426
    skew, 239
Loci, intersection of, 337
Locus, 327, 435
    in three-space, 342
Logic, 4
Lune, 527
Major arc, 254
Mathematical system, 169
Mean proportional, 348
Means, 348
Measurement
    of angle, 17
    of area, 444
    of segment, 14
Median
    of quadrilateral, 190
    of trapezoid, 186
    of triangle, 24
Mid-point, 23
Minor arc, 254
Minute, 18
Negative arc, 306
Normal, 240
Number
    line, 416
    rational, 416
    real, 416
Oblique
    angle, 21
    triangle, 24

Obtuse
  angle, 21
  triangle, 24
Octagon, 136
One-to-one correspondence, 61
Order, 139, 213
Ordered pair, 419
Ordinate, 418
Origin, 415
Orthocenter, 230
Pair, ordered, 419
Pairs of angles, 43
Parallax, 396
Parallel
  lines, 111, 433
  postulate, 112
Parallelepiped, 513
Parallelogram, 158
  altitude of, 444
  area of, 447
  base of, 444
Parts
  corresponding, 29, 111
  included, 31
Pentagon, 136
Perimeter
  of polygon, 392
  of triangle, 24
Perpendicular, 20, 25
  bisector, 23
  planes, 242
Pi, 257
Plane, 7
Planes, perpendicular, 242
Point of symmetry, 196
Points, correspondence of, 373
Point-slope equation, 430
Polar triangles, 532
Pole, 525
Polygon, 135
  angle of, 135
  apothem of, 475
  area of, 483
  center of, 475
  central angle of, 475
  circumscribed, 309
  concave, 136
  convex, 136
  diagonal of, 144
  exterior angle of, 137
  inscribed, 252
  radius of, 475
  regular, 469
  side of, 135
  spherical, 531
  vertex of, 135
Polygons, similar, 374
Polyhedral angle, 509

Polyhedron, 511
  interior of, 511
  regular, 512
Positive arc, 306
Postulate, 45, 542
  of continuity, 543
  parallel, 112
Prism, 512
  altitude of, 512
  base of, 512
  edge of, 512
  face of, 512
  rectangular, 513
  right, 513
  volume of, 520
Problem, 78
Projection, 243
Proof, 47
  direct, 46, 97
  indirect, 98, 547
Proportion, 347
  terms of, 348
Proportional
  division, 352
  fourth, 349
  mean, 349
Proposition, 78, 546
Protractor, 19
Pyramid, 515
  altitude of, 515
  base of, 515
  edge of, 515
  face of, 515
  volume of, 521
Pythagorean
  integers, 385
  theorem, 382
Quadrant, 419, 525
Quadrilateral, 136, 158
  median of, 190
Quantity, 48
Radical axis, 295, 401
Radius
  of circle, 11
  of regular polygon, 475
  of sphere, 525
Ratio, 347
  extreme and mean, 362
  of similitude, 374
  terms of, 348
Rational number, 416
Ray, 15, 503
Real number, 416
Reasoning
  deductive, 46
  direct, 97
  indirect, 98
Reciprocal, 426

Rectangle, 165
    altitude of, 444
    area of, 445
    base of, 444
Reflection, 64
    angle of, 397
Reflexive property, 122, 553
Refraction, angle of, 398
Regular
    polygon, 469
    polyhedron, 512
Rhomboid, 158, 167
Rhombus, 158, 167
Right
    angle, 20
    prism, 513
    section, 513
    triangle, 24
Rise, 424
Rotation, 16, 63
Run, 424
Scalene triangle, 81
Secant, 299
Second, 18
Section
    golden, 362, 390
    right, 513
Sector
    of a circle, 485
    spherical, 531
Segment
    of a circle, 485
    of a line, 8, 503
    measurement of, 14
    of sphere, 531
Segments, equal, 14
Semicircle, 258
Set, 6
    convex, 504
Side
    of angle, 15, 17
    initial, 17
    of polygon, 135
    terminal, 17
    of triangle, 24, 67
Similar polygons, 374
Similitude, ratio of, 374
Skew lines, 239
Slant height, 516
Slope-intercept equation, 430
Slope of line, 423, 432
Small circle, 525
Solid angle, 509
    vertex of, 509
Solid figure, 235
Space loci, 342
Sphere, 524
    area of, 532

cap of, 531
center of, 524
cone of, 531
diameter of, 524
great circle of, 525
lune of, 527
polygon of, 531
radius of, 525
sector of, 531
segment of, 531
small circle of, 525
triangle of, 526
volume of, 530
wedge of, 531
zone of, 529, 531
Spherical
    degree, 527
    excess, 533
    polygon, 531
    segment, 531
    triangle, 526, 528
Square, 165
Statement, conditional, 44
Straight
    angle, 16, 20
    line, 6, 429
Straightedge, 7, 9
Summation symbol Σ, 509
Supplement, 51
Symmetric
    property, 553
    relation, 71, 122
    triangles, 527
Symmetry, 196, 527
    axis of, 199
    center of, 196
System, mathematical, 169
Table of squares and square roots, 556
Tacit assumption, 45
Tangent, 207
    circles, 292
    common external, 294
    common internal, 294
    length of, 290
Terminal
    position, 17
    side, 17
Terms
    defined, 6, 540
    of proportion, 348
    of ratio, 348
    undefined, 6, 540
Tetrahedron, 511
Theorem, 46, 546
    converse of, 116, 547
    Pythagorean, 382
Three-space, 235
Tomahawk trisector, 309

Transformation, 62
  by reflection, 64
  by rotation, 63
  by translation, 62
Transitive relation, 71, 122, 553
Translation, 61
Transversal, 113
Trapezoid, 158, 186
  altitude of, 444
  area of, 452
  bases of, 186, 444
  isosceles, 186
  median of, 186
Triangle, 24, 67
  acute, 24
  altitude of, 26
  angles of, 24
  area of, 449
  base of, 79, 444
  center of gravity or centroid of, 231
  circumcenter of, 229
  determined, 70
  equiangular, 81
  equilateral, 81
  excenter of, 228
  exterior of, 67
  incenter of, 228
  interior of, 67
  isosceles, 79
  median of, 24
  obtuse, 24
  orthocenter of, 230
  perimeter of, 24
  polar, 532
  right, 24
  scalene, 81
  sides of, 24, 67

spherical, 526
  vertex of, 24
Triangles
  congruent, 29, 70
  similar, 374
Trihedral angle, 507
  face of, 507
Trisection of angle, 142, 308, 309
Union, 503
Unit
  of angle measure, 18
  of arc, 258, 301
  of length, 14
  point, 415
  of volume, 518
Value, absolute, 416
Vertex
  angle, 79
  of angle, 15
  of half-line, 15
  of polygon, 135
  of polyhedral angle, 509
  of triangle, 24, 67
  of trihedral angle, 507
Vertical angles, 53
Volume, 518
  of cone, 521
  of cylinder, 520
  of frustum, 522
  of other figures, 532
  of prism, 520
  of pyramid, 521
  of sphere, 530
  unit of, 518
Wedge, spherical, 531
Zone, 529, 531

ACKNOWLEDGMENTS

Grateful acknowledgment is made to the following sources for their kind permission to reproduce photographs in GEOMETRY.

PAGE
42 Baltazar Korab
66 CONVAIR, Division of General Dynamics
79 (*Top*) Shelburne Museum, Inc.; Shelburne, Vermont
    (*Left*) Gustavo Thorlichen
96 American Machine and Foundry Company
124 Photo — ENIT — Roma
193 International News Photo

250 (*Top*) PHOTO LIBRARY, George Holton
    (*Left*) Courtesy Smithsonian Institution Traveling Exhibition Service
333 The Christian Science Monitor
372 Union Carbide Corporation
399 The Christian Science Monitor (Gordon N. Converse)
442 H. Armstrong Roberts
538 Magnum (Erich Hartmann)